Childhood scenes: 1. Robert's birthplace at Willington Quay is at the left hand end of the row of cottages. (This view differs from the incorrect one in the pre-1862 editions of Smiles) 2. The cottage at West Moor, Killingworth, now known as 'Dial Cottage' where Robert spent his formative years. 3. Tommy Rutter's school house at Long Benton. 4. Bruce's Academy at Newcastle where he completed his schooling. 5. West Moor Colliery at Killingworth where he served his apprenticeship as a viewer. 6. The Davy safety lamp (left) and Stephenson's showing the similarity of concept.

ROBERT STEPHENSON:

RAILWAY ENGINEER

John Addyman and Victoria Haworth

NORTH EASTERN RAILWAY ASSOCIATION
AND
THE ROBERT STEPHENSON TRUST

Published by the North Eastern Railway Association

ISBN 1 873513 60 7

Layout by John Addyman

Printed in Great Britain by The Amadeus Press Ltd.

THE NORTH EASTERN RAILWAY ASSOCIATION

Formed in 1961, the NERA caters for all interested in the railways of north-east England, in particular the North Eastern Railway and the Hull & Barnsley Railway, from their early history down to the present day. This also extends to the many industrial and smaller railways that operated alongside them. Interests range over all aspects of development, operation and infrastructure of the railway, including such diverse activities as locomotive history, rolling stock, train services, architecture, signalling, shipping, road vehicles and staff matters – both for the general enthusiast and model maker.

With in excess of 690 members, regular meetings are held in York, Darlington, Hull, Leeds and London. A programme of outdoor visits, tours and walks is also arranged. There is also an extensive library of books, documents, photographs and drawings.

Members receive a quarterly illustrated journal, the NORTH EASTERN EXPRESS, and a newsletter, covering membership topics, forthcoming meetings and events in the region together with book reviews and a bibliography of recent articles of interest. Almost 180 issues of the EXPRESS have been published to date.

The Association also markets an extensive range of facsimiles of NER documents, including diagram books. timetables and other booklets from original NER material while it is developing an expanding range of original publications, available to members at discounted prices.

A Membership Prospectus can be obtained from the Membership Secretary: Mr. T. Morrell, 8 Prunus Avenue, Kingston Road, Willerby, Hull, HU10 6PH. www.ner.org.uk

A sales list of other NERA publications can be obtained from the Sales Officer: Mrs. C. E. Williamson, 31 Moreton Avenue, Stretford, Manchester, M32 8BP. (PLEASE ENCLOSE A STAMPED ADDRESSED 9" X 4" ENVELOPE WITH YOUR ENQUIRIES).

THE ROBERT STEPHENSON TRUST

The Robert Stephenson Trust was founded at the instigation of Victoria Haworth in 1988 with the objectives of bringing his achievements to the notice of today's public and preserving the remaining premises of the factory of Robert Stephenson & Co. at 20 South Street, Newcastle. The premises have been carefully restored and house exhibits and displays relevant to Robert Stephenson. These may be viewed by the public on open days. The Trust produces a twice-yearly journal, and publications relevant to Robert Stephenson.

The trust welcomes new members, and those interested in joining can obtain membership details from the Membership Secretary, The Robert Stephenson Trust, 20 South Street, Newcastle-upon-Tyne, NE1 3PE. www.robertstephensontrust.com

Title page illustration:
The Illustrated London News *of 29 October 1859 devoted a page of engravings to commemorate Robert Stephenson's funeral and some of his finest achievements. The Britannia Bridge over the Menai.Straits, the High Level Bridge over the Tyne and the Victoria Bridge over the St. Lawrence at Montreal are featured.*

Contents

Acknowledgements

The authors are most grateful to the librarians or archivists and staff at the following establishments: House of Lords Records, Guildhall Library of the City of London, Institution of Civil Engineers, Institution of Mechanical Engineers, National Archive (formerly the Public Records Office) Kew, British Library, Wetherby, National Railway Museum, York, the Literary and Philosophical Society, Newcastle, Durham County Record Office, Tyne and Wear Archives and the Scottish Record Office. The staffs of the following public libraries have also been most helpful: Darlington, Chester, Liverpool, Manchester, Newcastle and Pickering, as have numerous other librarians who responded to requests for rare tomes though the Inter Loan system.

Valuable information and help has been given by the following individuals: James Armstrong, Roger Bastin, Alan Blower, Tony Clamp, Alan Clothier, Christopher Dean, Colin Foster, Graham Hardy, Tony Hall-Patch, Adrian Jarvis, Bob Longridge, Ron Prattley, John Teasdale, Stanley Tyson, Mike Wild, David Williamson and Harry Wilson. Very considerable help has been given by Alan Bowman and Bob Roper.

Both authors would like to thank their families for their support and tolerance.

One of the authors is deeply indebted to Bill Fawcett, for lavish assistance in researching a variety of points that needed clarifying and discussing many others to help to resolve them. He has also provided illustrations, read through the text and made many helpful suggestions.

Any errors of fact or interpretation remain the authors' responsibility.

John Addyman and Victoria Haworth   September 2005

FOREWORD

The coming of the railways changed the lives of millions of people throughout the world and nowhere was the change greater than in Great Britain. The impact of the railways on the social, political and economic aspects was huge. The construction of tunnels, embankments and cuttings was one of the biggest projects ever undertaken and changed the face of the country more completely than any previous single event.

To achieve such change in such a short timescale demanded engineers of extraordinary skill and vision coupled with determination and stamina.

Few, if any, displayed these qualities more than Robert Stephenson. He was one of the giants of the railway age, delivering mechanical and constructed engineering not only in Britain but across the world. It is significant that amongst those other giants of the railways at that time was, of course, Isambard Kingdom Brunel. It is equally significant that Brunel regarded Robert Stephenson as a friend as well as a competitor. Brunel's visit to North Wales to witness the floating of the first of the Britannia Bridge's wrought-iron box section tubes clearly demonstrated their close relationship. This compliment was returned when Stephenson visited the *Great Eastern* during its launching. Of course, a key difference between them was their support for entirely different track gauges; Stephenson promoting the standard (4'-8½") and Brunel believing in the broad gauge (7'- 0¼").

Throughout the nation Stephenson's influence on the railways and the countryside remains today. Heavier and faster trains than could ever have been envisaged in the first half of the nineteenth century still pass over or under many of Stephenson's structures along the routes he directly designed. The High Level Bridge at Newcastle, the Royal Border Bridge at Berwick-upon-Tweed, Kilsby Tunnel and the Conwy Bridge are the most well recognised but these major structures are only some of the many bridges designed by Stephenson as he strove to create relatively level routes for the new railways. This sympathetic approach to traction needs reflects the, often less publicised, qualities of his locomotive designs that emerged from the Newcastle factory set up in his name by his famous father.

A testimony to Stephenson's contribution to society was as MP for Whitby for, surprisingly, 12 years. A great sadness is that he died at a relatively early age of 56, thus restricting the nation from benefiting further from his great genius.

This biography addresses some of the imbalances and lack of recognition previously opined by some authors, and is therefore welcomed. It is a privilege to have been invited to write this foreword and for me to be reminded of some of the achievements of Robert Stephenson and the part they played in my formative years at York and Newcastle.

Jim Cornell

INTRODUCTION

When the BBC *Look North* programme conducted a regional poll in 1999 to find the 'Man of the Millennium' George Stephenson was chosen above contenders from all walks of life; his son Robert did not even merit a mention. Again in 2001-2 when BBC 2 conducted a national poll to find the greatest Briton of all time, Robert did not even appear in the top 100.

Robert's accomplishments are too often undervalued nowadays, as are those of other outstanding engineers, practising in the century prior to 1860, with one notable exception – Isambard Kingdom Brunel. John Smeaton, Thomas Telford, Joseph Locke and the Stephensons *together* get far less media attention than Brunel, but with fair representation each could appear to the public equally great. Brunel's own view on Robert's engineering ability is illuminating. In his diary for 5 May 1846 he recorded: 'Stephenson is decidedly the only man in the profession that I feel disposed to meet as my equal, or **superior**, perhaps, on such subjects.'

If George Stephenson was the catalyst that made the elements of waggonways, steam power and public transport fuse together to start a railway system, then Robert gave much of the energy to that reaction. In the mid-1820s, the early locomotives on the Stockton and Darlington Railway were barely holding their own against the horses that were also employed on the line. In 1829, intelligent and respected engineers Walker and Rastrick had agreed in their report, commissioned by the Liverpool and Manchester Railway (L&M), that it could adopt a series of stationary engines using ropes to haul the trains. Robert had been away in South America, and had he remained there, railway development could easily have made this false start. It was Robert, and not George's, ability to defend and improve steam power, and to resolve the many early problems on railways, that probably advanced their development by at least ten years. An example of this ability was the London to Birmingham Railway. The original plan was to build a single line at a cost of £700,000 to be worked by horses. Robert's line, opened in 1838, cost £5,500,000 but was superbly aligned, with easy gradients, double track and, of course, was locomotive worked. However, despite the price, it was an immediate commercial success. And it was not only railways that had to be made to move forward in step with Robert's ideas, but the engineering industry as a whole. In the 1830s it was difficult for engineers to get wrought-iron wheels, axles or crankshafts to withstand normal wear and tear, but, within 20 years, this material was to resist much larger working stresses without the slightest problem – for example, in the tubular bridges.

It is paradoxical that Robert himself perhaps made a significant contribution to the lack of due recognition for his own achievements. When Samuel Smiles was researching his biography of George in 1854 he consulted Robert, who allowed his father to retain much more credit than he had earned on certain projects. Robert had been unable to refute his father's boasts during his lifetime (he must have been unaware of some of them until they appeared in the newspaper reports of George's speeches) so he could hardly do so after he was dead. George loved the limelight but Robert was far more self-effacing.

However, it is Smiles who is most to blame for the fact that Robert's very significant contribution to the early development of the locomotive is either generally ignored or transferred to George. Although many contemporary commentators regarded Robert as the greatest engineer of his generation, Smiles' biography of George (in its various editions) seemed set on eroding this reputation. Anyone reading 'Robert Stephenson's Narrative' that appeared as an appendix *only to the 1862 edition* of Smiles (reprinted 1968), would think that instead of actually designing and building the *Rocket* he had nothing to do with it: 'It was in conjunction with Mr. Booth that **my father constructed** the "Rocket"…'. The version in Robert's own handwriting, now in Devon County Record Office, which he had sent to Smiles on 20 August 1857, is very different: -

> 'I think it is perfectly needless to go into the absurd and ridiculous stories which some writers have hatched up about my father's conduct with Rocket at Liverpool – I had charge personally of the engine myself with Ralph Hutchinson

> my father did not really attend much to Rocket and whatever was done to the
> Engine was done under my own eye and direction.'

Smiles' transfers of credit have led to Robert remaining quite unjustifiably in the shadow of his father. They make the need for an accurate biography of Robert all the more pressing.

However, the twenty-first-century biographer has to overcome many of the myths perpetuated over the years by various authors. For example, posterity presents an image of Robert being a devoted and loving son, but what tends to emerge, on closer analysis, is that this applies only if George kept clear of Robert's projects. The difficulty for today's biographer is compounded by the fact that many documents available to contemporary biographers have either disappeared or been ignored, while the myths have prevailed. When the lawyer, John Cordy Jeaffreson, and the engineer, Professor William Pole, wrote their *Life of Robert Stephenson,* in the early 1860s, they had many thousands of letters, diaries and original plans to peruse. They could, and did, talk to many who had worked with him on his major projects, or knew him at different phases of his life. Samuel Smiles likewise had access to such primary sources, although like many who followed him he did not allow the facts to get in the way of a good story. Robert himself suffered from 'memory overload', which was not surprising considering the number of projects that he was involved with. He sometimes recalled an earlier decision, on what should have happened, rather than what did happen.

Every effort has been made to find the true explanation, but it is inevitable that some errors of fact or interpretation will have been made. 'Fortunate is the art that does not need an interpreter' wrote an early twentieth century composer, but he was only talking about the transient abuse of musical scores by performers. Unfortunately the writing of history, as Smiles has demonstrated, is far more vulnerable and the damage caused is permanent: 'The Moving Finger writes; and having writ moves on: nor all thy Piety or Wit shall lure it back to cancel half a Line, nor all thy Tears wash out a Word of it.'

It is hoped that this biography will redress the various imbalances which have become established and allow Robert to be given full credit for his achievements. Jeaffreson considered that had Robert died in 1844, when he had already completed a chain of railways from London to the Tyne and was participating in many of the others: -

> '... he would have left nothing to which history could point as a monument of original and distinctive genius. He had raised the locomotive by a series of beautiful improvements from the ill-proportioned and ineffective machine of 1828 almost to its present [1864] perfection of mechanism. He had, in conjunction with his father, so fixed the English railway system in continental countries, that throughout Europe his name was identified with the new means of locomotion. His engineering achievements were beyond all cavil works of great ability – but not of distinctive genius.'

In the same critical vein we could describe Brunel as an adapter and enlarger of others' ideas, and Locke as a mere railway builder, but would we get away with it? However, we must agree that it was the unprecedented scale and difficulties of the great bridges, of the next fifteen years, that were to grip the public imagination, and establish Robert's fame beyond all doubt. To give explanations of Robert's most innovative railway engineering and a brief summary of his life within a reasonable sized book means that well known subjects, such as the Rainhill Trials and the Gauge Wars, are given scant coverage, but these outstanding bridges will be dealt with in some detail. Fortunately three of them still survive, over 150 years old, as monuments to his genius.

N. B. Liberal use has been made of quotes throughout the work and the spelling and punctuation of the original documents has been kept. Christian names have been used to make it absolutely clear which Stephenson, Rennie or Moorsom one is talking about (contemporary documents often only refer to Mr. Stephenson, etc.). Footnotes are shown thus: - (5) when only book and page references are given and thus: - (5) where additional information is included.

CHAPTER ONE: EARLY LIFE; from Tyneside to Colombia

1803 - 1819

Robert Stephenson's birth on 16 October 1803 coincided with the advent of the steam locomotive. The pioneering genius of Richard Trevithick (1771-1833) opened the door through which both George and Robert Stephenson were to pass to exploit the locomotive and to leave a legacy of outstanding achievements.

Robert was born in a row of workers' cottages on the north bank of the 'Coaly Tyne' at Willington Quay, seven miles downstream from Newcastle; the family's one-roomed home was at the western end of the row. Robert was regarded by his family as a 'wee sickly bairn not made long for this earth', but the loving care of his mother, Frances, meant that he survived the critical months of infancy during which many of his contemporaries succumbed. Robert was deprived of a baptism in the local parish church, as mining subsidence had rendered it unsafe. Instead the ceremony had to take place in the schoolroom on Wallsend Green. (1) His father could not remember the date of Robert's birth, and 16 November was the habitual celebration day; it was even considered for, but not used on, the inscription on his tombstone in Westminster Abbey.

In 1803, shortly before the birth of Robert, George had gone to Willington Quay to work the ballast engine designed by Robert Hawthorn. They had first met when Hawthorn was the colliery engineer, or 'viewer', at Walbottle Colliery. (2) The viewers were responsible for the extraction and transportation of the coal, and for the colliery machinery; they were educated and capable men highly regarded for their skills. However, George's ambitions were limited by his lack of education, and, at the age of 22, he was approaching the apparent zenith of his career in the mining industry. A worker needed to make a good impression on the viewer to further his career, and cultivating a friendship with Hawthorn resulted in his appointment as a brakesman at Willington Quay. Hawthorn had been a very hard taskmaster to both George and to Joseph Locke's father. George wrote to William Locke in 1823, about Hawthorn, 'I daresay you will well remember he was a great enamy to me but much more so after you left.' (3) However, George was too shrewd 'to quarrel with the cleverest engine-wright of the district'. 'George stood in frequent need of the counsel and countenance of Hawthorn,' and he took part in the early discussions about steam power. (4)

The Stephensons' home at Willington Quay was overshadowed by a hill of ships' ballast, and subjected to dust and smoke. The unpleasantness of the location was increased by the continuous noise of clattering machinery. Nevertheless, under the influence of Frances the household was comfortable and clean, and we know George was very proud of his home. Frances has been described as having a sweet temper with charming modesty, kind of disposition and sound good sense.

When Frances became pregnant again, in 1804, George decided to move to the rural parish of Longbenton for the good of his wife's health. He was given charge of a steam winding engine for one of the nearby pits. Their new cottage, with one ground floor room and a loft, was at the western end of Paradise Row, a small terrace recently built for the workers sinking a new pit at West Moor, near the old settlement of Killingworth. (5) All the collieries surrounding Killingworth were owned by the 'Grand Allies', (6) and their horse-worked Killingworth Waggonway, which George was to make famous, was at the back of new his home and ran to the River Tyne, a distance of four miles.

Unfortunately, the move did not help Frances Stephenson; her baby daughter died aged three weeks in August 1805, and on 16 May 1806 the 37-year-old Frances followed her to the grave. (7) His wife's death was a terrible blow as, 'this domestic happiness was all to pass away; and George felt as one that had thenceforth to tread the journey of life alone.' An invitation to superintend the working of a low-pressure engine, which powered a large spinning works in Montrose, in north-east Scotland, offered George an opportunity for change. (8) He gratefully accepted the job, and made long-term arrangements for the three-year-old Robert to be cared for by Ann Snaith, an ideal surrogate mother, from nearby Longbenton. In March 1808 Ann married George's younger brother, Robert (1788-1837), in St. Nicholas' Church, Newcastle. When George returned to Killingworth his heart must have sunk when he found his cottage in Paradise Row empty and locked up. With some relief he found that his son was being well cared for by the newly-weds, and that a close bond was being formed between the two namesakes, uncle and nephew. (9)

'Recovering possession of his child, George Stephenson again established himself at West Moor', and resumed employment as a brakesman at Killingworth. During his long absence, George had managed to save £28, about half-a-year's wages. However, any renewed self-confidence that he felt in the face of adversity was to be dashed. He found that his father had been blinded by a blast of steam being accidentally let off in his face. George paid off his father's debts of £15 incurred by loss of work, and moved his parents to a comfortable cottage, adjoining the waggonway, near to his own home. Having his doting grandparents close at hand added another dimension to young Robert's life. 'Old

Bob' had gained a reputation among the children of Wylam as a great storyteller, and he no doubt fired his grandson's imagination with many stirring tales. (10) Robert recalled, 'I was a great favourite with the old man, who continued to be very fond of animals, and cheerful to the last; and I believe nothing gave him greater pleasure than a visit from me and my cuddy [donkey].' (11)

On his return to Killingworth, George had employed a new housekeeper who turned out to be a poor choice, so his sister, Eleanor (1784-1848), was invited to look after the household. 'It was a bright day for Robert when this young woman entered the cottage at West Moor, and took him into her affectionate keeping.' Eleanor was three years younger than George, she was described variously as 'a merry lass' or 'seriously inclined', but was good for Robert, and put up some resistance, on his behalf, to George's dominant ambitions for his son. The protracted war with France had sapped the economy and, as usual, the working people were to suffer the most. George with a relatively well-paid job and the money he earned from his clock repairs, cobbling and other activities was able to insulate himself and his family from the worst deprivations. Even so, with five mouths to feed in the Stephenson households meals were frugal and young Robert learnt that butter and eggs were a luxury. (12)

Robert was now 'growing up an active, intelligent boy, as full of fun and tricks as his father had been.' Like the children of other caring mineworkers of the district, Robert was sent to Tommy Rutter's school in Longbenton. The parish clerk could only offer a very limited education, but Robert, in George's words, 'was not in childhood to toil hard all day for a few pence.' When he visited the area with Smiles in 1854, Robert pointed to a house, 'that was Rutter's, where I learnt my A B C, and made a beginning of my school learning.' (13) One of Robert's earliest recollections was of having to trudge to school dragging miners' picks to be sharpened by the blacksmith in Longbenton, and returning in the evening with the repaired items. This was to earn a few pence towards the cost of his schooling. (14)

Robert's immediate environment was a main source of his education. The living room was full of models, clocks and intriguing apparatus, and the discussions that his father was habitually engaged in about machinery furthered Robert's practical knowledge. George was not only working for the colliery; he was also with partners erecting and repairing machinery in the neighbourhood. As soon as Robert was able to help his father, 'it was the proudest work the boy could take part in.' One project George was engaged in was the draining of a nearby quarry. 'When the little engine was set up at Ochre Quarry to pump it dry, Robert was scarcely absent for an hour.' (15)

Robert's childhood was dominated by the early development of the steam locomotive, which is expounded in Chapter 3. When Robert was only a baby and Richard Trevithick's locomotive was being assembled in Gateshead, 'Trevithick sat with Robert on his knee many a night: it was through him Robert was made an engineer.'! (16)

Like most parents, George was keen to give his son a better start in life than he himself had had. He recounted; 'In the earlier period of my career, when Robert was a little boy, I saw how deficient I was in education, and I made up my mind to put him to a good school, and give him a liberal training.' (17) On 14 August 1815, when Robert was sent to Mr. Bruce's school in Newcastle, George was earning at least £200 a year from his various activities. Bruce's Academy had a high reputation for excellence and was attended by middle-class boys and the sons of the minor gentry. Initially Robert was required to walk but his father soon had to buy him a donkey for the taxing 10-mile daily journey to school and back. Although the other pupils had homely Northumbrian accents, Robert stood out in the crowd by his guttural pit intonations, homemade attire, hob-nailed boots, which clattered on the floor, and his packed lunch of rye bread. The sensitive child was subjected to ridicule, but he withstood the bullying silently. Not defending himself proved to be the best course of action, and soon some of his fellow scholars became firm friends for life. However, his suffering may have had a profound effect on his personality at such an impressionable age. (18) His progress was good but not extraordinary, and after his death some of his former schoolfellows were quite astonished at the scale of his professional achievements. In later life he had written to the son of his tutor: -

'It was to Mr. Bruce's tuition and methods of modelling the mind that I attribute much of my success as an engineer; for it was from him that I derived my taste for mathematical pursuits and the facility I possess of applying this kind of knowledge to practical purposes and modifying it according to circumstances.' (19)

'During the time Robert attended school in Newcastle, his father made the boy's education instrumental to his own.' Also, 'In this spirit George caused his son to learn French, because it would be useful to him in business.' Robert spent some of his spare time in the library of the Newcastle Literary and Philosophical Institute from which: -

'Robert brought home standard popular works and encyclopaedic volumes of natural science and inventions [e.g. *Repertory of Arts & Sciences*]. These books his father read and compelled him to read; but the labour went very much against the boy's grain'. (20)

He made notes and sketches, from the books that could not be borrowed, and in the evening repeated what he had learnt for George's receptive mind. (21) The diligent boy soon attracted the attention of the Rev. William Turner, a Unitarian minister and secretary of the Literary and Philosophical Society for the first 44 years of its existence. Conversations about the Stephensons' aspirations would take place, and, undoubtedly, Robert would learn of William Thomas' paper read before the Society in 1805 *'On the propriety of introducing roads on the principle of the coal-waggon ways, for the general carriage of goods,'* Towards the end of his life, Robert Stephenson often spoke of the gratitude and esteem he felt towards his revered instructor. 'Mr Turner was always ready to assist me with books, with instruments and with council, gratuitously and cheerfully. He gave me the most valuable assistance and instruction, and to my dying day I can never forget the obligations which I owe to my venerable friend.' (22)

Together with his father Robert practised the ability to read engineering drawings, which he could soon do 'as easily as he would read a page of a book'. Samuel Smiles thinks 'A spirit of self-improvement was thus early and carefully planted and fostered in Robert's mind,' but the situation was coming extremely close to 'All work and no play…'! 'The neighbours sometimes thought George was an "o'er strict father," and pitied the poor boy who was kept so close to his books.' Jeaffreson takes up the negative implications of this: -

> 'Up to the time when he left Bruce's school, Robert did not exhibit any marked enthusiasm for the pursuits in which his father was most warmly interested. Possibly George Stephenson was too urgent that he should prosecute the study of mechanics, and by continually goading him to work harder and harder "at his buiks" gave him a transient distaste for the subjects to which he was naturally inclined.' (23)

At Killingworth George spent much of his weekends pondering on the problems of machinery and stripping down the winding engine under his charge in the hope of improving its efficiency by adjustments and fine-tuning. By his effective maintenance and modifications the pit's profits increased, and George Stephenson's name came to the notice of the viewer, Ralph Dodd(s) (1762-1821). This came about after the Grand Allies had installed a Newcomen type of engine to pump out the new Killingworth High Pit. No one could make it lower the water, and Kit Hepple, one of the sinkers, challenged George to make it work. George said, 'I could alter her man, and make her draw: in a week's time I could send you to the bottom.' Hepple reported the conversation, and Dodd, who was at his wits' end, let George have a go. The engine was modified and set up correctly, and within five days workmen were able to go to the bottom of the pit. (24) He had also achieved a wider reputation in the district as a skilled 'pump doctor', and gained numerous contracts to maintain other engines. In 1812, at the age of 31, George was rewarded with the salaried appointment of enginewright at Killingworth for the Grand Allies, after the previous incumbent had met with a fatal accident. George now had the scope to develop his ideas, while Robert was also becoming capable of making a valuable input; the improved Killingworth locomotives and the miners' lamp were notable examples of the father and son's early teamwork. (Locomotive development is covered in Chapter 3.)

There had been a need for a practical safety lamp for many years. A series of horrific explosions in mines around Tyneside culminated, in 1812, with the worst at Felling Pit, near Gateshead, by which no fewer than 90 men and boys were either suffocated or burnt to death. (25) An explosive, flammable gas from the coal, known locally as 'fire-damp', meant that it was difficult to mine the most valuable resources as the gas occurred in abundance in all the best seams. Candles caused the explosions but the miners needed light in order to work. Dr. William Reed Clanny (d. 1850), of Sunderland, had produced his version of a cumbersome, but safe, lamp in 1813. For some years George had been 'in his own rude way, making experiments in fire-damp in the Killingworth mine.' (26) In August 1815, when Robert started at Bruce's Academy, George rallied the forces: 'In making these experiments in his humble cottage at West Moor, Nicholas Wood [1795-1865] and George's son Robert usually acted as his assistants'. (27) Nicholas Wood's education, training and position, as under-viewer, helped to ensure the realisation of the Killingworth Miners Safety Lamp, which became known affectionately as the *Geordie*.

The team worked exceptionally quickly; both senior men had time-consuming jobs, and young Robert's schooldays were taxing as well, with his daily ten-mile journey either on foot or by donkey. Their work took place within a four-month period. 'After several evenings' careful deliberations,' (28) Wood prepared the drawings and they conducted the experiments within their empirical approach. The apparatus was completed and the first trial in Killingworth pit occurred on 21 October 1815. Further modifications were carried out, and the final version was completed and tested on 30 November. Nicholas Wood wrote: 'On Tuesday night December 5th we laid it before the Literary and Philosophical Society in Newcastle.' (29) While most present considered the lamp to be the most useful and simple yet, Dr Clanny, as a competitor, raised a voice of opposition. Prolonged and undignified antagonism was also to come from the eminent scientist Sir Humphry Davy (1778-1829).

In August 1815 a committee based in the North East had invited Sir Humphry Davy to turn his attention to the subject of a safety lamp. As a result, in December 1815, shortly after the Killingworth lamp had been pronounced a success, a lamp by Davy was exhibited to coal-miners at Newcastle. Those present appreciated that both lamps worked on the same principle. For George 'all the world's a stage' and Jeaffreson considered: -

> 'To George Stephenson one of the best consequences of his invention was the quarrel which it provoked between his friends and the supporters of Sir Humphry Davy. The coal-owners of the district formed themselves into two parties. A newspaper war was waged, in which the advocates of Stephenson were altogether victorious. The partisans of Sir Humphry gave him as a reward for his invention £2,000, awarding to George Stephenson 100 guineas for the lamp they professed to regard as a clumsy contrivance, if not an imitation. ...
>
> 'To make head against this demonstration of Sir Humphry's friends, George's supporters got up another testimonial, amounting to £1,000.' (30)

The Geordie lamp undoubtedly saved hundreds of lives, and was ultimately to prove safer than the Davy lamp, which was prone to overheat, causing serious accidents when used in Welsh and Yorkshire mines. Helping to produce the safety lamp was Robert Stephenson's first encounter with national fame, and he acted as amanuensis for his father during the newspaper controversy. This involvement in a long-standing war of words would not be his last. The events of 1815 had demonstrated how a worthy idea could be translated into reality by concentrated effort, and kindled a fascination with chemistry. Indeed, just before his official retirement from railway work in Britain, in 1850, Robert declared 'his knowledge of chemistry to surpass his attainments in engineering'. **(31)**

About this time William Losh (1770-1861)**,** the senior partner in Losh, Wilson and Bell, who owned Walker Ironworks and local chemical factories, was impressed by the success of the first Killingworth locomotive and kept a keen interest in the improvements then being made. Losh had been educated on the continent, and 'this highly cultivated gentleman,' had studied metallurgy in Sweden and chemistry in Paris. He saw George as 'a man well fitted to carry out his enterprises and to suggest new ones.' In early 1816 an arrangement was made by which George could work for two days a week for Losh, and three days for the Grand Allies, receiving £100 per annum from each of them. **(32)**

It was 'in token of his gratitude to him as his father's benefactor' that Robert made his earliest known drawing: a sundial copied from Ferguson's *Astronomy*. The lad presented it to Mr. Losh before embarking on the construction of an actual sundial. This out-of-school summer activity caused Robert Stephenson to say 'many a sore head I had while making the necessary calculations to adapt the dial to the latitude of Killingworth,' (33). A stone for the dial was hewn, carved, polished and dated MDCCCXV1 for placing over the new front door of the Stephensons' home. The cottage had been extended to the west for another living room and a bedroom above, with a staircase instead of a ladder. The dwelling still stands and is known as Dial Cottage.

Under Losh's expert eye, experiments were carried out to ascertain the strength of metals in order to produce two types of wheel, and cast-iron rails with half-lap joints to help to alleviate irregularities. On 30 September 1816 Losh and George Stephenson applied for a railway patent (No. 4067) encompassing rails, wheels and improvements to the design. (34) Robert's interest in metal properties almost certainly stemmed from this time. These were heady days before the limitations of scientific theory - anything was possible.

However, the first locomotives were cumbersome, unreliable beasts, and their failure to supplant the horse may well have caused George to contemplate emigrating to the United States with his sister Ann, her husband, John Nixon, and young family. There seemed 'little prospect of introducing the locomotive into general use so George saw the germ of a great revolution in navigation' **(35)** especially going into the steamboat trade on the Great Lakes. The Nixons accepted this exciting challenge, emigrating after their son's birth in 1818. Other opportunities were to divert George Stephenson from this track.

Robert's paternal grandparents died in 1817 and 1818, and Aunt Eleanor left the house at West Moor soon after their deaths; she married Stephen Liddle in 1824. Around 1819 George decided he should re-marry. According to spurious legend, George's first love, in the days of his youth, was Elizabeth Hindmarsh who, being the daughter of a well-off farmer, had been considered to be far above the station of a young colliery workman. **(36)** George was now a man of means, and she was still a spinster; they married on 29 March 1820 and Robert acted as witness at the ceremony.

July 1819 – July 1824

Robert left school in July 1819 and was apprenticed to Nicholas Wood, to train as a viewer in Killingworth Collieries. The position of viewer, at the top of the tree in the mining industry, had always been beyond George's reach because of his lack of education, but to his son he could now afford this opportunity. Robert's three years' training to become a viewer needed him to gain familiarity with all aspects of mining. It was 'not only hard but hazardous.' **(37)** Robert was extremely fortunate to have a teacher of Nicholas Wood's calibre, and Wood taught him that systematic experiment was essential before arriving at a conclusion. Because Nicholas Wood was often involved in George's other activities it is certain that Robert spent a lot of time away from the colliery.

However, when he was there it was sometimes extremely hazardous. The Grand Allies had adopted the Geordie lamp for use in their pits, and a fine of half-a-crown (12.5p) was imposed on workmen using candles, but it was difficult to enforce the rule and even the managers broke it. Once a fortnight Robert was required to accompany Wood down the Killingworth mines for an inspection of the workings. On one occasion Wood decided to use a candle, instead of the very dim Geordie lamp, in a part of the mine where he thought it should have been safe. 'The spot was more foul than the viewer supposed, and an explosion instantly ensued.' Fortunately, Nicholas Wood only received minor injuries and Robert and the under-viewer were shocked but unhurt, but it did make a strong impression on them of the value of the safety lamp, dim though its light might have been! (38)

On another occasion Robert was nearly roasted alive. George had installed three underground haulage engines in the Killingworth pits, nicknamed 'Geordie', 'Jemmy' and 'Bobby'. The flues from the engines were carried to the surface through brick lined boreholes, but this was not without hazards as George explained in a letter of 21 December 1819. 'The soot in the Geordie Flues caught fire beside the damper and set the Coal on fire nearly all the way to the Jemmy. We got it under [control] last night.' Robert added a postscript to the letter about the dangers; 'My father has almost wrought me to Death in the Flues but he himself has been two or three times dropt with the choak damp but I took care not to go as far as that. But where I was I think I would not have been long in making a joint of Meat Ready.' (39)

From 1819, during the completion of the sinking of Hetton Colliery, in County Durham, George planned its waggonway. It ran from the River Wear at Sunderland and continued southwards over Warden Law to serve the new pit. The seven-mile long line was undulating and difficult, and the summit on Warden Law was 560 feet above sea level. It had to be worked by a combination of stationary steam engines, self-acting inclines and initially three, later five, locomotives. The resident engineer for the line's construction was George's brother, Robert, and, as Nicholas Wood was also involved, so must have been young Robert. Work on the railway started in March 1821, and it opened on 18 November 1822. **(40)** The track was to the Losh/Stephenson patent of 1816, but soon: - 'It was found, however, that the railway was affected very injuriously by locomotive haulage, and it is now preferred to draw the wagons forward and backward by stationary steam-engines.' (41) Regardless of the initial problems it was carrying over 300,000 tons of coal per annum by 1826, and locomotives were certainly reported as fully employed at the Sunderland end in 1828. The Hetton Railway, the first in the world to be built with the intention of using steam locomotives, remained in use for 136 years. Again the Grand Allies permitted George to be paid for this work without any reduction of his Killingworth salary, which was now virtually a 'retaining fee'.

George's next railway project was on a much grander scale. Ideas for reducing the cost of the transport of coal from the South Durham coalfield to Darlington, Yarm and Stockton had been under consideration from the late 1760s. A canal, a canal and tramway, and a railway scheme were all considered. In 1821 a second attempt to get an Act for a railway almost foundered when it was found to be undersubscribed. (42) Darlington Quaker, Edward Pease (1767-1858), saved the day by increasing his investment from £3,000 to £10,000. The Stockton and Darlington Railway (S&D) proposals were well known in Killingworth, and when the second Bill was progressing through Parliament George Stephenson, together with Nicholas Wood, met Edward Pease in Darlington. The date quoted for one meeting, 19 April 1821, was significant as that on which the first S&D Act was due to receive Royal Assent. **(43)** Having guaranteed almost an eighth of the £82,000 required, Edward Pease was worried, even at this late stage, that the best scheme had not gone through Parliament. George Stephenson easily convinced the shrewd Quaker that the original plans for the line should be re-examined. The result of the interview was that George was asked to make a careful investigation of the original route; this was to be done in the autumn of 1821, 'as soon as the crops are off the ground'.

Robert, 'a slight, spare, bronzed boy' assisted in the survey, together with John Dixon (1796-1865). 'He heartily enjoyed the work. Spending the entire day in the clear balmy air, eating frugal meals of "bread, butter, milk, and potatoes" under sheltering hedgerows, lodging at night in roadside inns'. (44)

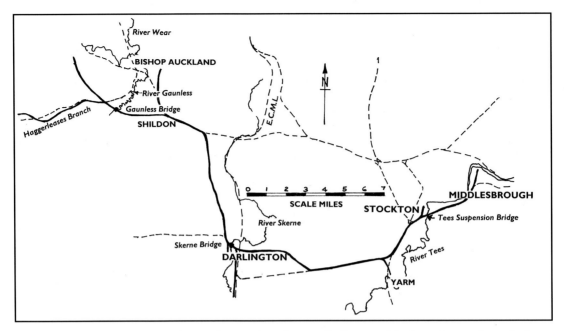

Figure 1.1: plan showing the Stockton and Darlington Railway and its branches at the end of 1830, and, dotted, later railways in the district. J. F. Addyman.

One of George's many gifts was a natural aptitude to choose the best route for a railway, and his line offered economies over the previous schemes in all aspects of its construction. The S&D board decided to promote his line in a new Bill during the 1823 session of Parliament, and include a significant clause allowing locomotives to be used to haul both passengers and merchandise. The estimated cost was a little over a third of that of a canal, and £7,700 below the earlier railway scheme. George was appointed Engineer of the S&D on 22 January 1822 with a salary of £660 out of which he 'was to provide for the services of assistants'. (45)

There were important outcomes for Robert from the S&D project. 'Several gentlemen who came in contact with him during the survey for the line had been struck with his natural force of intellect that they represented to his father the propriety, and indeed the imperative duty, of him giving him a college education.' George, with his salary from the S&D and other emoluments, could well afford to send Robert to Cambridge, but 'he did not wish to make his son a gentleman.' Instead, Robert went to Edinburgh University for one academic year, which extended from late October 1822 to April 1823. (46) His letters and later recollections imply that he studied Natural History, Natural Philosophy, Mathematics and Chemistry. He enjoyed a geological expedition to the Scottish Highlands with Professor Jameson (1774-1854); this was also attended by George Parker Bidder (1806-1878), who was to become one of Robert's closest friends. Many years later he said to Samuel Smiles, 'I have travelled far, and enjoyed much, but that delightful botanical and geological journey I shall never forget.' (47) Professor (Sir) John Leslie (1766-1832), who had recently transferred from the chair of Mathematics to that of Natural Philosophy, awarded Robert a prize for solving 'some mathematical questions'. (48) 'The six months' study had cost his father £80; but he was amply repaid by the better scientific culture which his son had acquired'. (47)

It is of interest to compare George's much exaggerated account of Robert's education in a speech he gave in 1848 at the celebration dinner following the completion of the first Conwy tube. He said: -

'...he had put his son from school to school, as his little means had allowed him, and in every school he had taken the lead. He at length placed him in one of the first schools in the north of England, with Mr. Bruce, of Newcastle, and he believed his son had proved the best mathematician ever raised at that school. That did not satisfy him (the father), but he had him trained as a mining engineer, and sent him to college at Edinburgh, to study mineralogy, chemistry, and mathematics, under Professor Leslie, and he was proud to say that he took the mathematical prize at that college.' (49)

At the end of the university term Robert naturally returned to assist his father on the S&D, which was to receive Royal Assent on 23 May 1823. The 1821 S&D Act had made provision for a branch to Evenwood, but the owner of collieries further west soon demanded that the branch should be lengthened to serve them. When this was presented as a possible objection to the 1823 Act, Robert was delegated to survey and prepare the deposited plans for an extended branch to Hagger Leases Lane.

The proposed line, on an entirely new alignment, was four-and-a-half miles long, and, following the valley of the River Gaunless, it rose from its junction with the main line at an average gradient of 1 in 120. (50) Lack of funds deferred the start of the Haggerleases branch for another four years. The line was completed in 1830, under the supervision of Thomas Storey (1789-1859), and was renamed the Butterknowle branch in 1899; it remained in use until 1963. (51)

The S&D required a crossing over the River Gaunless at West Auckland, and the ingenious cast and wrought-iron bridge (Fig. 1.2) is usually credited to George Stephenson as Engineer-in-Chief of the railway. But was this structure, that has been described as the prototype of Brunel's Saltash Bridge, really his idea? (52). The late J. G. James, whose worldwide research on early iron bridges was published in the *Transactions of the Newcomen Society*, (53) suggests that the Gaunless was the first to use the idea of lenticular construction. The inspiration for this, and the bowstring arch, possibly went back to the beginning of the seventeenth century when a Croatian bishop, Faustus Verantius (1551-1617), produced illustrations of each type in his *Machinae novae*, which was published in 1616. (Fig. 1.2) The alternative of an iron or stone bridge over the Gaunless was mentioned in the S&D minutes of 27 December 1822, and Robert had returned from Edinburgh University before the bridge was built. Discussions with his mentors while he was there, or with engineer and lecturer, George Buchanan (1790-1852), might have suggested the design that was used. George Stephenson had become a partner, from 1821 until December 1824, in John and Isaac Burrell's small foundry at Forth Banks, Newcastle, where the bridge was fabricated. By the time it was being built Robert Stephenson & Co's works had been established next door to the foundry, and this makes it even more likely that Robert had a hand in its success. The other major bridge on the original line was taken out of George's hands, during Robert's absence in South America, and given to a Durham architect, Ignatius Bonomi (1787-1870). This bridge, over the Skerne, had to be a stone structure, and this implies a lack of faith by the directors in George's ability as a bridge designer. Most of the early specifications and quantities for the railway are in Robert's handwriting, and contractors were required to report to him at Killingworth.

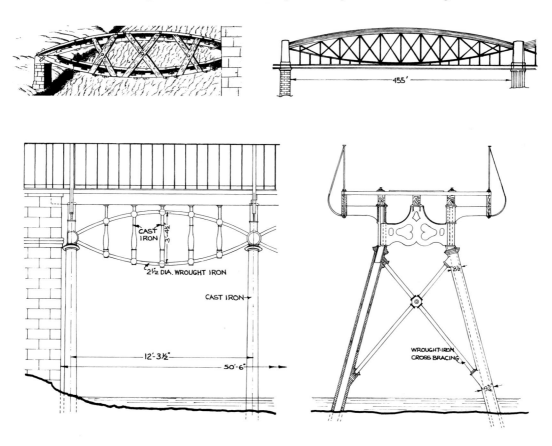

Figure 1.2: Faustus Verantius's early seventeenth century design which may have influenced the cast and wrought-iron bridge over the River Gaunless and later I. K. Brunel's Saltash Bridge (top right).

The S&D needed to address the major obstacle to the widespread use of locomotives - the damage that they caused to the track. (George's first estimate had allowed £6,200 for stationary engines but made no mention of locomotives.) (54) Malleable or wrought-iron rails, plates or bars had been used with success on some tramways. Lord Carlisle's Railway at Tindale Fell, near Brampton, in Cumberland, had used malleable-iron rails of a uniform section from 1808. A fish-bellied shape had been patented as early as 1789 by William Jessop (1745-1814) for cast-iron rails. In order to reduce breakages this gave the deepest section midway between the supporting chairs, where the maximum bending moment occurs, and was adopted by others, including Losh and Stephenson in their 1816 patent. John Birkinshaw (1777-c.1855), agent to Bedlington Iron Works, had devised a method of rolling malleable rails to the fish-bellied shape which he patented on 23 October 1820 (No. 4503) (55). These were developed, at the behest of the manager, Michael Longridge (1785-1858), primarily for use on a new waggonway, built at the Works' expense, to transport coal cheaply from Willow Bridge (later Barrington) Colliery, about two miles distant. (56) George Stephenson paid £700 for a half-share in the lease of this colliery from 5 December 1820, fortunately just too late to suggest the use of the inferior cast-iron rails of the 1816 patent. (57)

One of the many visitors to Killingworth in 1821 was William James (1771-1837), a land agent and surveyor, who had been interested in the promotion of railways on a national scale for many years. His horse-worked Stratford and Moreton Railway had just received Royal Assent, but his visit to the North East assured him that the way forward was to use locomotives instead of horses. He also visited the Bedlington Iron Works, and in June he wrote to a friend of Edward Pease, 'I pronounce my Candid Opinion that the Malleable Iron Rail Road at Bleddington Works is by far the best I have ever seen both in respect of its Material and form.' (56) William James and George Stephenson, with the same goal in view, were aware that if they did not use these superior rails the inevitable breakages of the cast-iron ones could put their dream of a national system of locomotive-worked railways in jeopardy.

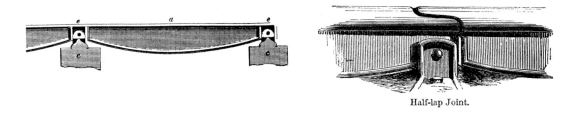

Half-lap Joint.

Figure 1.3: The fish-bellied rails and joints to the Losh and Stephenson patent. (Wood and Smiles)

One would have thought that an agreement incorporating the ideas of malleable iron and the rail joints of the Losh/Stephenson patent could have been forthcoming. However, George was prepared to advocate the use of the new rails for the S&D, without securing any financial arrangement, so he and Losh are each reputed to have lost £500 in potential royalties from their 1816 patent. When George reinforced other recommendations for the malleable rails to the S&D board they accepted them in October 1821. This led to a bitter row with Losh and virtually ended the Stephensons' relationship with him. (55)(**58**) William James and Michael Longridge were both to step into Robert's life and form friendships which would have a considerable influence on him.

The sort of agreement that could have been negotiated between the Bedlington Iron Works and Losh and Stephenson is illustrated by a contemporary one with the Jameses. William James's son, William Henry (1796-1873), had applied for a patent, and such was the mutual respect, at this time, that an agreement, dated 1 September 1821, allowed Stephenson and Losh 'to adopt any improvements and the introduction of tubes to their boilers as contained in the letters patent of W. H. James.' (**59**) Included in the agreement was a clause allowing the Jameses a proportion of the profits on any locomotives, incorporating their patent, sold to work on railways south of a line drawn from Liverpool to Hull. The friendship between the Jameses and the Stephensons was such that the summer of 1822 saw Robert assisting William James's team with the first proper survey of the Liverpool and Manchester Railway (L&M). (60)

James's 1822 survey of the L&M was started too late to meet the 30 November deadline required by Parliamentary Standing Orders. The survey and plans were not finished until late September as explained in this mature letter to William James from Robert dated 3 September 1822: -

My Dear Sir,

Hugh [Greenshields] and I set off last night to see you but we were so unfortunate as to lose our guide. I am sorry we cannot meet your expectations in arriving at Manchester with the survey. It is utterly impossible. Had the weather been favourable to us we might have accomplished it. In our present situation we may arrive on Wednesday evening but not sooner and with the regard to finishing the survey and plan on or before the 16th it is quite impracticable and let me assure you (however it may derange your business) that no effort has been spared by Mr. Padley [James's brother-in-law] and myself. We even by ourselves surveyed the greater part of Sunday – for God sake! Don't depreciate Mr. P's exertions he is very much concerned at your request. I should be glad to see you if convenient at the Canteen this evening when we may talk matters over. Mr. P. went over (yesterday afternoon) Mr. Bradshaw's land and just as they were leaving the last field three men came running up to dismiss them but fortunately we had got finished. We commence at the canal today and shall make every effort in our power to arrive at Manchester tomorrow evening. From there I should wish very much to go over the other end of the line with you. I am quite delighted with this part of the line for I feel confident by care in setting it out after the act is got it may be made a very complete line of Railway.

Should you be under the necessity of having the plans finished by the 16th I should advise another assistant (a competent surveyor) to be procured immediately.' (61)

The survey was seen by the L&M committee for the first time in mid-October. This meant that it was far too late for them either to alter the route or negotiate to avoid the strong opposition that was coming from major landowners. The first S&D Bill (1819) had failed because of opposition from landowners, and it is hard to fathom why James, as a very experienced land agent, had not been aware of the strength of the opposition during the L&M survey and taken steps to avoid it. Other problems were looming for James. His daughter admitted later; 'From being so much engaged in railway business about the years 1821 and 1822, W. James's other affairs languished for a want of requisite attention.' (62) William James's financial difficulties had become such that he was imprisoned from 18 November 1822 until 19 February 1823, and again from 30 May to 22 October 1823. Another annual deadline for the railway was missed, and when he was jailed for the third time, on 14 May 1824, the very tolerant committee decided to replace him. At the end of 1823 they had already asked Jesse Hartley (1780-1860), the designer of Liverpool Docks, to report on the route. In early May 1824 four members of the L&M committee visited Killingworth, the Hetton Colliery Railway and the uncompleted S&D, and on 20 May George was invited to replace James. **(63)**

William James was a very convincing talker, and Robert came very much under his spell resulting in a friendly exchange of ideas and sympathies that is evident from their correspondence. George Stephenson must have become aware of James's growing influence over Robert during the L&M survey. Although James's behaviour towards George was faultless, George always ignored James's crucial role in promoting the L&M. This became so blatant that Robert was provoked to write a letter to W. H. James in 1844 acknowledging that: -

'I believe that your late father was the original projector of the Liverpool and Manchester
Railway, and that he spent a great deal of money and time in bringing the project to bear,
and though he was unsuccessful in the first attempt, it no doubt led the way to future
results.' **(64)**

The relatively remote location of Killingworth and the fact that George had upset one of the Grand Allies, with the S&D route, made the idea of a new site to build locomotives very attractive. George, who later *claimed* to have built about 55 engines, including 16 locomotives, between 1813 and 1825, agreed it was essential that a proper works was opened to achieve a higher standard of workmanship. (65) On 23 June 1823 the first factory in the world specifically to build steam locomotives was founded in Newcastle-upon-Tyne. The firm known as 'Robert Stephenson & Co.' had an initial capital of £4,000 divided into ten shares. The signatories of the agreement were: Edward Pease (four shares, two of these were paid for by Pease's cousin Thomas Richardson), Michael Longridge, George and Robert Stephenson (two shares each). Robert had to borrow £500 from Edward Pease to pay for his stake. Robert's valuable input to the design of the later Killingworth locomotives was acknowledged by him being made, at the age of 19, the managing partner '...upon condition that his Father George Stephenson furnish the Plans, &c., which may be required, and take general charge of the Manufactory as long as required by the Partners.' (66) However, from this time George made no real contributions to the works or to locomotive development, and often rejected improvements suggested by Robert. A very relevant account is given by Smiles from the Killingworth days, while Robert was serving his apprenticeship: -

'One who used to drop in at the cottage of an evening, well remembers the animated and
eager discussions which on some occasions took place, more especially with reference to
the growing powers of the locomotive engine. **The son was even more enthusiastic
than the father on this subject. Robert would suggest numerous alterations and
improvements in details of the machine. His father, on the contrary, would offer
every possible objection defending the existing arrangements,** – proud, nevertheless,
of his son's suggestions, and often warmed and excited by his brilliant anticipations of
the ultimate triumph of the locomotive.' (67)

Land was leased beside Burrell's foundry in South Street, Newcastle, and Robert was given the task of setting up the engine works: -

> 'It was a trying position for a young man, only twenty years of age. To be so trusted was the grandest sort of education – but it was an education fitted only for an able man. He had to supervise the building operations, engage men, take orders, advise on contracts, draw plans, make estimates, keep accounts, and in all matters, great or small, govern the young establishment on his own responsibility.' (68)

As early as December 1823 the works had delivered its first engine to the Earl of Carlisle. It is difficult to imagine how the Stephensons managed to find time for all their activities during 1823. In September they had managed to squeeze a visit to London, and Ireland, to obtain some orders for the engine works, before returning home via the historic ironworks at Coalbrookdale. Partner, Thomas Richardson (1771-1853), the wealthy founder of Richardson, Overend and Gurney's discount house, had asked them to report on a rival type of engine being widely publicised by its American inventor, Jacob Perkins (1766-1849). When George and Robert were able to stop it, even when it was working at a pressure of 200 lbs per square inch, by grabbing hold of the flywheel, Robert was to write 'I am convinced, as well as my father, that Perkins knows nothing about the principle of steam engines.' (69)

At the end of 1823 Thomas Richardson had become interested in the 'Colombian Mining Association' which hoped to exploit abandoned, but once extremely profitable, Spanish gold and silver mines by using modern machinery. He asked George about many of the requirements for the project, and Robert was soon brought into the consultations, 'and he did the work in such a manner that Mr. Richardson formed a yet higher opinion of his energy and capacity.' Robert was asked if he would like to accompany the expedition, and 'the proposal put the young man in a fire of excitement... Moreover, the dreams of wealth, which had fascinated apparently cautious and practical men like Mr. Richardson, seemed to Robert Stephenson's young mind no visionary hopes, but realities beyond the reach of doubt.' (70)

At the end of February 1824 Robert, and his uncle Robert, went to Cornwall at the behest of the agents for the American mining venture; Messrs. Herring, Graham and Powles. The result of the trip was an elaborate joint report on all facets of the Cornish mining industry, which were expected to be more akin to the working of Colombian mines than the collieries of the North East. Robert also took the opportunity to inspect the Bristol steam boats, and visit the Neath Abbey Iron Works. He had to stay most of March in London and was there again from the end of April; this was partly in connection with the preparations for Colombia and partly to attend the committee stages of the 1824 S&D Bill. During this period he was becoming more obsessed with the idea of going to Colombia, which promised the extra inducement of an annual salary of no less than £500, plus expenses. In mid-March he had not plucked up enough courage to mention his hopes to his father, but he wrote to Michael Longridge from London on the 19th: -

> 'There are some new prospects here in agitation, which I look forward to with great satisfaction. It is making a new road in Colombia. This new scheme of the road or railway is also connected with four silver mines at Mariquita. The road is projected between La Guayra and the city of Caracas. ...Mr. Powles is the head of the concern, and he assures there is no one to meddle with us. We are to have all the machinery to make, and we are to construct the road in the most advisable way we may think, after making surveys and levellings.' (71)

He was only able to put off writing to his father until the beginning of April: -

> 'But now let me beg you not to say anything against my going out to America, for I have already ordered so many instruments that it would make me look extremely foolish to call it off. Even if I had not ordered any instruments, it seems as if we were all working one against the other. You must recollect I will only be away for a time; and in the meantime you could manage with the assistance of Mr. Longridge, who, together with John Nicholson, would take the whole of the business part off your hands. And only consider what an opening it is for me as an entry into business; and I am informed by all that have been there that it is a very healthy country. I must close this letter, expressing my hope that you will not go against me for this time.' (72)

Robert was only concerned about his commitment to the engine works, whose slim order books could be swelled by the requirements of engines and mining machinery for South America. There were plenty of surveyors who could assist George with the projecting and building of railways. Robert's mother had died of tuberculosis, and there were fears of him developing the disease, hence the reference to the 'very healthy country' as a little arm twist. **(73)** The enthusiastic support of Thomas Richardson, the exciting prospect, the high salary, his independence, and the warm healthy climate all added up to an extremely valid incentive for Robert to go to South America.

The preparations for the three-year South American expedition included Robert taking lessons in Spanish and in 'Mineralogical Chemistry' during his sojourn in London while awaiting orders to start his journey. (74) Initially, he was instructed by the Colombian Mining Company's agents to depart from Falmouth, but, at the very last moment, he was told to sail from Liverpool instead. He had actually paid for, and loaded over a ton of luggage on to the Falmouth coach, which was about to depart, when the message came. The change of departure was fortunate as George had to be in Liverpool to attend a meeting with the L&M committee, and they dined together in Joseph Sandars' opulent house on the evening of 12 June 1824. George was most impressed by the rich merchant's lavish hospitality, and wrote to Michael Longridge: -

'What changes one sees! – this day in the highest life, and the next in a cottage – one day turtle soup and champagne, and the next bread and milk, or anything that one can catch… The merchants are clever chaps, and perseverance is stamped on every brow. There is a Doctor Trail, a clever mineralogist, and some famous mathematicians that we have dined with. I was much satisfied to find that Robert could acquit himself so well amongst them. He was much improved in expressing himself since I have seen him before; the poor fellow is in good spirits about going abroad, and I must make the best of it.' (75)

Robert's matchless experiences of the last two years, which had included his university training, projecting railways, attending Parliamentary Select Committees, setting up an engine works, and planning a mining expedition, had made him ready to face any challenge. The Colombian project was to be the first of his many major adult challenges.

Robert sailed from Liverpool in the afternoon of the 18 June 1824 on the *Sir William Congreve*. His last act before sailing was to instruct his agents to transfer £300 from his salary each year to Robert Stephenson & Co. He was aware, as were the other partners, that it would be necessary to inject cash into the company for several years before the demand for engines would be sufficient for it to become the highly profitable concern that they all expected. (76)

Colombia: July 1824 – November 1827

The 35-day journey to South America was the first real period of relaxation Robert had enjoyed since he started school, and its benefits undoubtedly induced him to purchase, in later life, his own yacht in order to 'get away from it all'. On 23 July 1824 he recorded in his log-book: -

'Early in the morning I saw the Colombian coast, and at two o'clock cast anchor opposite La Guayra; observed with silence the miserable appearance of the town. The hills behind the town rise to a height that gives a degree of sublimity to the scenery in the eyes of a stranger.' (77)

The sad appearance of the town was the first of many disappointments to be faced during his stay in South America. He investigated a breakwater or pier at La Guayra, and a railway to Caracas 8 miles away. He carefully sounded out local opinion regarding storms and as a result decided on a breakwater in favour of a pier. The terrain between La Guayra and Caracas, which necessitated a gain 3,000 feet in such a short distance, would have made the railway extremely difficult to construct and to work. He submitted that it would cost at least £160,000, and considered with the amount of traffic likely to be generated (less than 6,000 tons per annum) it was doubtful that it would be profitable. The hills behind the town lost 'their degree of sublimity' when he had to travel over them! 'Mounted on a mule he surveyed the road between the two towns, and found it "a wonderful example of human industry – not human skill." The ascents and descents were so precipitous that he wondered how his brute contrived to keep on its legs.' It provided a foretaste of the type of tracks to be encountered on his 700-mile journey to the capital, Bogotá, and the problems to be faced in transporting the heavy machinery, even short distances, over such roads to the mines. (78)

He completed his explorations around Caracas by the 21 October, and started his long mule journey to the interior accompanied by a German servant and interpreter. The journey was prolonged by the need to fulfil his remit to investigate and report on the roads and mineral prospects of the country that he passed through. A number of days were wasted by following up false leads, and he did not arrive at Bogotá until mid-January 1825. However, he was sufficiently impressed to write to his father 'expressing great confidence in the mineral wealth of the country.' He met Mr. R. S. Illingworth, the commercial representative of the Mining Association, in Bogotá. He then proceeded about 70 miles north west, crossing the Magdalena River at Honda, to reach the once prosperous, but now almost deserted, city of Mariquita. The main mines, for which the Colombian Mining Association had negotiated a lease, were Santa Ana and La Manta, on the eastern slopes of the Andes just a few miles beyond Mariquita. **(79)**

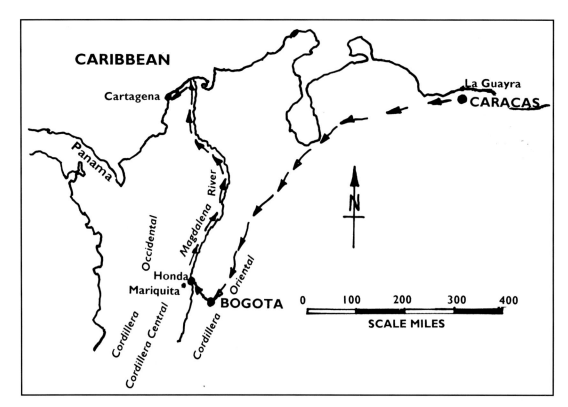

Figure 1.4: map of Gran Colombia showing Robert's main journeys between 1824 and 1827.

The Magdalena River was navigable from the rapids at Honda to the Caribbean, some 450 miles away, and steamboats had been introduced on it in 1822. This made the river appear far more attractive than attempting the 800 miles of mule tracks to get to La Guayra. **(80)** Honda was only 20 miles from the mines, but the route rose steeply from the river; even the first climb out of Honda was precipitous. However, for the main part of the journey the roads were good by Latin American standards.

'A moderate amount of labour would have rendered them passable for wheeled carriages, except at certain points where it was clear that wheels could never run.' Two rivers had to be forded, but often on the worst parts of the route, which could not be improved, 'the way ran over bare rocks, through narrow passages worn by the floods of the wet season, and down declivities so nearly perpendicular that no beast of burden, except a mule, could descend them.' 'In the precipitous portions of the route, which mules took two hours to cross, Robert Stephenson saw at a glance difficulties of which he had not been forewarned, and for which he was consequently unprovided. The heavier portion of the machinery could not be moved across the country except on wheeled carriages.' (81)

The Mining Association's idea of re-opening the best of the old Spanish mines, employing steam engines to work the pumps and machinery, was very plausible. But, incredibly, having arranged to transport bulky equipment over thousands of miles of water, through storm and floods, they found that they were unable to move it the last 20 miles on land. The directors' failure to have made even the basic inquiries, before they took the lease, to see if was possible to get the essential machinery up to the mines gave Robert the impression that 'he was at the head of an enterprise projected by visionary speculators'. **(82)** His early reports about the difficulties must have come as quite a shock to them! However, his suggestions on how to help the situation were generally ignored, though this may have been partly due to letters taking up to five months to reach their destination.

Robert was well aware that to be connected with an ill-conceived venture would not do his reputation any good, and he must have felt bitterly disappointed when all those dreams of fame and wealth had vanished. He hoped to extricate himself from the project when letters from home left no doubt that his talents could be far better employed in England rather than supervising, now traditional, mining operations in Colombia. His partners in Robert Stephenson & Co., with the exception of Thomas Richardson, urgently required that he return home. Richardson, who may have pinned any hope of saving the Colombian venture on Robert, was against it. (83) The others felt that he was under no legal obligation to the Colombian Mining Association, but, in spite of his frustration, Robert felt bound to stay until the end of the three-year engagement, unless, as Richardson suggested, he was given the formal permission of the directors to quit his post earlier.

When his assistant, Charles Empson (1792-1861), and the first party of the miners arrived at Honda they had to leave all the machinery on the banks of the Magdalena, only taking up to the mines the light tools and implements that could be carried on the backs of mules. Robert immediately sent an urgent message to England requesting that all further machinery be sent out as a kit of parts small enough to be carried by the mules.

> 'Instead of supplying him with the machinery for which he had written, the directors sent out fresh cargoes of costly and ponderous apparatus, which could no more be conveyed over bridgeless rivers, and up mountain passes, than they could be wafted from the earth's surface to another planet; and to add to his chagrin, the projectors wrote to him, complaining that he had not already sent home a freight of silver.' (84)

All this machinery had to be left to rust on the banks of the Magdalena and its absence at the mines delayed even the preliminary work. It was not until the end of October 1825 that sufficient miners had arrived to enable the operations to begin in earnest.

The miners were an even worse problem. They had been recruited in Cornwall and little effort seems to have been made to select reliable workers. They had a reputation for being unruly in England but now, free from the social constraints of their homeland, they degenerated into an insolent, undisciplined, drunken rabble.

> '...the terms on which these miners had been hired were far too high. Insolent from prosperity, and demoralised by the long-continued idleness of the voyage, they no sooner entered Honda than they roused the indignation of the inhabitants by excesses which outraged even South American morals. Before Robert Stephenson made the acquaintance of the men, he received a formal and angry remonstrance from the Governor of Honda with regard to their conduct.' (85)

Robert hoped that by taking a carefully reasoned line as to their responsibilities and by setting them to work he would be able to control them, but easy access to alcohol made them ungovernable. They particularly resented that Robert was not a Cornishman and that he was so young. He wrote to Illingworth, in Bogotá, 'They plainly tell me that I am obnoxious to them, because I was not born in Cornwall; and ...that it is impossible for a north-countryman to know anything about mining.' Their promotion was through the ranks and to their minds it was unthinkable for anyone who had not reached a senior position in this manner to know anything about mining. There must have been a much more enlightened attitude in the North East as Nicholas Wood was only in his mid twenties when he became viewer at Killingworth. As was customary in Cornwall the gangers or foremen of the teams gloried in the title of 'captain' so they deliberately gave the impression to the locals that they were really in charge, and Robert was not the Engineer-in-Chief but only a youth sent out to pay their wages. The Association did take a strong line to remove this misapprehension. (86)

The miners' behaviour was so bad that on two nights Robert's life was in real danger from their riotous, drunken invasion of his bamboo cottage at Santa Ana. In order to moderate their more obvious vices Robert tried to interest them in sports, games and trials of strength during the evenings. Here his own prowess gained him some grudging respect. In spite of all his efforts he was never able to 'get from any man more than half a day's work each day, and he always had nearly a third of his hundred and sixty subordinates disabled by drink'. (87)

There were some advantages of being in Colombia. The climate in the foothills of the Andes was every bit as good as he had been led to expect, and the profuse, beautiful and varied flora and fauna gave the impression of an earthly paradise. The Stephensons had always had a love for birds and animals and here their noisy, endearing and often amusing activities were a source of pleasure to Robert. His cottage was positioned to give him a superb view over an extensive and varied panorama with the added bonus of the amazing sunsets. He wrote to Michael Longridge in December 1825 saying that his health was good, but 'not as strong as when I left England'. (88) He suffered from bouts of fever and a 'visceral derangement'. (89)

He profited by the company of visitors from Mariquita and Bogotá. For several weeks his guests were Jean Baptiste Boussingault (1802-87) and a Dr. Roullin, who was nominated to be the professor of mathematics at the university that was to be re-established in Bogotá. Boussingault, who was to become professor of chemistry at Lyon and make significant discoveries about plant life, had been educated in the School of Mines at St. Étienne before coming to South America in support of Simón Bolívar's successful revolution. (It was this revolution which had provided enough stability in 'Gran Colombia' to enable the mining operations to recommence.) He was now employed by the Mining Association as a chemist and geologist. Both these gentlemen generously shared their special knowledge with Robert. 'Under their guidance Robert Stephenson studied with system and accuracy the higher branches of mathematics, and various departments of natural science.' (90)

He wrote to his step-mother to say that he was dividing his time 'between eating and study'. This may have been true in the wet seasons, but at other times he explored large tracts of the surrounding country prospecting for minerals. He made assays of the specimens of ore that he found, and wrote reams of letters and reports. Jeaffreson, who had access to the reports, thought that they had 'considerable literary merits'. **(91)** It was clear from the letters, which he had written since leaving university, that he wrote in good idiomatic English. He was not very happy about his speech though, which still had traces of his colliery background, and he implored the few Englishmen, that he came in contact with, to correct his lapses into the vernacular.

In the three years from 31 December 1824 the Colombian Mining Association had expended nearly £200,000 on their venture, but a large proportion of the sum had been wasted by their own maladministration. The only viable operations had been carried out under Robert's direction; 'in everything for which he individually could be held accountable the expedition had been successful.' Before he quit Robert suggested a strategy, which if followed, 'could be made to pay them a handsome, though not enormous, dividend.' (92)

On completion of his three year agreement Robert was asked to wait at least long enough to allow his grudging replacement to arrive; he could not agree and R. S. Illingworth had to come from Bogotá to hold the fort. If Smiles is to be believed, one of the directors even approached George Stephenson and offered 'to make it worth his while' to allow Robert to extend his three-year stay. (93) He left Santa Ana in late July 1827 with his friend and assistant, Charles Empson, (94) and joined a boat at Honda for the passage down the Magdalena to Cartagena on the Caribbean. He had been very enthusiastic, in his letters and reports, about the possibility of building a road or canal over the Isthmus of Panama in order to avoid the voyage around Cape Horn. He had hoped to get some idea of either's feasibility before his journey home, but this was not possible in the time available.

In Cartagena Robert met Richard Trevithick whose mining ventures in Peru had been erroneously reported in Cornwall as making him an enormous fortune and earning him £100,000 a year. (95) He was, in fact, penniless. In his biography Francis Trevithick only quotes rather contradictory letters about his father's meeting with Robert. Francis' later position as the London & North Western Railway's locomotive engineer means he must have met Robert several times in the quarter century after his father's death, but he obviously did not bother to find out the facts first hand. Robert is accused of being initially aloof and making no attempt to talk to Trevithick, but the two had not met since Robert was a baby so it is hardly surprising that neither one recognised the other. Also Robert was wearing the Colombian attire, that he had adopted three years earlier, and Trevithick's garments were much the worse for wear. One report suggested that they became involved in a slanging match, but their raised voices may just have been the result of two enthusiasts releasing their pent up ideas to each other. We can only speculate on the amount of influence that their exchange of ideas had on the future development of the steam locomotive. Robert had saved £100 for his journey home, and he gave half of it to Trevithick to enable him to sail via Jamaica to England. **(96)**

There was an epidemic of yellow fever in Cartagena, which recommended as brief a stay there as possible. As there was no ship immediately available for the direct voyage to England, Robert's party, which had now swelled to five, decided to take passage on one bound for New York, from where there were frequent sailings to Liverpool or London. They had been joined by a Mr. Gerard and the two small Montealegre boys who were under his care. **(97)** Their voyage was uneventful until they approached Cuba when they had to rescue the pathetic survivors from two hulks that had been dismasted in storms. They were fortunate to have been becalmed and so avoided the storms, which had struck a little to the north of them and 'wrecked every vessel exposed to their violence'. They did not finish their journey unscathed as, nearing New York, their brig, *Bunker Hill*, ran aground about midnight. 'The vessel soon filled with water, and, being surrounded by the breaking surf, the ship was soon split up, and before morning our situation became perilous.' Although it must have been a terrifying experience, fortunately no lives were lost, and the passengers were taken ashore about 8 o'clock. Robert lost his money and all his belongings except his prized collection of mineral specimens. **(98)**

Robert had no problems in getting money when he arrived in New York in mid-September, but he and his party could not face another long voyage immediately after seeing the results of the other shipwrecks and experiencing their own. He wrote to Illingworth, '…had I not been on the American side of the Atlantic, I guess I would not have gone to sea again.' (98) They went on a tour to the Niagara Falls and Montreal; a round trip of about 1,000 miles. In spite of the urgent requests for him to return home as soon as possible, this trip delayed his arrival by over a month. He wanted to find out more about 'the finest steam-boats in the world', being built by the Stevens and others, which also intrigued his father. **(99)** To cover the 1,000 miles in less than a month must have required using boats for most of the journey. In the twenty years since steam navigation had been introduced on the Hudson River considerable advances had been made in the design of the craft and their engines, and they were now widely used on the rivers, canals and lakes of North America. Obviously any information Robert could obtain about their boilers, mechanism and performance would be invaluable on his return to the locomotive works.

Robert did not find the Niagara Falls as impressive as the Tequendama Falls in Colombia, and we are told: -

> 'At Montreal he threw aside his Colombian dress, and, equipping himself in the ordinary costume of an English gentleman, went into the best society of the city. After attending a succession of balls and routs given by the colonial dignitaries, he returned to New York, and with his four companions and a servant took his passage to Liverpool in a first-class packet – the *Pacific*.' **(100)**

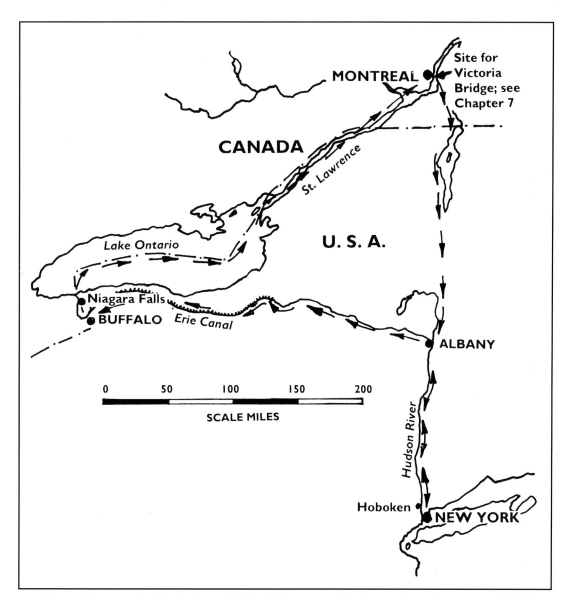

Figure 1.5: map showing Robert's 1,000 mile journey in North America in the autumn of 1827.

The *Pacific* arrived in Liverpool between 11 and 16 November 1827. Here Robert found his father in charge of constructing the Liverpool and Manchester Railway, and settled in a comfortable house in Upper Parliament Street. **(101)** During Robert's absence, of over three years, George had enjoyed the triumph of the opening of the Stockton and Darlington Railway, and endured the disappointment and embarrassment of the failure of the first L&M Bill. Regardless of having been let down by the inaccurate L&M survey, and being torn to shreds by the legal vultures at the committee stages of the Bill, George was now well on his way to vindicate his claims about railways.

Within six months of Robert's departure to South America another company was being set up in Newcastle, 'for opening an office of Engineering and Railway Surveying'. Mindful of the cause of

James's financial problems, this was a means of providing the funding to allow George to survey and project many further railways, and advance his ambition for a monopoly in railway construction. That monopoly was a dream that could not happen, but the 'sleeping partners' must have benefited considerably over the years from the efforts of George, his son and the large pool of engineers and surveyors that they employed. The company was inaugurated on 1 January 1825, under the name of 'George Stephenson & Son'. The five equal shareholders were: George Stephenson, Robert Stephenson, Edward Pease, Thomas Richardson and Michael Longridge. Clauses 4 and 6 stated: -

'4. All expenses for Clerks, Surveyors and other Salaries, and all other expenses shall be first discharged, after which Geo. Stephenson and Robt. Stephenson shall be paid for their joint use £1,500 per annum as a compensation for their services, and then the profits be divided according to their respective shares, providing the work done and the money received amount to the sum above named.

'6. Robt. Stephenson is at liberty to conclude his present foreign engagement before he render any personal service to this company, yet the benefit to arise from any other foreign engagement is to go into the common stock. **If within three months after his return to England, it is the said Robt. Stephenson's wish to terminate this agreement, it shall end upon his giving three month's notice**.' **(102)**

Robert had a crucial decision to make: whether to pull out of the partnership or stay within it but contrive to get as much freedom as possible. He chose the latter course, although he knew Locke and Vignoles were having problems working with his father on the L&M. George did the route planning for many of the lines that Robert built, but it was extremely rare for them to work together on their construction.

NOTES AND REFERENCES

1. J. C. Jeaffreson and William Pole, F.R.S., *The Life of Robert Stephenson, F. R. S. Volume 1,* (1864) (Jeaff. Vol. 1) pp 7-8. For a modern work on R. S's early life see Victoria Haworth, *Robert Stephenson: Engineer and Scientist: The Making of a Prodigy.* (2004)
2. Ibid. p. 6. Robert Hawthorn founded an engineering works in 1817, where his sons were later to produce locomotives next door to Robert Stephenson & Co's.; the latter took them over in 1937.
3. Ibid. p. 60.
4. Ibid. pp. 6, 23.
5. Ibid. pp. 12-13.
6. The Grand Allies were a group of colliery owners: Earl Strathmore (1769-1820), Sir Thomas Liddell (later Lord Ravensworth) (1775-1854) and the Rt. Hon. James Stuart-Wortley-Mackenzie (later Lord Wharncliffe) (1776-1845).
7. Jeaff. Vol. 1, p. 15. She died on 14 May.
8. Samuel Smiles, *Lives of the Engineers. The Locomotive, George and Robert Stephenson,* (1862 edition, reprinted 1968), pp. 45-6. Samuel Smiles (1813-1904) was secretary to the Leeds & Thirsk Railway and, later, to the South Eastern Railway. Oddly, Prof. Simmons considered the Stephenson book as 'honest and careful' but L. T. C. Rolt, in his foreword to the 1968 reprint, rightly considered 'It is one of the defects of Smiles' writing that he makes his chosen characters appear as faultless paragons of virtue... Smiles unwittingly does his characters a disservice.' Adrian Jarvis' searching paper 'The credibility of Samuel Smiles in early railway history', given to the First International Early Railway Conference in 1998, has appeared in the *Gazette* of the Robert Stephenson Trust, Vol. V No. 2 and Vol. VI No. 1 (2004-5).
9. Jeaff. Vol. 1, pp. 15-6.
10. Ibid. p. 2 also Smiles, p. 47.
11. Smiles, p. 65.
12. Jeaff. Vol. 1, pp. 16-9.
13. Smiles, p. 65.
14. Jeaff. Vol. 1 p. 29.
15. Smiles, p. 59.
16. Francis Trevithick, *The Life of Richard Trevithick,* (1872), Vol. 2. p. 172.
17. Smiles, p. 61.
18. Jeaff. Vol. 1, pp. 34-6.
19. Smiles, p. 63.
20. Jeaff. Vol. 1, pp. 43-4.
21. Smiles, pp. 63.
22. Ibid. p.114, also *Lit & Phil. Bicentenary Lectures 1993,* pp. 72, 196.
23. Jeaff. Vol. 1, p. 44.
24. Smiles, pp. 51-2.
25. Ibid. p. 104.
26. Ibid. p. 108. This is confirmed by the under-viewer, John Moody's, statement of 23 Dec. 1816.
27. Ibid. p. 113.
28. Ibid. p. 109.
29. Northumberland Record Office NRO 602/21

30. Jeaff. Vol. 1, p. 39.
31. J. A. Francis, *A History of the English Railway,* (1851), Vol. 1, p. 197. After R. S's death successive presidents of the Institution of Civil Engineers, J. Locke and G. P. Bidder, both commented on the extent of his scientific knowledge.
32. Jeaff. Vol. 1, p. 33. The 1815 date he quotes is incorrect.
33. Ibid. p. 44.
34. J. G. H. Warren, *A Century of Locomotive Building by Robert Stephenson & Co.* (1923) p. 35.
35. Smiles, p. 139. This was the second time that George had considered emigrating.
36. Jeaff. Vol. 1, pp. 3, 50. Smiles, p. 150. Both Jeaffreson and Smiles originally accepted the legend, but later Smiles was able to disprove it.
37. Jeaff. Vol. 1, p. 52. In 1923 Warren op. cit. (p39) regretted that Nicholas Wood had been ignored by our national biographers; eighty years later it is still the case. Wood's preference for making careful observations and experiments before carrying out modifications may not have been in accord with George Stephenson's more impatient rough and ready approach. Although he remained a friend of the Stephensons he did not become involved in George's railway building or in Robert Stephenson and Co. where his influence could have been extremely valuable. He continued to make and repair locomotives at Killingworth after the Newcastle works had been founded. His interest in the scientific approach to railways resulted in him being consulted on many railway projects during his life. He preferred to remain in the mining industry where, through his ability and shrewd purchase of collieries, he amassed a fortune of £400,000. His *A Practical Treatise on Rail-Roads* was published in editions of 1825, 1831/2 and 1838.
38. Ibid. pp. 52-3.
39. W. O. Skeat, *George Stephenson. The Engineer and His Letters,* (1973), pp. 35-6.
40. Smiles, pp. 140, also Jeaff. Vol. 1 p. 49. Smiles says that George was employed to *alter* a waggonway to Hetton *in 1819*. No evidence of this waggonway is shown on contemporary maps. Work on sinking Hetton Colliery had ceased by 1819 because of financial problems of the then owner; it was not re-started under new management until December 1820. It is feasible that the planning did start in 1819, but at whose behest?
41. C. Von Oeynhausen and H. Von Dechen, *Railways in England 1826 and 1827,* (1971) pp. 32-3.
42. W. W. Tomlinson, *The North Eastern Railway; Its Rise and Development,* (1914), pp. 40-86, gives an extensive description of the events leading to the opening of the S&D.
43. There are conflicting accounts of this meeting by those involved; the Peases, George Stephenson, Nicholas Wood and John Dixon. Warren, op. cit. (p. 44 footnote) is certainly correct when he says there is confusion between two distinct visits. The legendary, unannounced *evening* visit was well before the 19 April *morning* visit. The Peases obviously needed some time to check out the claims of a pair of uninvited strangers before putting the railway project into George's hands. John Dixon said that he was sent to Killingworth to summon George for, undoubtedly, the second meeting. This meeting resulted in the formal letter, asking George to review the scheme, being sent immediately afterwards, and George responding to it on 28 April.
44. Jeaff. Vol. 1, p. 54.
45. Tomlinson, p. 80.
46. Jeaff. Vol. 1 p. 55.
47. Smiles, p. 148.
48. Jeaff. Vol. 1, pp. 54-9.
49. *Manchester Guardian,* 20 May 1848.
50. Deposited Plan, 1823.
51. Tomlinson, p. 140.
52. P. S. A. Berridge, *The Girder Bridge,* (1969) p. 1.
53. *The Transactions of the Newcomen Society,* Vols. 52 and 59.
54. Smiles, p. 158.
55. B. Woodcroft, *Abridgements of Specifications Relating to Railways 1803- 1866,* (1873), p.7.
56. Charles E. Lee, *The Evolution of Permanent Way,* (1937), pp. 52-3.
57. Jeaff. Vol. 1, p. 51.
58. Ibid. p. 65. This may be a simplified account of the failure of their relationship as Losh had already appreciated the value of malleable iron. In the previous month (14 September 1821) he had taken out his own patent for 'fixing bars of malleable iron on the upper surface of a line of cast-iron rails...' (Patent 4591).
59. Warren, p. 30. W. H. James's boiler, which *was* patented in 1825, had concentric water tubes surrounding a single fire tube. The one he *considered* patenting in 1821 may have been of a more conventional design.
60. Smiles, p. 188.
61. Original letter Liverpool City Library.
62. E. M. S. P. *The Two James's and the Two Stephensons,* (1861, reprinted 1961), p. 72.
63. R. H. G. Thomas, *The Liverpool & Manchester Railway,* (1980), pp. 16-18. This work gives a well researched account of the railway, although Professor Simmons considered, in his foreword, that: 'Mr. Thomas is ungenerous towards George Stephenson – though he might fairly point out that George himself was very rarely generous to others [!].'
64. E. M. S. P., pp. 105-7, vi. In June 1846 Robert's name was at the top of a committee of sympathetic senior engineers 'for promoting a general subscription for the three sons and one daughter of William James, deceased.' A very sour view appears eight years later when he sent copies of their correspondence to Samuel Smiles: -'There is a bundle of James's letters, which characterise the man very clearly as a ready, dashing writer, but no thinker at all on the practical part of the subject he had taken up. It was the same with

everything he touched. He never succeeded in anything, and yet possessed a great deal of talking talent. His fluency of conversation I never heard equalled, and so you would judge from his letters.'

65. Warren, p. 53.
66. Ibid. pp. 53-8.
67. Smiles, p. 144.
68. Jeaff. Vol. 1, p.66.
69. Ibid. p. 62. Letter to Michael Longridge dated 10 Sept. 1823.
70. Ibid. pp. 67-8.
71. Ibid. p. 73.
72. Ibid. pp. 70-1.
73. Smiles, p. 243 states that George took Robert for a medical examination by Dr. T. E. Headlam in Newcastle. 'Robert afterwards used to say that he felt as if he were upon trial for life or death.'
74. Jeaff. Vol. 1, p. 72.
75. Ibid. pp. 74-6.
76. Ibid. pp. 74-6.
77. Ibid. p. 78.
78. Ibid. pp. 78-81. Robert's own description which appeared in *National Magazine and Monthly Critic* during 1837 (pp. 40 and 44) states that the main road was well paved and drained, but it was the roads from it to the plantations that were 'in some cases so steep that it was difficult to sit on the mules.'
79. Ibid. p. 81-3. When questioned on his work in Colombia during his evidence for the 1829 Newcastle & Carlisle Bill (p. 128) R. S. was asked if he had been employed in mining, he answered; 'Yes; and also road making; I made some surveys in that country; indeed that was the ostensible object that I went out for.' When asked; 'Did you go out with a view to the erection of machinery?' he answered 'No' [Who did then?].
80. *Encyclopaedia Britannica,* (1973), Vol. 14 p. 566. It is possible that the Mining Association did not appreciate the navigational prospects of the river, hence the reason for exploring the roads.
81. Jeaff. Vol. 1, pp. 84-5.
82. Ibid. p. 93, also *The Larchfield Diary,* (1876). In 1825 Thomas Mewburn (1786-1867), 'the first railway solicitor', wrote in his diary (p. 7) 'The London speculators allege that British industry and British capital will effect what cannot be accomplished by the natives, and they fondly hope that by transplanting British miners and establishing railways and steam engines the difficulties which the natives have encountered will be overcome.' He recorded in 1826; 'Nearly all these speculations have entirely failed.'
83. Ibid. p. 95.
84. Ibid. p. 98.
85. Ibid. p. 87.
86. Ibid. pp. 87-90.
87. Ibid. p. 91.
88. Ibid. p. 96.
89. Smiles, p. 247.
90. Jeaff. Vol. 1 pp. 92, 98.
91. Ibid. p. 92, on the other hand Smiles (p. 246) found them 'dry and uninteresting'.
92. Ibid. p. 101.
93. Smiles, p. 250.
94. Jeaff. Vol. 1. p. 105.
95. Smiles, p. 252.
96. Trevithick, Vol. 2, pp. 272-3. Both Smiles and Jeaffreson say that Trevithick accompanied Robert to New York but this is incorrect.
97. Jeaff. Vol. 1, p. 105 states that (John Mair) Gerard was an employee of the Mining Association but this may be incorrect as he could have been freelancing. The elder of the Montealegre brothers, Jose, later became President of Costa Rica, and the younger, Mariano, assisted on District 5 of the London & Birmingham, which included Kilsby Tunnel. Information kindly supplied by R. S. Roper
98. Smiles, pp. 252-3. The mineral collection survives in a museum in Cheltenham.
99. Jeaff. Vol. 1, p. 97. Col. John Stevens (1749-1838) of Hoboken, New Jersey, and Robert Fulton (1765-1815) did much of the pioneering work on these steamboats.
100. Ibid. pp. 109-11. Robert's letter quoted on pages 109-10 makes no mention of the steamboats, and Jeaffreson says that the journey was made *on foot.* We know Robert was in New York on 21 Sept. and the packet to England must have left New York in late October to arrive in Liverpool before mid-November – so how could he and his party have covered 1,000 miles on foot, and still have time for three or four days in Montreal? The Hudson River and Erie Canal (opened 1825) gave direct access to Buffalo (for Niagara), and much of the return journey via Montreal could be accomplished also by using boats.
101. PRO RAIL 371/1, L&M minutes, George was formally appointed on 3 July 1826 at a salary of £800 on condition that he was in attendance for 9 months out of every 12.
102. Warren, pp. 63-4. One of the routes anticipated to need an immediate survey in 1825 was the 'London and Northern Rail Road'. The partners must still have expected Robert's rapid return from Columbia as he was nominated to take charge of a team of seven surveyors earmarked for this scheme. Unfortunately, nothing other than the first ledger, giving some tantalising details of George Stephenson & Son, has survived; this is now in the NRM Library at York. The company was formally wound up soon after George's death in 1848.

CHAPTER TWO: RETURN HOME

November 1827 to September 1833

There were a number of things that required Robert's immediate attention on his return from America.

He was very concerned about a satisfactory conclusion of his affairs with the Colombian Mining Association so he must have been relieved to find that they had accepted their reduced scale of operations, and 'received him with gratifying expressions of respect.' He agreed to give advice on their future projects, and in January 1828 visited Alston Moor, in Cumberland, to recruit some lead miners for work in Colombia and Mexico. (1)

Edward Pease and Thomas Richardson had both written in early 1827 threatening the closure of Robert Stephenson & Co. Pease wrote: -

> 'I can assure thee that thy business at Newcastle, as well as thy father's engineering, have suffered very much from thy absence, and, unless thou soon return, the former will be given up, as Mr. Longridge is not able to give it that attention it requires; and what *is* done is not done with credit to the house.' (2)

Robert was well aware of his responsibilities. He had written to R. S. Illingworth in March 1826; 'My prosperity is involved in that of my father, whose property was sacrificed in laying the foundations of an establishment for me; his capital being invested in a concern which requires the greatest attention…' His father and Michael Longridge had not been able to devote much time to the business, and Pease's criticism was justified; the well-equipped factory was running at a loss. A drastic reorganization was required: designs, estimating, workmanship, the securing and delivering of orders all needed considerable improvement to assure the firm's future. Robert put some real effort into turning the fortunes of the firm around, but its reputation may have suffered, in the short term, by its previous poor performance. In June 1829 the L&M directors resolved to enforce a hefty penalty of £500 if the firm did not deliver the winding engine for the Liverpool tunnel by 4 November. **(3)**

During Robert's visits to London, prior to going to South America, he had met the nubile and intelligent, Miss Fanny Sanderson, and had been sufficiently attracted to wish to renew their acquaintanceship very soon after his return. She was described as '…not beautiful, but she had an elegant figure, a delicate and animated countenance, and a pair of singularly expressive dark eyes.' After her death a close relative added: 'She was an unusually clever woman, and possessed of great tact in influencing others, without letting anyone see her power. To the last her will was law with her husband; but, though she always had her way, she never seemed to care about having it.' (4)

Robert did not immediately commit himself 'to the position of a suitor.' Almost a year after his return to England he met his father by chance in London, and took him unannounced to Broad Street to meet the lady. She survived the ordeal! 'She did not appear confused, and the visit passed off extremely well.' Two months later Robert proposed to her with the intention of their getting married in early 1829. Michael Longridge recommended that the couple should settle in Bedlington, and Robert prepared to take a house there. His work meant that he would have long absences from home, and Fanny would have felt very isolated in the village after spending her life in London. His family and friends were so very much against the idea that he abandoned it, thus delaying his marriage by some months. A suitable new house, No. 5 Greenfield Place, was rented on the, then, western outskirts of Newcastle, about half-a-mile from the factory. This 'small and unassuming dwelling' overlooked the verdant Tyne valley, and 'Newcastle had few more pleasant places.' (5)

Robert had many commitments during the first six months of 1829, but he did contrive to spend a lot of time in London, and receive the censure of his peers. Richardson, of all people, '…went so far as to reprove him for wasting on a pair of bright and laughing eyes the time that might be more profitably spent in paying court to the magnates of Change.' Robert was indignant: -

> 'You do me injustice in supposing that the ladies in Broad Street engross the whole of my time; I am at present so ardently engaged in the [Newcastle and] Carlisle opposition that I have neither time to visit Broad Street or the Hill (i. e. Stamford Hill, Mr. Richardson's residence), though a visit to either place would give me great pleasure. You are really too severe when you imagine, or rather conclude, that I neglect business for considerations of minor importance. [!] I am well aware that it is only by close attention to my business that I can get on in the world.' (6)

On Wednesday 17 June 1829 the wedding ceremony took place in the parish church of St. Botolph, Bishopsgate. Fanny's family was not rich, and the factory was still absorbing most of the money that Robert and his father could earn, so the celebrations were modest. At the end of their short honeymoon in North Wales he established his wife in Greenfield Place, and got busy with the building of *Rocket*. (7)

Between Robert's return to England and his appointment as Engineer-in-Chief of the London and Birmingham Railway (L&B), in September 1833, he became involved in the construction of a number of small railways, and in giving opinions and evidence for or against others. This, together with his other consultations, provided a much needed source of income, but some of these commitments were to embarrassingly increase his workload during the projecting and engineering of the L&B.

1829 Evidence against the Newcastle and Carlisle Railway Bill

According to Joseph Locke's (1805-60) evidence George Stephenson was employed, in 1825-6, by major local landowners, the Greenwich Hospital Commissioners, to survey an alternative route for the Newcastle & Carlisle Railway (NCR) to that proposed by William Chapman (1749-1832) and Benjamin Thompson (1779-1867). The rival line, which was surveyed by Locke (Robert was in South America), was required to run to the north of the Tyne from Hexham and on to the Town Moor at Newcastle. **(8)** It employed inclined planes to reach the higher ground to avoid the flooding, which would have been a major problem with parts of the Chapman/Thompson alignment. **(9)** Michael Longridge wrote to Robert in November 1825, 'Your father has been employed by the party who oppose this railway, and in examining the line has found greater errors in the levels than were committed by his assistants in the Liverpool Road. Robert! my faith in engineers is wonderfully shaken.' (10) Robert was to give evidence against the second N&CR Bill, in February 1829, particularly with regard to the possibility of flooding south of the river between Newcastle and Hexham. Although other engineers opposed the Bill, on the same grounds, it was passed and the levels were altered during the building of the line to resolve the problem. In February 1830 George Stephenson expressed his regrets that the N&CR, which passed within sight of his birthplace, was not to be built by him, but he still hoped that, by default, its construction might subsequently fall into his hands. A letter, from Robert to Thomas Richardson, dated 25 January 1830, speculated how he and George would have divided the work on the railway. It gives an early insight to his attitude on delegation and his reluctance to work directly with his father: -

> 'I have consulted with my father on the subject of the Carlisle end of the railway. He is quite agreeable to take the west end of the line and leave it chiefly to my management for something between £500 and £700 a year. They would not expect my whole time to be devoted to it, as an assistant to be always attending would be requisite; so it would not require me to confine my attention to that neighbourhood entirely. I should then have the Lancashire [linking the Bolton and Leigh to the L&M] and the Warrington and Newton to attend to. Amongst them I should divide my attention, and I see no difficulty in doing that, when I have a confidential assistant at each place to see that my plans are carefully and strictly attended to ...' (11)

A year later he became involved in another railway from Newcastle. In January 1831, Joshua Richardson, then the resident engineer of the Leicester and Swannington Railway, issued a pamphlet proposing a line from Newcastle to North Shields. Enough interest was generated for a meeting to resolve that Robert Stephenson and Richardson should prepare a survey. The promoters failed to reach a decision regarding the best route, and before the year's end the project came to a standstill. In 1835, another line was suggested, and, with some modifications, was completed in 1839. (12)

The Canterbury and Whitstable Railway.

An alternative to the turnpike roads was required for the transport of coal and merchandise between the sea and Canterbury. This gave rise to a number of schemes for the improvement of the navigation on the River Stour between its mouth at Pegwell Bay, near Ramsgate, and the city. Ironically, just as a solution was being reached to improve the river, William James proposed a railway on a much shorter route over the hill from the sea at Whitstable. **(13)** The engineering talents that became involved were Telford and Chapman, for the river improvements, the Stephensons, Locke, John Dixon, Thomas Cabry and Edward Fletcher for the railway, and James Walker for Whitstable Harbour. **(14)**

George Stephenson supplanted the bankrupt William James, as he had on the Liverpool and Manchester. He made some minor alterations to the plans, but the line that was built was basically the one that had been deposited by James in November 1824, and granted Royal Assent on 10 June 1825. (15) After authorization, George was appointed Engineer for the line, but had little personal involvement in it: -

> 'I merely gave the general levels from the map presented to me, and sent Mr. Locke to lay out the line in the best way. They had not enough money to execute the line properly, and could not pay more than one resident engineer. I did not see it more than once or

twice, and observed that the walls of one of the bridges were bulging I remarked that it would come down, however, the bridge is still standing; the engineer did the best he could, but he was a young engineer.' (16)

Joseph Locke was only employed for a few weeks, about the time that the Act was granted, to do the primary setting out. John Dixon (1796-1865) supervised the line's construction from immediately after the completion of the S&D in September 1825 until he went to the L&M at the beginning of 1827; Joshua Richardson was his assistant. **(17)**

The single line railway was six miles long and required a steep climb of around 220 feet from Whitstable Harbour to the summit at Clow's Wood. A mile of easy gradients followed before a steep descent from Tyler Hill to Canterbury; there was a tunnel 842 yds long on the Canterbury incline. Initially, there were stationary engines at Tyler Hill and Clow's Wood, which together worked just over four miles of the railway from Canterbury to Bogshole. From Bogshole, for the remaining two miles, the locomotive *Invicta,* horses or gravity were used. By June 1827 the tunnel was finished, but work, on the almost complete railway, stopped as there was a shortage of cash. Around May the following year Robert took over the little outstanding work, with Thomas Cabry (1801-73) in charge of the erection of the stationary engines. (18) The railway was officially opened on 3 May 1830, beating the Liverpool and Manchester by over four months. (19)

The locomotive and the two 25 horsepower winding engines were supplied by Robert Stephenson & Co. (20) In 1832, after *Invicta* had problems working heavier trains, the company provided another 15 horsepower stationary engine at the top of Church Street incline. **(21)** Francis Whishaw reports that by 1839 the locomotive had been dispensed with. **(22)** In 1825 George Stephenson had advised against the use of locomotives, and had proposed three stationary engines with the easier gradients being worked by horses. (23) Possibly the confidence arising from the success of the *Rocket* led to the introduction of a locomotive on the railway. *Invicta* is preserved, but, like the *Rocket,* little remains of the original machine, and again its appearance is much altered. (24)

The Warrington and Newton Railway.

When Robert was being questioned about his previous experience of civil engineering works, at the London and Birmingham inquiry, he cited the Warrington Railway as one of them. (25) This was a five-mile branch that ran south from the mid point of the Liverpool and Manchester towards the Mersey at Warrington. John Cass Birkinshaw (1811-67) assisted with the survey, and the line was authorised on 14 May 1829. Initially, it connected to the L&M only by a ten-chain curve towards Liverpool, and it crossed to the north of the main line to tap Haydock collieries. It bifurcated at Warrington to serve Dallam Lane and Bank Quay. The line was opened from Dallum Lane to the south end of Newton, to serve Haydock Park races, at the beginning of June 1830, and the west curve on to the L&M was ready on 25 July. The branch to Bank Quay, which also became part of the West Coast main line, was not completed until 1835. (26)

Before the end of 1829 Robert had proposed to the Warrington and Newton Company that it should extend the railway southwards across the Mersey as far as Sandbach, to form the first stage of a line to Birmingham. However, the opposite occurred when the Grand Junction Railway (GJR) was projected from Birmingham to Warrington. After somewhat protracted negotiations the GJR managed to purchase the W&N, thus avoiding having to build its own link from Warrington to the L&M; this was authorised by the Act of 12 June 1835. (27)

A new Act was granted to the W&N on 29 May 1830 to construct an east curve to allow direct running to Manchester or Wigan. Robert surveyed this line, which, having a considerably better radius than the west curve would have been about 1½ mile long. (28) It was not built and another ten-chain radius curve was substituted before the opening of the GJR in 1837. (29) In 1864 the LNWR built the Winwick-Golborne high-speed cut-off to link the mid point of the W&N with the Wigan branch, leaving just two miles of Robert's railway on the West Coast main line.

The Leicester and Swannington Railway

Another railway that Robert had been involved in as Engineer-in-Chief, before the London & Birmingham, was the 16-mile-long Leicester and Swannington. This line was destined to become the oldest part of the Midland Railway. In 1828 the usual problems with the inadequacy of the roads for the transport of coal and lime led a local mine owner to explore the Stockton and Darlington Railway. He was impressed and later, with his partners, he visited George Stephenson in Liverpool for advice on how to get a railway approved and built. George and Robert visited the locality and, as a result, on 12 February 1829 a committee was formed to promote the line. Initially Robert was engaged with a local surveyor to do the survey and present estimates. The works would be fairly light but a tunnel, about a mile long, and inclines of 1 in 29 and 1 in 17 would be needed; the cost was estimated at just over £75,000. George became the major shareholder, but not a director, at the outset. The first Act was granted on 29 May 1830, allowing the company to raise £90,000 capital and £20,000 loans. Robert was appointed Engineer on 9 July, (30) two months before he was plunged into the parliamentary work for the London and Birmingham (L&B). During the three-year period that he was engaged for the line he was very heavily committed on the L&B, and most of the work was left to three resident engineers employed by George Stephenson and Son. Joshua Richardson served for almost a year before returning to the Canterbury and Whitstable as manager. W. E. Gillespie, who had worked for George both on the Nanttle Railway and the L&M, held the post until December 1832, when he disappeared 'under a cloud' following the discovery of errors in the quantities and payments for the large Battleflat cutting. John Cass Birkinshaw replaced him. Birkinshaw and Robert finished with the line on 21 October 1833, a month after the latter had been formally appointed Engineer-in-Chief to the L&B. (31)

There were problems not only with the resident engineers and the inexperienced local contractors, but also with the tunnel. This was expected to be entirely through rock but one third of its length was found to be in sand. The problem came to light in March 1831, during the critical surveying and design stages of the L&B. Robert made a hasty visit and suggested the use of a temporary timber shield at the head of the excavation, while the tunnel should be lined throughout with brickwork 14 to 18 inches thick. With George being a major shareholder, he was called in a month later to report on the works for the now worried directors. He backed his son, and his recommendations were acted upon. Copeland and Harding, who had worked on the L&M tunnel and later completed the Watford contract on the L&B, were employed to finish the tunnel. (32) Robert reported, on 21 June 1832, that the tunnel was 'sound' but not perfect, and the line was officially opened on 17 July. (33) The original estimate for the railway was £5,603 per mile and the final cost, in spite of all the difficulties, came to only £7,970. (34)

The 1 in 17 gradient was against the flow of the loaded wagons, and the directors resolved, on 15 February 1833, '...that a Stationary Engine be immediately ordered for the inclined plane at Swannington and that the Engineer prepare proper plans and specifications'. Robert complied and his elegant design was put out to competitive tender resulting in the Horseley Iron Company being awarded the contract at the end of April. The engine suffered some teething troubles in its early days due to the manufacturing difficulties inherent at that time. The single-cylinder engine worked at a steam pressure of 80 lb. per sq. in., and the (then extremely innovative) piston valves were operated by gab motion similar to that introduced on contemporary locomotives. The flywheel was connected to the winding drum via a clutch, and a band brake was fitted to control descending wagons. (35)

The collieries served by the engine ceased working in the late 1870s, and from 1892 the Swannington engine was used to lower coal to a pumping engine needed to maintain the safety of other mines. In 1947 the pumping engine was converted to electric power, and the incline was officially closed in February 1948. (36) The Swannington engine was saved, and is now on display in the National Railway Museum at York. (Colour Plate 2)

Robert Stephenson & Co. provided the locomotives for the railway, but the first were found to be deficient in power for the unexpectedly heavy passenger and goods traffic. The company designed a powerful 0-6-0, *Atlas,* which was delivered in February 1834. Writing in 1923, J. G. H. Warren said: -

'This locomotive for the Leicester and Swannington Railway, built in 1834, may be justly called the prototype of the English six-coupled goods engine which has been – and is today – the maid-of-all-work of the British railway. Particulars of more than six hundred locomotives, obtained from various builders and railway companies, and published in 1840 [1842 Whishaw], show that up to that time the dimensions of this engine had been exceeded in a few instances only'. (37) (Fig. 3.13)

After the first four Stephenson locomotives had been delivered to the railway some directors felt that other manufacturers, like Edward Bury (1794-1858), should be invited to tender. As George was a major shareholder his opinion was sought and he is reputed to have replied: -'I have no objection, but put them to a fair test; hang one of Bury's engines on to one of mine, back-to-back; then let them have a go at it'! (38) It was obvious that Bury's smaller locomotive could not handle the heavy trains that Robert Stephenson's 0-6-0 could.

Early in 1831 the Snibston Estate, which was close to the railway, was to be auctioned, and Robert realised from the geological features that there would be profitable coal seams under it. 'This opinion he urged upon his father so forcibly, that the latter persuaded two of his Liverpool friends, Mr. Joseph Sandars and Sir Joshua Walmsley, to join him in purchasing the Snibston Estate.' There was, as usual, a snag in the form of a 20 feet thick layer of extremely hard igneous rock, 'green whinstone', which took two years to penetrate. They then found an excellent seam of main coal, at a depth of 600 feet, and Snibston Colliery turned out to be 'a most lucrative concern'. (39)

The Stanhope and Tyne Railway.

Around 1826 William Harrison, a bold entrepreneur, had been involved with the highly profitable Fawdon waggonway, and in 1831 this experience led him to become interested in a Durham railway project to link limestone quarries and kilns at Stanhope, in Weardale, with collieries at Medomsley, just north of Consett. The original plan was then to convey the coal and lime to the Tyne above Newcastle via the Derwent valley, probably by relaying the old Pontop waggonway. William Harrison soon abandoned this idea, and boldly proposed taking the new railway all the way to the Tyne below Newcastle and serving Medomsley with a branch off it. The terminus was ultimately chosen as South Shields, at the mouth of the Tyne.

The other promoters included William's brother, John Fairweather Harrison, and the latter's future son-in-law, Antonio Freire Marreco. William's son, Thomas Elliot Harrison (1808-1888), had served as a pupil under William Chapman, and had then worked on the London & Birmingham, assisting in the preparation of the deposited plans, for Robert Stephenson in 1830-1. In 1832 Robert was asked to become the consulting engineer for the 'Stanhope and Tyne Railroad Company' (S&T), with T. E. Harrison as engineer for the works. (40) In spite of what happened later on the S&T Harrison and Stephenson became lifelong friends, and were to collaborate on the building of the East Coast route between Darlington and Berwick.

The total length of the railway and its branches was to be just less than 38 miles. The quarry at Stanhope and colliery at Medomsley were roughly the same altitude, but the direct route out of Weardale required a two-mile climb of 650 feet over Weatherhill, which was 1445 feet above sea level. This climb was achieved by the use of two fixed engines; the Crawley engine (at 1120 ft.) hauled the wagons up gradients as steep as 1 in 8; the Weatherhill engine, at the summit, worked the slightly easier higher slopes. (41) The engines were standard designs, and manufactured by Hawks and Co. of Gateshead. (42)

As with the Hetton Colliery Railway, it was decided that the rest of the railway should be worked by a combination of stationary engines, self-acting inclines, horses or locomotives as the gradients dictated. Again by following the lie of the land, the engineering works were kept extremely light for a railway through such hilly country. It had been intended to provide a viaduct over a 150ft. deep ravine, called Hownes Gill, but Robert decided to use two inclines of 1 in 2½ and 1 in 3 assisted by a 20 horse power engine at the bottom of the Gill. (43) The cost of the viaduct together with the poor ground conditions, at the bottom of the ravine, and the presence of old mines must have influenced this decision. **(44)**

The railway was opened on 10 September 1834, and the usual celebrations included a banquet where everyone remotely connected with the undertaking was toasted, with one notable exception – Robert Stephenson. Even T. E. Harrison failed to mention him when responding to a toast. (45) Robert had accepted the role as consulting engineer at an agreed fee, **(46)** but later, because of the new railway's shortage of cash, which was expected to be temporary, he had been asked to accept his payment of £1,000 as ten shares in the company. **(47)** This acceptance was later to cost him dearly when his involvement with the railway was suddenly and devastatingly acknowledged.

The promoters had decided to enter into wayleave agreements with the landowners affected by the railway, as this avoided the delays and expense of getting an Act of Parliament and buying land. This was a common practice for short colliery lines in the North East, but when it was decided to extend the railway to South Shields it would have been prudent to promote a Parliamentary Bill. The wayleaves were cheaply acquired on the upland section between Weardale and Consett, but the hard bargains forced by landowners further north resulted in the company being saddled with a total annual rent of £5,600. (48) There were other very significant disadvantages of not getting an Act. Due to Government dithering the Limited Liability Act did not come into force until 1855, and without its protection every shareholder in any railway, based on a deed of partnership, was personally responsible for all the liabilities of their company. (49) Also, had the railway been incorporated by an Act, its borrowing would have been limited, wisely, to a third of the share capital. By 1840 the money borrowed by the Stanhope and Tyne was no less than three times the amount of the share capital raised. (50)

The traffic did not match up to expectations, and the ambitious schemes and borrowing entered into by the directors soon had the railway in serious financial difficulties. Jeaffreson, with his legal training, was highly critical. He condemns everything from the acquisition of the wayleaves and the purchase of land to the general financing and running of the company, and sums up: - 'From first to last, method and business exactness were neglected in the affairs of the Stanhope and Tyne line.' **(51)** Tomlinson adds, on behalf of the shareholders, that by the end of 1840: - 'They then found that, in the management of their affairs, every principle of sound finance had been thrown to the winds.' (50)

Until the end of 1840 Robert had not been aware of his exact position with regard to his liabilities in the S&T. He then learnt to his horror that, as the most reputable and wealthy of the 49 shareholders, he was the most vulnerable to the demands of the creditors. When the first bill, that the directors could not pay, was presented to him for payment, he dashed in panic to his friend and solicitor, Charles Parker, for assistance. Parker proved himself to be a very sound ally in mitigating the effects of the disaster, which could have made Robert bankrupt. On Parker's advice an extraordinary general meeting of the S&T was held on 2 January 1841, where it was resolved that the company should be dissolved and a new one, with capital of £400,000, should be incorporated by an Act of Parliament. The assets of the dissolved company possibly exceeded £300,000, but its liabilities were nearly £441,000, and, 'It remained for the greater men with the greater interests at stake to advance their thousands on the effort of retrieval.' Unfortunately Robert was one of these men, and he had to find £20,000 towards floating the new company, which became known as the 'Pontop and South Shields Railway'. In anticipation of having to raise the money he had to consider the transfer of half of his share in Robert Stephenson & Co. to his father. **(51)**

When he wrote to Edward Cook, at the Newcastle works on 4 January 1841, he was more or less resigned to the situation, but naturally angry with the perpetrators: -

> 'Your view as to my wishes respecting one half of my interest in the factory is exactly what I wish. The transaction is not intended to be otherwise than *bona fide* between my father and myself. The fact is, that I owe him nearly £4,000, and I have not now the means of paying him as I expected I should a month or two ago. All my available means must now be applied to the Stanhope and Tyne. On the 15th of this month I have £5,000 to pay into their coffers. The swamping of all my labours for years past does not now press heavily on my mind. It did so for a few days, but I now feel master of myself; and though I may be poor in purse, I shall still have the treasure of satisfaction amongst my friends who have been friends in my prosperity. The worst feature of the case is the all-absorbing character of my attention to the rectification of its embarrassments, which if produced by legitimate misfortune would have been tolerable, but when produced by **** men who are indebted to me, they become doubly afflicting. I am not without hopes that before the 15th of this month we shall have succeeded in bringing the affairs into a tangible state, and about that date I hope to be in Newcastle.' **(51)**

The Pontop and South Shields obtained its Act on 23 May 1842, and on 29 August 1842 Robert Stephenson became its first chairman. **(52)** With sound management the potential of the railway was realised, and a section of it even served, for a short time, as part of the main line from London to Scotland. The southern end of the line, which had been abandoned briefly in 1839, was taken over first by the Derwent Iron Company, and then by the Stockton and Darlington, when it also became a viable part of the railway system. Within the next 50 years, all the inclines were bypassed to allow locomotives to work throughout, though some were retained for many more years to serve local industries. A very circuitous detour avoided Crawley and Weatherhill inclines, and these remained in use until 28 April 1951. (53)

NOTES AND REFERENCES

1. Jeaff. Vol. 1, pp. 114-5.
2. Ibid. p. 101, and Smiles (1862), p. 250.
3. PRO RAIL 371/1, L&M minutes 8 June and 5 Oct. 1829. The contract was not signed until June, but delivery was on time in spite of the vessel carrying the engine being shipwrecked near Aberdeen in September!
4. Jeaff. Vol. 1 p. 137.
5. Ibid. p. 134.
6. Ibid. p. 135.
7. Ibid. pp. 135-6.
8. *Evidence taken before a Committee of the House of Commons on the Newcastle & Carlisle Railway Bill* (1829) p. 174. There is nothing in the Greenwich Hospital records to suggest that they were anything but in favour of a railway. Information kindly supplied by Bill Fawcett.
9. W. W. Tomlinson, *The North Eastern Railway its Rise and Development*, pp. 191-7. Both George and Robert had been involved in a route at the western end of the N&C for the Earl of Carlisle. See letters dated between August 1824 and March 1828 in B. Webb & D. A. Gordon's *Lord Carlisle's Railway*, (1978) pp. 117-122.
10. Jeaff. Vol. 1, p. 112.
11. Ibid. p. 153.
12. Tomlinson, pp. 209, 282-3.
13. Rev. R. B. Fellows, *History of the Canterbury and Whitstable Railway*, (1930), pp. 7-11. The Act for the 'navigation of 70 miles' was granted on 22 June 1825. The length of the railway was six miles, and even the easier graded alternative, proposed by William James, was only 11 miles long.

14. Ibid. pp. 5, 7. These included the president of the I. C. E. and three future presidents, also the first two presidents of the, later founded, I. Mech. E. Thomas Cabry became responsible for the maintenance of the infrastructure of the southern half of the North Eastern Railway, and Edward Fletcher became its first loco. superintendent. Fletcher drove *Invicta* for the opening of the Canterbury and Whitstable.

15. Ibid. p. 22.

16. S. C. Brees, *Appendix to Railway Practice,* (1839), p. 94. G. S's evidence for GWR Bill.

17. *Evidence for the Newcastle and Carlisle Bill,* (1829) p. 168, makes it clear that Dixon was in charge of the construction of the railway and not Joseph Locke as often stated.

18. Brian Lewis, *The Cabry Family,* (1994), p. 14.

19. Fellows, p. 28.

20. Ibid. p. 79.

21. Ibid. p. 41. *Invicta* was despatched from R. S. & Co. on 15 April 1830. It cost £635.

22. Francis Whishaw, *Railways of Great Britain and Ireland* (1843) p. 50. Whishaw (1804-56) had worked as a civil engineer with James Walker and then with G. S. and T. L. Gooch on the Manchester and Leeds Railway surveys. He was secretary of the Royal Society in the mid-1840s, and inspired the setting up of the Great Exhibition of 1851. He wrote the best railway reference work of the period. Unfortunately, he died, as he had once described W. James, 'a poor and neglected man'. *Proc. I. C. E. Vol. 16*, pp. 143-150 gives his obituary.

23. Fellows, pp. 87-8.

24. Ibid. p. 69.

25. Jeaff. Vol. 1, p. 176.

26. Brian Reed, *Crewe to Carlisle,* (1969), pp. 14-17.

27. Reed, p. 31.

28. Ibid. pp. 14 and 19.

29. Henry Booth, *An Account of the Liverpool and Manchester Railway,* (1839), map facing p. 1.

30. C. R. Clinker, *The Leicester and Swannington Railway,* (1977) pp. 5-8.

31. Ibid. p. 49. Also PRO RAIL 359/2 L&S Minutes Nov. 1832 to Feb 1833.

32. Ibid. p. 10.

33. Ibid. p. 12.

34. Clinker, pp. 41-3.

35. Whishaw, p. 187.

36. Ibid. p. 44.

37. J. G. H. Warren, *A Century of Locomotive Building,* (1923), pp. 314-5.

38. C. E. Stretton, *The Development of the Locomotive,* (1896) pp. 60, 62.

39. Jeaff. Vol. 1, pp. 164-5.

40. Tomlinson, pp. 212-8.

41. Ibid. p. 243.

42. T. E. Rounthwaite, *The Railways of Weardale,* (1965) p. 19.

43. Tomlinson, p. 244.

44. *Proc. I. C. E. Vol. 22,* pp.44-47. W. Cudworth, 'The Hownes Gill Viaduct on the Stockton and Darlington Railway.' The inclines limited the transfer of wagons to 12 per hour, and an alternative was needed by the S&D, who now owned this part of the railway. In 1853 a premium design by Thomas Bouch was provisionally accepted by the S&D board, for a delicate 150ft-high viaduct to replace the inclines. On behalf of the railway, R. S. vetted the design, and visited the site in October 1854. He suggested that there was no margin for foundation problems, inferior material, or workmanship. Bouch arranged to take some trial boreholes, and, as expected, the ground conditions were found to be poor, and the viaduct had to be redesigned, on R. S's recommendation, with wider piers throughout, and the use of inverted arches in the bottom of the ravine. Its cost of £15,750 would certainly have been too high for the original S&T to afford. The original 20 h.p. engine supplied by R. S. & Co. cost less than £1,000.

45. *Newcastle Journal,* 13 Sept. 1834.

46. A letter in the Science Museum from R. S. to his father on 24 Sept. 1832 says that the fee was to be £300 per annum, which suggests he was employed by the company until the end of 1835.

47. *Early Railways,* Edited by Guy and Rees (2001) pp. 325-341. 'The Stanhope and Tyne Railway: a study in business failure.' by J. H. Baldwin, quotes J. F. Harrison's business plan, of 1833, which anticipated annual profits from the mines, quarries and railway of £48,000. Half this profit was expected from the railway, but it made an operating loss every year, and these had accumulated to over £70,000 by 1841. This essay also gives other valuable information, to those interested in the S&T, which does not appear in the earlier histories.

48. Tomlinson, op. cit. p. 216

49. Jeaff. Vol. 1, p. 217.

50. Tom. p. 442.

51. Jeaff. Vol. 1, pp. 245-51. Somewhat coyly, Jeaffreson does not include the mild expletive in R. S's letter. Robert's finances in 1841 may not have been as bad as he first imagined. According to F. S. Williams' *The Midland Railway* (pp. 54-5), in 1841 he waived half of the fees due to him on the North Midland Railway and halved the salary that they wished to pay to retain him as locomotive superintendent. As the fee for the S&T survey was payable to George Stephenson & Son is it possible that the consultancy stood the loss?

52. Tom. p. 444. *The Railway Times* 4 Mar. 1843 states: 'The Directors are gentlemen of high character and standing, and the undertaking could not be under better guidance.'

53. Rounthwaite, p. 22.

CHAPTER THREE: LOCOMOTIVE DEVELOPMENT

1803 – 1828

Robert Stephenson's childhood coincided with the early development of the steam locomotive by various pioneers. He was only one year old when the first ever locomotive in the North East was being assembled to Richard Trevithick's designs. Following his 1802 patent Trevithick had been trying to drum up business in the region for his high-pressure engines and locomotives. In 1803 John Whinfield, who owned a small foundry on the banks of the Tyne in Pipewellgate, Gateshead, had been selected by Messrs. Trevithick, Vivian and West as their northern agent, 'to make, sell, and erect Steam Engines, upon the Principles for which we have obtained a Patent'. (1) When Christopher Blackett heard of the success of the locomotive at Penydarren he ordered one from Trevithick for his five-foot gauge wooden waggonway from Wylam Colliery to the staiths on the Tyne at Lemington.

The construction of the 'Gateshead Locomotive', between October 1804 and May 1805, was supervised by a gifted local man, John Steele, who had been apprenticed at Whinfields before helping Trevithick on the Penydarren project. The locomotive had a return-flue boiler, a single horizontal cylinder and a flywheel, with power being transmitted to the smooth wheels by means of gears. The use of a wrought-iron rather than a cast-iron boiler meant the weight was kept below five tons. (Fig. 3.1) She was demonstrated on a short length of track within the cramped foundry site 'for the quality to see her run', but Blackett reneged on the deal and the locomotive never ran on a waggonway. He may have received reports about damage to the track at Penydarren and concluded that she was much too heavy for his own. The engine was used for over 70 years to power a blower for the foundry's cupola. (2)

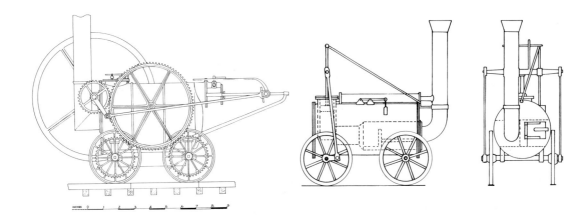

Figure 3.1: (left) Trevithick's Gateshead locomotive of 1804-5, and (right) his demonstration locomotive Catch-me-who-can *of 1808 using one of his cast-iron stationary engine boilers. Each had a single cylinder and smooth wheels. Science Museum/John Farey/Trevithick Vol.1/ J. F. Addyman.*

An important side effect of Trevithick's high-pressure steam engine promotion in the North East was the dialogue which developed between himself, George Stephenson, Robert Hawthorn and John Steele. George was an unknown colliery worker but he must have been very persuasive as all three accepted invitations to his Willington Quay cottage for discussions on steam power. The Gateshead locomotive was being built about the time that George moved to Killingworth in 1805, and then it is likely that most of the discussions took place in Newcastle on 'pay nights'. George had risen through the ranks of fireman, plugman and brakesman with a determination to understand the workings of Newcomen and Watt low-pressure engines, but it was to Trevithick and Steele that he was indebted for his enthusiasm for the high-pressure steam locomotive.

> 'Every word that came from Steele … George Stephenson stored up in his memory.
> Steele was never weary of prophesying, that "the day would come when the locomotive
> engine would be fairly tried, and would then be found to answer." No wonder that
> George Stephenson caught enthusiasm from such a teacher.' (3)

Towards the end of the Napoleonic wars horses became scarce, as did fodder to feed them. As a result stockpiles of coal accumulated and some industries almost ground to a standstill. The Brandling brothers, of Gosforth House, near Newcastle, were the owners of mines served by the nearby Kenton & Coxlodge waggonway and of a mine just outside Leeds. The first ever commercially successful railway came about in Yorkshire, when the Brandlings introduced locomotives to transport coal on about one-and-a-half miles of their line from Middleton Colliery to the staiths at Leeds. It was here that their engineer, John Blenkinsop (1783-1831), introduced his rack and pinion system. (4) (Fig. 3.2)

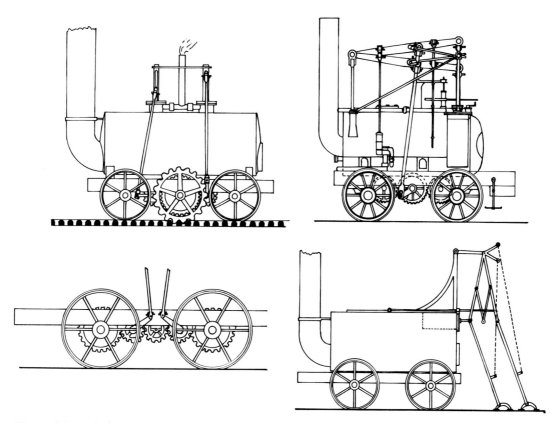

Figure 3.2: early locomotives 1812-1814; (clockwise from top left) Blenkinsop/Murray, Hedley (in later condition), Brunton's, and the chassis of the first Stephenson locomotive. Various sources.

Not surprisingly when Matthew Murray (1765-1826), of Messrs. Fenton, Murray and Wood, had been commissioned to construct the motive power for John Blenkinsop's system, he closely followed Trevithick's locomotive design, consequently paying the inventor £40 patent dues. (5) The experienced and innovative mechanical engineer was able to set two vertical cylinders into a single flue wrought-iron boiler. His *Prince Regent* made a debut on 24 June 1812, followed by the *Salamanca* a few months later on 12 August; both gave over twenty years service. When Murray's third locomotive, costing £350, was almost complete, a request came from John Watson, the Brandlings' viewer at Kenton, for it to be transferred to the North East. (6)

> 'September 2nd, 1813. An ingenious and highly-interesting experiment was performed in the presence of a vast concourse of spectators, on the railway leading from the collieries of Kenton & Coxlodge, near Newcastle, by the application of a steam-engine, constructed by Messrs. Fenton, Murray, and Wood, of Leeds, under the direction of Mr. John Blenkinsop, the patentee, for the purpose of drawing the coal waggons. About one o'clock the new invention was set a-going, having attached to it sixteen chaldron waggons loaded with coals, each waggon with its contents weighing four tons or thereabouts, making altogether an aggregate weight little short of seventy tons. Upon perfectly level road the machine, so charged, it was computed, would travel at the rate of 3½ miles per hour; …Under all the circumstances, it was very highly approved of, and its complete success anticipated.' (7)

Uncle Robert was the 'Engineman' at Coxlodge, (8) and his brother's position gave George an opportunity for detailed scrutiny of Murray's locomotive. Young Robert, still at Tommy Rutter's school, must have had the chance of exciting rides on the new mechanical replacement of the horse.

Not to be outdone, a number of colliery owners followed the Brandlings' lead. Christopher Blackett had re-laid the track on the Wylam waggonway, and he again asked Trevithick to provide a locomotive, but, unsurprisingly, the request was declined. (9) William Hedley (1779-1843), the Wylam viewer, and the enginewright Jonathan Foster took up the challenge, and their first practical locomotive was under trial in 1813. They had to carry out experiments to confirm what Trevithick had already proved - that traction was possible using smooth wheels on smooth rails. Other pioneers, William Chapman (1749-1832) and William Brunton (1777-1857), remained unconvinced, and the former advocated chain haulage whilst the latter patented a 'walking locomotive' (10).

The Grand Allies gave every encouragement to their own engineering contingent: viewer Ralph Dodd, under-viewer Nicholas Wood and enginewright George Stephenson started work immediately after the Kenton demonstration. Samuel Smiles paraphrases Wood's description of the resulting two-cylinder Killingworth locomotive, which incorporated ideas of Trevithick, and Murray: -

> 'The engine was, after much labour and anxiety, and frequent alterations of parts, at length brought to completion, having been about ten months in hand. It was placed upon the Killingworth Railway on 25th July, 1814; and its powers were tried on the same day. On an ascending gradient of 1 in 450, the engine succeeded in drawing after it eight loaded carriages of thirty tons weight at about four miles an hour; and for some time it continued regularly at work.

> '...."Blutcher" was nevertheless a somewhat cumbrous and clumsy machine. The parts were huddled together. The boiler constituted the principal feature; and being the foundation of the other parts, it was made to do duty not only as a generator of steam, but also as a basis for the fixings of the machinery and for the bearings of the wheels and axles. The want of springs was seriously felt; and the progress was a succession of jolts, causing considerable derangement of the machinery. The mode of communicating the motive power to the wheels by means of the spur-gear also caused frequent jerks, each cylinder alternately propelling or becoming propelled by the other, as the pressure of the one upon the wheels became greater or less than the pressure of the other; and when the teeth of the cogwheels became at all worn, a rattling noise was produced during the travelling of the engine.' (11)

Smiles goes on to explain that the economy of the locomotive, when compared with the horse, was very much in the balance, and it 'might have been condemned as useless'. Smiles also says, incorrectly, that the blast was introduced at this stage, but the necessary pipes are not shown in Dodd and Stephenson or Losh and Stephenson patents of 1815 and 1816. **(12)**

In order to eliminate the jerks and jolts, first it was decided to use coupling rods, but the manufacture of cranks presented severe difficulties and a continuous chain proved easier (Fig. 3.3) The first engine embodying the chain was tried at Killingworth on 6 March 1815, 'and found to work remarkably well.' **(13)** Coupling rods were included in the 1815 patent, but Nicholas Wood wrote in his 1825 *Treatise*: 'Many plans have been devised to obviate the use of this chain but nothing superior has yet been devised.' (14)

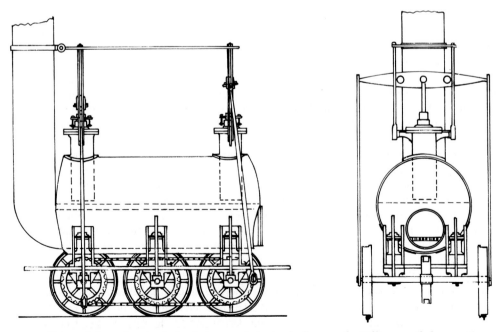

Figure 3.3: a six-wheeled, chain-coupled, single flue, early Killingworth locomotive showing the steam springs of the 1816 Losh/Stephenson patent. Nicholas Wood.

The lack of springing for the early locomotives did not help the fragile track and brittle case-hardened wheels. Steel springs had been in use on road coaches for some time, but may have been considered too expensive by the Killingworth team so a substitute had to be found. 'Steam' springs in the form of small cylinders with pistons attached to the axles used water at boiler pressure on the upper face of the piston to produce cushioning or springing for the locomotive. (Fig.3.3) The successful operation of this ingenious precursor of the shock absorber depended on the working pressure of the boiler being maintained constantly, and no leakage of water past the pistons. **(15)**

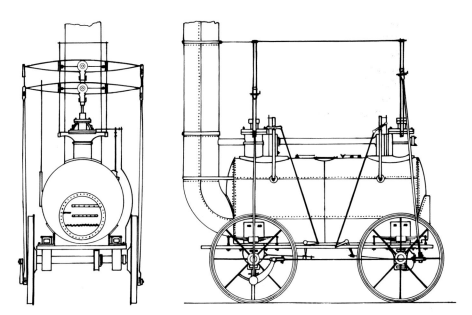

Figure 3.4: a later Killingworth locomotive incorporating improvements by the George and Robert Stephenson and Nicholas Wood; plate springs and coupling rods are used. Wood 1838 edition.

The fabrication of the more efficient return flue boiler, pioneered by Trevithick, added another problem to the many still to be resolved, and the fact that it required a driver and fireman to be at its opposite ends meant that some of the pioneer locomotive builders avoided it. Generally the single flues were able to evaporate 900 to 1,000 lbs of water per hour, which produced sufficient steam to move about 40 tons at 5 mph. (16) Trevithick's idea of turning the exhaust steam into the chimney was used on the Killingworth locomotives, built under Robert's auspices in 1821, to create the blast and 'accelerate the velocity of the current of heated air accordingly.' (17) However, if fuel economy was to be taken into account George considered that the blast was not really necessary and was wasteful of coal. (18)

The thermodynamic advantages of placing the cylinders within the boiler must have been far outweighed by the mechanical disadvantages of the complicated mechanisms needed to turn the wheels. Robert did not like them, particularly the 'parallel motion'. When he visited the Neath Abbey Iron Company in March 1824 he wrote: '…there is not one of them who understand the parallel motion thoroughly. They seemed to doubt me when I told them I had never seen one mathematically true, not even in principle.' (19) Having said this an early surviving drawing, which was prepared around 1822 for what became known as *Locomotion No 1*, raises questions. Warren points out: 'The drive from the cylinders, and the half beam parallel motion on the first Stockton and Darlington locomotive appears to be a retrogression from the more simple construction of the Killingworth and Hetton engines.' Even more bizarre, the return to gears to drive the axles, abandoned seven years earlier, was considered. (20) Did George insist on these retrograde steps or did Robert try to get his own way by making the design unacceptably convoluted? Robert was in South America when *Locomotion* was completed with its complex motion but with coupling rods linking the wheels.

In 1813 Hedley's Wylam team had placed the cylinders outside the boiler but had not taken advantage of their situation to simplify the drive from the pistons to the wheels. There was a continued reluctance to place the cylinders on each side of the boiler until Robert Wilson broke the mould when he constructed his locomotive with two vertical cylinders on each side of the boiler; it went into service on the Stockton and Darlington Railway in December 1825. **(21)** The first Stephenson locomotive to do so was the 'Liverpool Travelling Engine', which was in use on the Bolton and Leigh Railway in late July 1828, being renamed *Lancashire Witch* on 1 August. (22)

1828 – 1846

The education and experience that Robert had already received would have enabled him to consider many possible locomotive improvements during his stay in South America. His meeting with Richard Trevithick in Cartagena must have provided an opportunity for a particularly fruitful exchange of ideas, and his examination of the steam boats in North America given him inspiration from their practical developments. He did not plunge into locomotive improvements immediately upon his return. In London he had business to deal with for the Mining Association and for Robert Stephenson & Co., and was forced to visit northern France in December 1827 to sort out an earlier order for the Works. Robert still had to convince his father about the need to upgrade their designs, as shown in a letter written to his friend and confidant, Michael Longridge, on 1 January 1828: -

> 'Since I came down from London, I have been talking a great deal to my father about endeavouring to reduce the size and ugliness of our travelling-engines, (colour plate 6) by applying the engine [cylinder] on either side of the boiler or **beneath it entirely**, somewhat similar to Gurney's steam coach. He has agreed to an alteration which I think will considerably reduce the quantity of machinery as well as the liability to mismanagement. Mr. Jos. Pease writes to my father that in their present complicated state they cannot be managed by 'fools', therefore they must undergo some alteration or amendment.'(23)

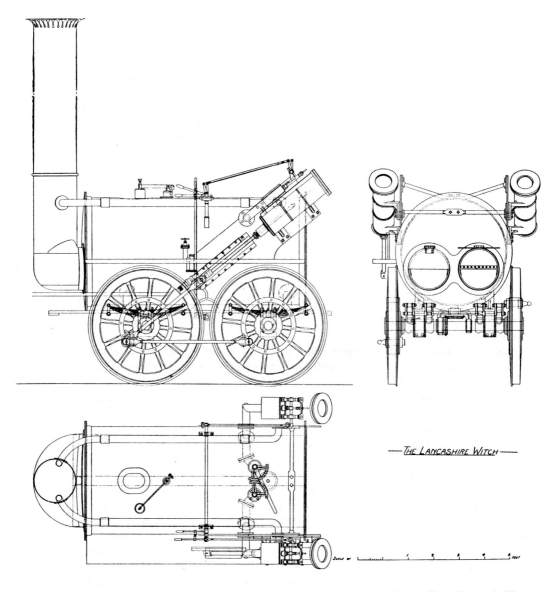

Figure 3.5: Lancashire Witch *was the reboilered and renamed 'Liverpool Travelling Engine'. Warren*

Early in 1827 the Liverpool and Manchester (L&M) secretary, Henry Booth (1789-1869), and George Stephenson had carried out experiments to produce 'Steam without Smoke' to fulfil the clause in the Act which prohibited smoke from the locomotives. On 30 April 1827 the development of the experiment, which was to overcome the anticipated difficulties of using coke instead of coal, had been approved by the L&M board. However, the work on the resulting 'Liverpool Travelling Engine' did not start until January 1828, after Robert's return. He implemented an idea for a coke-fired boiler and used a large central flue which split at its far end and bent into two smaller return flues, one on each side of it. There were two water tubes within the large fire-tube. The locomotive was an 0-4-0 with outside cylinders mounted at 45°, coupling rods and steel springs. When it was first steamed George wrote: 'We have tried the blast to it for burning coke and I believe it will answer. There are two bellows worked by eccentrics underneath the tender.' The original boiler had given problems and very soon it had acquired twin fire-tubes. (Fig. 3.5) When Robert overcame George's resistance and added the blast *pipes* the bellows were not needed to get the coke to produce sufficient steam. **(24)**

Another significant innovation on *Lancashire Witch* was the ability to cut-off the steam at half-stroke of the piston, by means of bevel gears, allowing expansive working when required. The French observers, Coste and Perdonnet, described the method of working: 'Ordinarily the cut off is operated at the beginning of the run in order to economise on steam when only a small quantity has been formed, and it is used without expansion when in full activity.' (25) The working of the valve gear was gradually improved by Robert Stephenson & Co. and by other manufacturers during the next 15 years.

Just as some progress was being made with the steam locomotive its use was to be questioned on the L&M. At the planning stage George had favoured inclines worked by stationary engines, only where the terrain was difficult, in order to avoid more expensive earthworks. As early as 1826, Josias Jessop (1781-1826) had recommended a large cutting with 1 in 530 gradients to replace George's one-and-a-half miles long 1 in 96 inclines on each side of the Rainhill Level. The extra expense, estimated at £37,000, made the inclines seem an awful lot more attractive. **(26)** In a letter of 23 February 1827 George boasted to Robert, who he knew was against the inclines: -

> 'I want these [stationary] engines to be constantly moveing with an endless Rope so that
> the locomotive engines take hold of the Rope and go on with out stoping … my new plan
> will be a huge job … you will think I have some mistaken ideas about this but I think not
> – and you may depend upon it that if you do not get home soon every thing will be at
> perfecttion and then there will be nothing for you to do or invent'! (27)

The inadequacies of the materials and machining techniques available for manufacturing the early locomotives meant that they were clumsy and unreliable in service. Those on the Stockton and Darlington were further hampered by the operating difficulties caused by it being only a single line, and were struggling to maintain superiority over the horses also used on the railway. Some L&M directors, led by James Cropper (1773-1840), advocated an idea of Benjamin Thompson to use stationary engines and rope haulage to completely oust locomotives from the line. As a result a deputation went to inspect the S&D and colliery lines in the North East in October 1828, but their findings were inconclusive. George Stephenson submitted strong economic and practical arguments against the use of stationary engines in a report of 5 November. **(28)** Unfortunately, it did not swing the case. On 17 November the board decided to invite civil engineer, James Walker (1781-1862), and iron founder and engineer, John Urpeth Rastrick (1780-1856), to make an independent investigation into the railways of the North East. **(29)**

Walker and Rastrick's final report came out on 9 March 1829, and was more in favour of stationary engines, particularly if heavy traffic was anticipated immediately after the line opened. If the traffic was to build up gradually, they left the way open to encourage locomotive development by '… something in the way of a premium, or an assurance of preference, might be held to the person whose Engine should, on experience, be found to answer the best.' **(30)** Joseph Locke and Robert had been doing their own investigations and experiments to produce a report in favour of the locomotive, which they presented to the board. **(31)** This forced the issue, as on 20 April the directors followed Walker and Rastrick's suggestion: -

> 'Resolved that a Premium of £500 be advertised for a Locomotive Engine which shall be
> a decided improvement on those now in use, as respects the consumption of smoke,
> increased speed, adequate power, and moderate weight, the particulars of which shall be
> specified in detail by the Preparation Committee.' (32)

This was a significant decision for the future of locomotive development, resulting in the Rainhill Trials and the success of Robert Stephenson's *Rocket*. Had *Rocket* failed, as the other competitors did, the locomotive could have been condemned and the advance of British railways somewhat delayed. 'Never was a premium more opportunely offered. It set engineers throughout the kingdom on the alert. Now was the time for a house to put itself at the head of the trade.' (33)

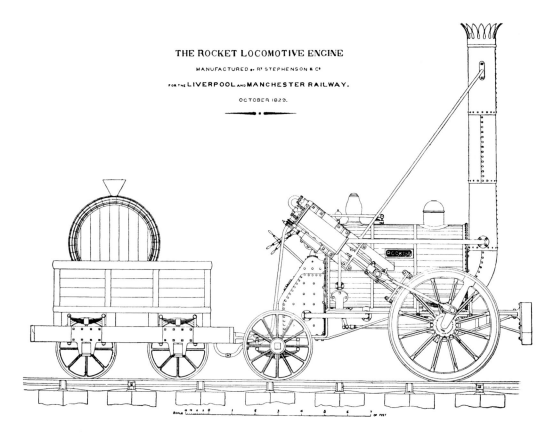

THE ROCKET LOCOMOTIVE ENGINE

MANUFACTURED ʙʏ Rᵗ STEPHENSON & Cᵒ

ꜰᴏʀ ᴛʜᴇ LIVERPOOL ᴀɴᴅ MANCHESTER RAILWAY.

OCTOBER 1829.

Figure 3.6: Rocket *from an 1859 drawing based on information available at that time to J. D. Wardale, then chief draughtsman at Robert Stephenson and Co, note the sloping back to the firebox.*

Contrary to popular belief George Stephenson had *no* involvement in the design and construction of *Rocket*. Robert was assisted in the task by George Henry Phipps (1807-88), who came to the works as a draughtsman in 1828, after he had served an engineering apprenticeship in London. (34) He recalled having assisted Robert in chalking out *Rocket* on the floor of the drawing office, and: -

> 'Having made the original drawings under Mr. Robert Stephenson, I can bear witness to the care and judgement bestowed by him upon every detail. In the arrangement of the tubes, with the method of securing their extremities, the detached firebox and many other matters of detail, all requiring much consideration. Mr. Stephenson was well aided in the mechanical details by the late Mr. William Hutchinson' (35)

Both Ralph and William Hutchinson were involved; they had started working with Robert in 1821 during the building of his improved 'Killingworth' locomotives for the Hetton Colliery Railway. **(36)**

The concept of *Rocket's* tubular boiler is usually attributed to the L&M secretary, Henry Booth, but the idea of multi-tube boilers had been around for over a quarter of a century. John Stevens (1749-1838) had patented a multi-tube boiler for use in his steam boats in America in 1803, and his second son had taken out the English patent on his behalf in 1805. **(37)** In 1825 W. H. James had patented a water tube boiler, and in March 1826 James Neville of London was granted a patent for a boiler with vertical fire-tubes. **(38)** Goldsworthy Gurney's October 1827 patent for his steam road carriage incorporated an ingenious design for a water-tube boiler. Frenchman, Marc Séguin (1786-1875), had employed a fire-tube boiler in a steam boat on the Rhone in 1825 and in a locomotive which was first tried in December 1829 – two months after *Rocket*. Séguin used the small tubes only to take the place of the return half of the return flue, but he was never granted a British patent. **(39)** In order to be granted a patent in Britain the applicant needed to be 'the true and first inventor'. When *Rocket's* boiler was built it was not patented and no claim for royalties was made by anyone, which suggests that the fire-tube boiler was already established. **(40)**

It was a huge step from Henry Booth suggesting a tubular boiler to Robert implementing it in practice. Making the boiler watertight, when subjected to the required hydraulic test at 150 lbs per square inch, presented almost insuperable problems. The ends of the tubes were at first brazed into the holes in the tube-plates but the plates tended to buckle under the pressure and cause the joints to leak.

After a number of frustrating attempts, the ends of the tubes were expanded and riveted or 'clinked' into the tube-plates while longitudinal stays were used to stop the ends of the boiler from bulging. **(41)**

The use of a multi-tube boiler meant that a separate firebox was necessary, and Robert designed a water jacket to surround the top and three sides of the firebox. This gave *Rocket* a total of 143 square feet of heating surfaces in contact with the water, but Robert carried out tests which proved that although only 17½% of this area was from the firebox it actually produced 75% of the total steam generated. (42) The firebox was made from copper and, to prevent distortion under pressure, the inner and outer walls of the water space were tied together by numerous stays; this practice was followed as long as steam locomotives were being built. (43)

A certain amount of secrecy was needed during the construction of *Rocket*, and having the firebox fabricated in Liverpool by a firm of coppersmiths aided this ideal. (The tender was also built in Liverpool by Thomas C. Worsdell (1778-1862) grandfather of two North Eastern Railway locomotive superintendents.) The locomotive was probably assembled in part of an addition to the original premises of Robert Stephenson & Co. on the opposite side of South Street. The completed locomotive was tested on three miles of the Killingworth waggonway, where Robert found 'that the engine did not work so well in one direction as the other.' *Rocket* was dismantled and taken by road to Carlisle for shipment to Liverpool to arrive, as stipulated, before 1 October 1829. **(44)**

As many as 15,000 people turned out to see the Rainhill Trials, and the dainty appearance of Braithwaite and Ericsson's *Novelty* made it by far the popular favourite. Nevertheless, *Rocket* was the only competitor to fulfil all the conditions and to satisfactorily complete the trials. Timothy Hackworth's *Sans Pareil* was over the stipulated weight and its hasty construction, needed to meet the deadline, meant that its return-flue boiler and its components were not as reliable as they should have been. **(45)** The steam blast in *Sans Pareil* was much too fierce resulting in a coke consumption, per pound of water evaporated, two-and-a-half times higher than *Rocket's*. (46) Robert had carefully judged the relationship of the double blast pipes, chimney diameter and the total cross sectional area of the tubes to get the best performance from *Rocket*. (47) The Rainhill prize money of £500 was shared between Booth and the Stephensons, although only one of them seems to have really earned it!

Rocket was built specifically to fulfil the conditions laid down for the trial and to win the event, but to produce a locomotive for normal service would require more development. The much-lauded boiler and firebox only achieved 75% of *Sans Pareil's* steam production rate and an increase of just 15% over the old single-flue Killingworth locomotives. (46) In fact, the vast improvement in *Rocket's* efficiency had been brought about by the simplification of the mechanism, a concept that Robert had been arguing with his father for years. The next modification was to place the cylinders as near to the horizontal as possible to provide more stability at the much higher running speeds.

Figure 3.7: James Nasmyth sketched Northumbrian *under trial on the 13 September 1830, and later made this painting. It shows a spring safety valve, splashers over the locomotive wheels and a level, or slightly sloping, footplate along the boiler. No Work's drawing survives for this important locomotive.*

In *Rocket,* and the four succeeding locomotives built for the L&M, the base of the chimney had been spread to cover the ends of the tubes, and a removable plate was fitted to allow their cleaning. Contemporary illustrations show that the next two, *Phoenix* and *North Star,* were provided with smokeboxes for the ash to accumulate and doors to permit cleaning. (48) Robert's final improvement implemented on *Northumbrian,* in July 1830, was to lift the firebox. (Fig. 3.7) Now the boiler heating surface had been trebled by providing more numerous smaller diameter tubes, and the size of the firebox had increased by 50% over *Rocket's.* **(49)** The modern boiler had arrived; all it would need in future was strengthening and enlarging to suit higher pressures and greater demands for steam.

Some of the L&M directors were still unwilling to acknowledge the superiority of Robert Stephenson's locomotives, and pinned their hopes on two enlarged versions of *Novelty* from Braithwaite and Ericsson; regrettably they wasted £2,000. The *Mechanics Magazine* supported the *Novelty* type but the *Manchester Guardian* thought 'their engines will not work – at all events to any useful purpose, whilst those of Mr. Stephenson perform their allotted tasks in the admirable manner which most of our readers have, no doubt, witnessed.' One of the directors, (Sir) Hardman Earle, described a trial of one of the Braithwaite and Ericsson engines; 'it was impossible to imagine a more signal failure, she could not make steam'. (50) Just a fortnight after the Rainhill Trials the leading anti-Stephenson director, James Cropper, tried to introduce another red herring and, 'read a letter which he had received on the subject of Mr. Gurney's Locomotive Steam Carriage, mentioning that Mr. Gurney had 18 or 20 Steam Carriages building for common roads.' **(51)** He cannot have got anywhere as there is no record of the ensuing discussion in the L&M minutes.

The Liverpool and Manchester Railway opened on 15 September 1830, and *Phoenix* and *North Star* showed their mettle when each ran more than 15,000 miles on it in the first year. (52) Robert anticipated that the rapidly increasing traffic on the railway would require something much more powerful and his *Planet* was delivered, within three weeks of the opening of the line, on 4 October. A significant improvement with *Northumbrian* had been the provision of frames to support the cylinders; with *Planet* the cylinders were placed *inside* the frames and under the smokebox in order to reduce heat losses. (Fig. 3.10) The use of inside cylinders required the forging or fabrication of a crank axle, something which George had had to abandon 15 years earlier. It was still an extremely difficult and fraught operation given the iron quality and the techniques of the time. Failure of the axle, when the locomotive was moving at speed, could result in a serious accident so Robert arranged for it to be supported at no less than six points. (Fig. 3.8) **(53)**

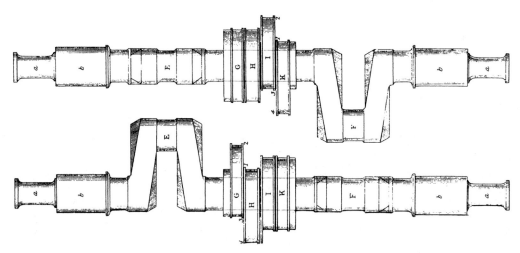

Figure 3.8: the complex problems of forging, fabricating and machining a six-bearing crankshaft in 1830 can be judged from these drawings of Planet's. *Wood 1838 edition.*

Problems in managing the coke fire, due to inexperience, meant that the Planet prototype averaged a little over 10 mph when hauling 80 tons from Liverpool to Manchester; later it averaged over 30mph when running light engine. (54) Such speeds were neither good for the locomotives nor the track. One of the drivers, Patrick Fenwick, was reprimanded by the board, in December 1832, for running *Vulcan* from Liverpool to Manchester in 68 minutes (26.5 mph)!

In July 1832, Hardman Earle considered that the Planet design 'came nearer to what was considered perfection, relatively of course, to any which had succeeded her.' The Planet type could be supplied either with a single pair of driving wheels or as a four-coupled locomotive and the design was imposed as a standard by the L&M for other manufacturers to supply. Edward Bury, who had established a locomotive works in Liverpool in 1829, wanted to supply his own designs and demanded a trial. His locomotive, *Liverpool*, could not steam and broke its crank axle, both of which did not impress the L&M board! (55)

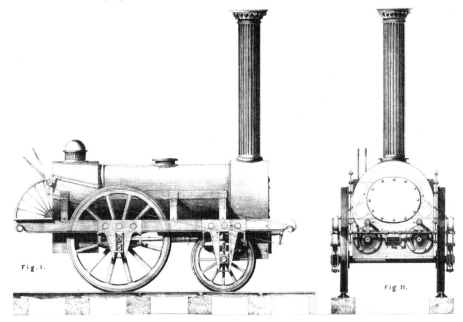

Figure 3.9: the first of the Planet type as drawn by G. H. Phipps. Much better weight distribution than Northumbrian's *was achieved by placing the cylinders at the front of the locomotive. Wood 1831.*

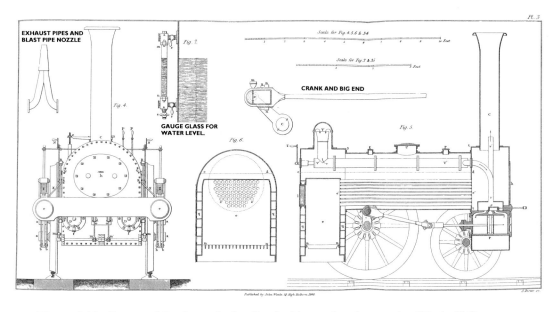

Figure 3.10: Coste and Perdonnet's details of a Planet class locomotive. Weale 1840.

George's fixation with the use of stationary engines for the Whiston and Sutton inclines, on either side of Rainhill, had precluded any compromise to increase the earthworks and reduce these gradients. The rapid development of the locomotive made the stationary engines unnecessary, but the inclines were to severely tax the early locomotives and banking engines were often needed. The stationary-engine lobby had said that locomotives would only be able to move their own weight up the inclines. However, on test, *Northumbrian* had proved capable of maintaining full boiler pressure while hauling 50 tons up one of the 1 in 96 inclines at 7½ mph. (56)

The board appreciated the gradient problem and, only five days after the opening of the line, ordered two locomotives 'of a more powerful description to be used on the inclined planes.' The two four-coupled locomotives, *Samson* and *Goliath*, enlarged versions of the *Planet,* were delivered from Robert Stephenson & Co. early in 1831. The cylinder diameter was increased by 3 inches to 14 inches and the driving wheel diameter reduced by 6 inches to 4 feet 6 inches. **(57)** In February 1831 *Samson* hauled 151 tons from Liverpool to Manchester in a net time of 2 hours 21 minutes for the 30 miles (12.8 mph). It needed three assisting engines on the incline where, later experience suggested, it was happy on its own hauling 80 tons. Its efficiency was monitored, and the consumption of coke was found to have been reduced to a very creditable figure of around a third of a pound per ton mile. (58)

Turning to other railways, Robert Stephenson & Co. continued to build locomotives for the S&D until 1832, both to their own and to Hackworth's designs; two Planet type locomotives were built for the line in 1830. The Canterbury and Whitstable opened four months before the L&M, and its *Invicta* was an 0-4-0 based on earlier designs rather than *Northumbrian* or *Planet's*. Although, it was the first locomotive to have its cylinders at the front, its inadequate performance is suggested by the fact that there was no locomotive in use on the line by 1839. (59) The fourth British public railway to be opened with Robert Stephenson & Co.'s locomotives was the Glasgow and Garnkirk Railway on 1 June 1831. It bought a 2-2-0 and an 0-4-0 of the Planet type, and, according to a contemporary author, these 'fully sustained the high character acquired for their engines by these eminent engineers.' (60)

The first Stephenson locomotive in America, supplied in 1829, was similar to *Lancashire Witch*, and had bar frames which became standard American, but not British, practice. **(61)** From 1831 to 1836 several fledgling American railroad companies purchased locomotives from Robert Stephenson & Co., usually single or four-coupled variations on the Planet type. The famous *John Bull*, built to R. L. Stevens' specifications, was supplied to the Camden and Amboy Railroad in 1831. **(62)** Low-cost construction giving curves with radii as small as 400 feet (6 chains) was contemplated on American railroads. When Robert was told this he is said to have recommended bogie locomotives to the deputation that visited Newcastle in 1828. **(63)**

The bogie or articulated locomotive had been patented by William Chapman in 1812, but it was virtually ignored in Britain for another 50 years. **(64)** In 1833 Robert Stephenson & Co. supplied their first bogie locomotive to the Saratoga and Schenectady Railroad. It was very similar to *Brother Jonathan,* an 1832 design by J. B. Jarvis for the Mohawk and Hudson Railroad (M&HRR). Trouble with broken crank axles led to modified drive on the company's bogie locomotive for the M&HRR, and a return to outside cylinders on one built for the South Carolina Railroad. It was inevitable that the Americans would soon start to build their own locomotives, based on British achievements, but modified to suit their very different working conditions. (65)

Figure 3.11: the bogie locomotive for the Saratoga & Schenectady Railroad. J.F.A.

At the end of 1830 Robert was involved in setting up another locomotive works on Merseyside as it was anticipated, with the number of railways being projected, there would be a great demand for locomotives in Lancashire and Yorkshire. He got the consent of the other partners in Robert Stephenson & Co., under very strict terms, and went into a two-year partnership with L&M director, Charles Tayleur, founder of what later became known as Vulcan Foundry. (66)

The great demand for locomotives did not materialise at once, and with the two factories and rival concerns now seeking work a run down of commissions from the leading British and American railways could not have occurred at a more embarrassing time. Both factories were helped by small orders for the Belgian, French, German and Russian railways; Tayleur & Co. also built 11 locomotives for the L&M between 1834 and 1837. (67) After two lean years orders started to pick up, especially from 1837 when a number of main line railways were opened. The delay with the London & Birmingham Act, until 1833, removed the prospect of one immediate outlet – in any case nice Messrs. Cropper and Rathbone were to ensure that Robert Stephenson & Co. got no orders from that railway for a decade. (68) The early output from the Newcastle works is shown in this table giving locomotives delivered in each year from 1825 until 1843: -

1825	2	1831	25	1837	29
1826	4	1832	13	1838	29
1827	2	1833	9	1839	30
1828	4	1834	14	1840	50
1829	6	1835	22	1841	38
1830	14	1836	18	1843	32

The large number of Planet type locomotives being built made it the first successful 'class' of locomotives, but soon further developments were necessary to meet traffic demands. In view of the growing number of locomotive manufacturers benefiting from copying Robert's hard-won improvements he decided to patent several new ideas. The patent was taken out 7 October 1833 for an improved locomotive carried on six wheels, and for the steam brake. To try and obviate the breaking or bending of the crank axle its 'driven' wheels were to be flangeless. The first of the class to incorporate the ideas was known as the *Patentee,* but it was the last locomotive by Robert Stephenson & Co. to be supplied to the L&M. **(69)** Warren considered: 'The type was however adopted elsewhere as a standard, both at home and abroad, and in fact determined eventually the general design of the British passenger locomotive for about fifty years.' (70)

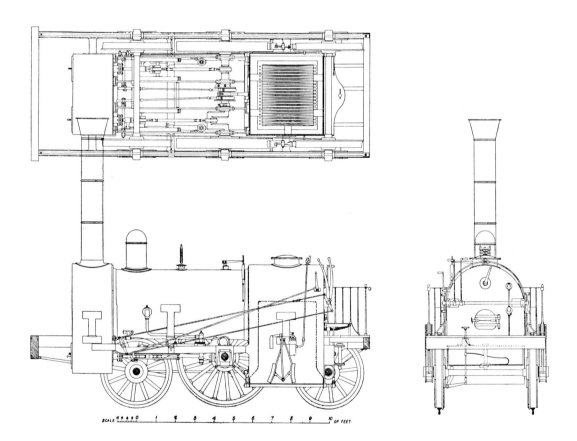

Figure 3.12: the Patentee *based on the original Work's drawings. J. G. H. Warren.*

The Patentee type was supplied on three axles as a single, four or six-coupled locomotive. The extra pair of wheels was needed to carry the larger boiler and firebox. Robert's description included: -
> 'Increasing the magnitude of the boiler, giving a larger extent of heating surface thereto, and working the enlarged boiler with a more moderate intensity of fire, is the true remedy, and will save fuel as well as avoid the rapid destruction of the boiler, because the steam will be allowed to escape more freely from the cylinders.' [The latter, he had already explained, was achieved by reducing the force of the blast.] **(71)**

Unlike later practice, when scores or even hundreds of identical locomotives could be turned out to a single design, considerable variations in wheel, boiler, firebox and cylinder dimensions were apparent in the Patentees. The prototype had a smaller total heating surface than a Planet, but had a lot larger grate and firebox area. At the other extreme, the boiler diameter of the powerful Leicester and

Swannington 0-6-0, mentioned in chapter 2, was 3ft - 11½in, and the firebox being the same width made it the maximum permitted by the spacing of the main frames. (Fig. 3.13) It had a heating surface 60% larger than the *Planet* in order to supply its 16 in diameter cylinders with their 20 in stroke. (72) The amount of steam produced by this boiler was five to six times as much as those of four years before when Robert and Locke had written: 'The effect of high-pressure is now almost universally admitted to depend not so much on the size of the cylinders as the quantity of steam which the boiler can generate and upon the degree of its elasticity [pressure].' (73) With this aim in view a modification to some of the Patentees was the provision of a domed or haystack firebox, which, unlike those introduced earlier on Edward Bury's locomotives, remained rectangular in plan.

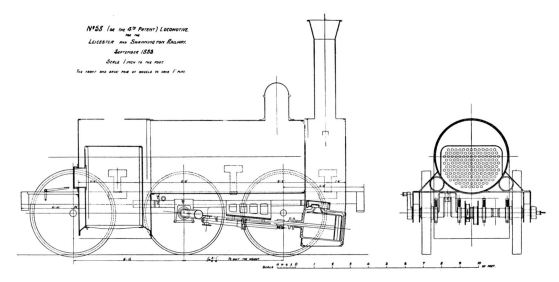

Figure 3.13: the powerful Leicester and Swannington 0-6-0 locomotive was completed in 1834. In spite of the boiler having over 150 tubes the firebox produced 589 out of a total of 656 square feet of heating surface. J. G. H. Warren from original Robert Stephenson & Co. drawings.

Many locomotive manufacturers were basing their designs on Robert's ground-breaking achievements, to which they were adding their own improvements. A number of established foundries and engineering works had gone into locomotive building, some under licence to Robert's designs, and soon there was little to choose between the products of the best of them. A significant number who had served at Robert Stephenson & Co. left to build locomotives elsewhere. James Kennedy, who had managed the works for 18 months during Robert's absence in Colombia, later became a partner of their keen competitor, Edward Bury. Robert wrote to his father on 18 December 1832: 'If Kennedy had not obtained a great deal of information from us here, we should have stood much higher as Locomotive Engine Makers than we do now. Bury never would have made an Engine.' From 1836 Michael Longridge started to build his own locomotives at Bedlington, although he remained a partner in Robert Stephenson & Co. until November 1842. Apprentices were causing a problem by taking hard-won information to competitors, and Robert regretted having: -

'…made any arrangements for allowing some of them to come into the office to become acquainted with every detail of our plans, &c. They have no sooner done so, than they leave and carry away what has cost us a great deal of money and more thought.' (74)

Inevitably, I. K. Brunel was an exception. When he turned his mind to locomotive design, for the broad gauge Great Western Railway (GWR), in 1836, he ignored Stephenson's hard-won knowledge and came up with his own very strange criteria. He stipulated low piston speeds, light axle loads and, most oddly, a 'force of traction' of 800 lbs at 30 mph which was less than two thirds of that achieved by *Northumbrian* six years earlier. (75) The respected GWR historian, E. T. MacDermot, considered: -

'It may be safely stated, without exaggeration, that in the whole history of British railways there has never existed such an extraordinary collection of freak locomotives as those which were built for the Great Western and delivered during a period of about eighteen months from November 1837.' (76)

Amongst those trying to fulfil the weight and piston speed limitations was T. E. Harrison who came up with two very peculiar locomotives. (Fig. 3.14) In order to keep the weight down the boilers were carried on a separate truck from the cylinders, resulting in leaky steam pipes and the loss of both adhesive weight and thermal efficiency. (77)

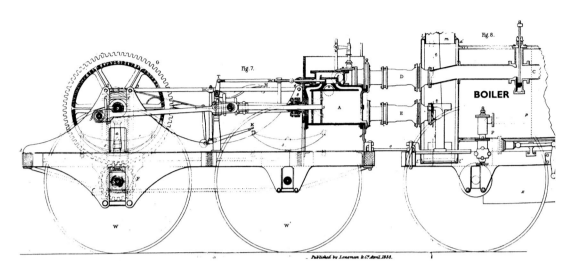

Figure 3.14: details of Thunderer, *one of T. E. Harrison's two designs for the GWR, this one with geared drive giving the equivalent of 18 feet diameter wheels. He also designed ones with 10 feet wheels for the GWR and Stanhope and Tyne Railway. Wood 1838 edition.*

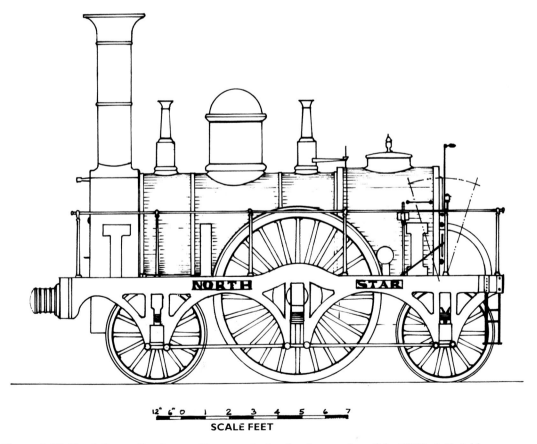

Figure 3.15: North Star *a Stephenson Patentee design for the opening of the GWR. J. F. Addyman.*

Fortunately, (Sir) Daniel Gooch (1816-89) managed to get Brunel to appoint him to look after the locomotives on the GWR from 14 August 1837. Gooch had worked for nine months at the fledgling Vulcan Foundry in 1834 and, for a similar period in 1836, in the drawing office of Robert Stephenson & Co. at Newcastle. Unfortunately, the orders had already been placed for the 'freak locomotives' prior to his appointment, with two notable exceptions from Robert Stephenson & Co. These, which became known as *North Star* and *Morning Star,* were based on the Patentee design. They had been intended for the 5 ft 6 in gauge New Orleans and Carrollton Railroad, but financial worries caused the American company to cancel the order, leaving the factory with two wider-than-standard gauge locomotives on its hands. The factory had declined Brunel's first request for locomotives, presumably because of the design limitations, but when an urgent order was placed for broad-gauge locomotives, on 4 July 1837, Robert decided just to re-gauge the *North Star* and provide it with 7 feet driving wheels. *North Star* was delivered on 28 November 1837 and *Morning Star,* with 6 ft 6 in wheels, on 24 January 1839. (78) Brunel commented on *North Star's* appearance: 'we have a splendid engine of Stephenson's it would be a beautyfull ornament in the most elegant drawing room ...'! (Fig. 3.15) (79)

Robert Stephenson & Co. had delivered twelve locomotives of this 'Star' class to the GWR by November 1841. These had an average working life of 29 years compared with six for the earlier L&M locomotives. The 'Stars' set the standard for early Great Western locomotive design as well as getting Brunel out of a very embarrassing motive power situation that did not please his directors.

> 'Gooch's standard passenger engines of 1840-1842 were direct derivatives of Messrs. Stephenson's 'Stars', and if the general drawings of both classes be compared, it will be found that in most essential particulars the designs were very similar, though there were differences in dimensions, modifications in the latter having been made as a result of experience gained in the working of the 'Stars' already in service. It is in no way derogatory to Gooch's high merit as a Locomotive Engineer of great ability to state that he took Stephenson's engines as his model; on the contrary, he acted in the best interests of the Company in basing his designs upon engines which had proved generally efficient in service, at the same time improving their details. The Company had already had more than enough of experimental failures.' (80)

Daniel Gooch designed his first locomotives in 1840, known as the 'Firefly class'. The 62 locomotives were built by seven contractors, the best being produced by the pioneering Leeds firm, now known as Fenton, Murray and Jackson. **(81)** When Brunel suggested to the Gauge Commission that the performance of broad and standard gauge locomotives should be compared it was appropriate that *Ixion,* one of the Leeds engines, be chosen to represent the GWR. Needless to say the improved broad-gauge engine performed very well indeed, but, because of other major concerns, this could not influence the Commissioners' decision in favour of the standard gauge. (82)

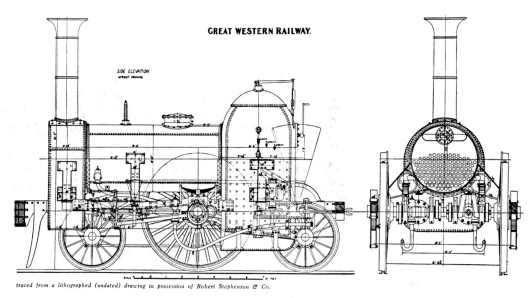

Figure 3.16: the GWR contender in the gauge trials was Ixion, *which Gooch based on the Patentee design. The locomotive performed very well for speed, reliability and ride quality, and was only out-performed by the standard gauge* A *on boiler efficiency. J. G. H. Warren.*

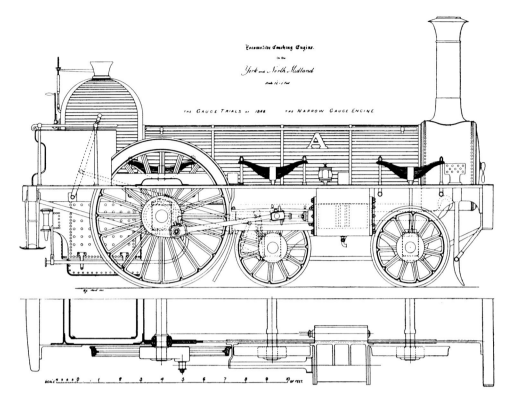

Figure 3.17: A *the long-boiler 2-2-2-0 built for the York & North Midland and used in the gauge trials.*

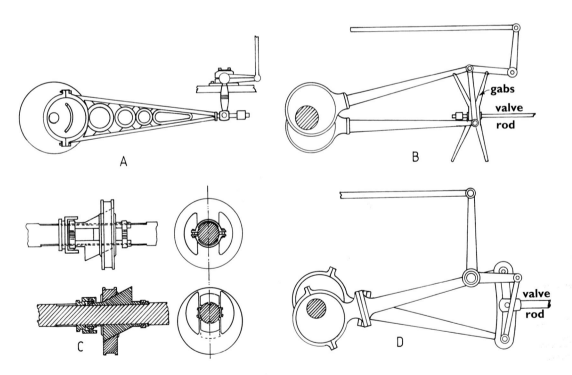

Figure 3.18: (a) loose eccentric as applied to the later Killingworth locomotives (b) four fixed eccentrics with gabs combined on the valve spindle, as applied by Robert Stephenson in 1841, (c) Dodds' shifting eccentric wedge motion, 1839, (d) four fixed eccentrics united with the slotted link, by Williams and Howe 1841-2. Various sources/ J. F. Addyman.

Some concepts like valve gears, which had originated elsewhere, were advanced in Stephenson's works. In 1712 an ingenious boy, Humphrey Potter, devised a system of ropes and strings to save him from having to open and close the cylinder valves manually on one of the first Newcomen engines. By adjusting the string 'linkages' to get the ideal opening and closing points of the valves the operating speed of his engine had been increased from 10 to 16 strokes per minute. (83) Since then many engineers had taken up the challenge to improve the efficiency of steam engines by devising linkages to optimise valve events; the early nineteenth century had seen a number of these. On the 1821 Killingworth and Hetton locomotives eccentrics were used on the axles to control the entry and exit of steam to the cylinders via slide valves. (Fig.3.18a) **(84)** Like hundreds of thousands of locomotive men who were to follow, Nicholas Wood noted that the exhaust did not always sound 'on beat'. Experiments were done by providing adjusting screws on the valve rod and it was 'soon found that there was a certain time, at which the opening into the cylinder could be made, when the effect was the greatest'. (85) Although, as yet, the cut-off point of the steam entering the cylinder could not be varied to suit the loading conditions it was, at least, being controlled to enter and leave at the optimum points of the piston stroke. Although, *Lancashire Witch* had introduced variable cut-offs in 1828, the first successful variable valve gear the 'wedge eccentric motion' was used on the Sheffield and Rotherham Railway. (Fig. 3.18c) It was patented in 1839 by Isaac Dodds (1801-1882), the nephew of the Killingworth viewer.

An arrangement invented by Charles Carmichael of Dundee in 1818 had been adopted in 1835 by Robert Stephenson & Co., and improvements continued to be made until a real breakthrough in 1841. Then Robert is reported as saying to the North Midland locomotive superintendent; 'there is no occasion to try any further at scheming valve motions; one of our people has now hit on a plan that beats all other valve motions.' A draughtsman at the Newcastle works, William Williams, had come up with what was developed to become known as the 'Stephenson Link Motion'. Some modifications carried out by a patternmaker, William Howe (1814-1879), ensured it worked correctly. (Fig. 3.18d) (86) From 1843 to around 1910 the Stephenson link motion, further improved by others, became the most popular type. After 1910 the Belgian Walschaert's valve gear, invented in 1844, gained precedence.

The final milestone in Robert's quest for increased efficiency was his introduction of the 'long boiler' type of locomotive in 1841, incorporating the new valve gear. This was partly to match the better steam production potential of the larger diameter boilers and wider fireboxes being introduced on the broad gauge, but also to overcome a problem. With the knowledge that the firebox produced most of the steam those on almost all locomotives had their surfaces enlarged without a corresponding increase in the heating surface of the boiler tubes. This meant that too little heat was transferred to the water via the tubes resulting in the smokebox and chimney being destroyed by the excessively hot gases passing through them. When Robert found that the temperature in the chimney was over 770° F (410°C), (about a third of the temperature within the firebox) he knew that the tubes must be lengthened with suitable modifications to the blast or draughting arrangements. The increase in boiler length was to be a significant 40 to 50 percent from around 8 ft 6 in to over 12 feet, resulting in better evaporation rates and a drop in smokebox temperature of 330° F (184° C). (87)

The wheelbase could not be lengthened to suit the long boiler because of the small size of the numerous locomotive turntables in use (a constraint to be encountered frequently by later locomotive engineers). It was overcome, on the long-boiler type, by keeping to the established wheelbase and placing all three axles in front of the firebox. (88) However, regardless of the size of the turntables it soon became inevitable that the wheelbase and number of wheels must be increased to carry heavier locomotives and to produce a 'better ride'. The ludicrous practice of separating the engine and tender to turn them individually on the tiny turnplates made it high time that proper turntables of adequate length for future developments were invested in by all railways. **(89)**

A recent writer has described the quality of the early locomotives by Robert Stephenson & Co. as 'execrable in the standard of construction and detail design.' (90) When judged by modern standards this is perfectly true, but had Robert waited for materials and manufacturing techniques to improve the evolution of railways would have been much slower. He and other pioneers went ahead with their ideas dragging technology forward in step with their requirements; this is still normal in many developments. Inventors and machine tool manufacturers: Bramah, Clement, Fox (of Derby), Maudslay, Murray, Nasmyth, Roberts and Whitworth all made significant improvements in the quest for speed and accuracy in the manufacture of component parts. (91) Ironworks were greatly advancing their smelting techniques and were becoming aware of the effects of various trace elements, found in ores from different localities, on the quality and strength of the finished iron. Both allowed increased reliability of locomotive components and economies in design. By the early 1840s this meant that crank axles were a lot easier to make and less liable to failure, so the new long-boiler locomotives were built with single iron plate frames inside the wheels instead of the much more expensive and heavier double or multiple frames used previously.

There were three long-boiler prototypes; a 2-2-2, a 2-4-0 and an 0-6-0, with driving wheel diameters of 5 ft 6in, 4 ft 6 in and 4 ft 9 in respectively. These prototypes had inside cylinders and the fashionable haystack fireboxes. (92) The improvements incorporated in these locomotives gave them a potential for much higher speeds so the instability inherent in the short wheelbases, imposed by the turntables, was becoming a real problem. Bogie locomotives were still avoided in Britain even though Robert found the most stable arrangement to be the 2-2-2-0, with the third axle being driven, which was really crying out for a leading bogie. A peculiar quirk of human nature is the mixture of extreme boldness and extreme conservatism, or even timidity, in the decisions we make. If Robert had gone for the bogie at this, or an even earlier, stage most British and continental manufacturers would have seen its advantages and followed him as they did in most other respects. **(93)**

A long-boiler locomotive with the 2-2-2-0 wheel arrangement was built in 1845 with 6ft 6in diameter driving wheels but outside cylinders placed between the leading pairs of wheels. It was known as 'A', and took part in the gauge trials where the results from the larger boiler were spectacular. (Fig. 3.17) The boiler pressures of A and broad-gauge competitor *Ixion* (Fig. 3.16) had been increased from the then normal 50 up to 75 lbs per square inch. On test *Ixion* evaporated 7 lbs of water per pound of coke whereas A, with its better proportioned boiler, evaporated 8.8 lbs. (94) Having achieved a figure 60% more than *Rocket's,* little further improvement could be made and most twentieth century locomotives' evaporation rates were within the 7 to 9 lbs range. For example, in 1923 one of the famous Gresley class A1 Pacifics, like *Flying Scotsman,* averaged less than 8 lbs of water per lb of coal on test. (95)

Locomotive Type	Date	Firebox	Tubes	Total
Killingworth single flue	1825		40-50	40-50
S&D return flue	1827		100	100
Lancashire Witch	1828		66	66
Rocket	1829	25.2	117.7	142.9
Northumbrian	1830	36.6	379	415.6
Planet	1830	37.3	370.4	407.7
Samson	1831	40.2	416.8	457
Patentee	1833	52.2	312.2	364.4
Leicester & Swannington	1833	67.5	589	656.5
Broad gauge *Ixion*	1841	97	602	699
Standard gauge *A*	1845	59	880	939

Table showing the heating surfaces in square feet for various early locomotives.

Although the boiler had reached its limit of thermal efficiency its size was being governed, to a large extent, by the inherent instability of most locomotives at speed. The widely held theory that the centre of gravity of the locomotives needed to be kept as low as possible to help stability precluded the use of larger diameter boilers. In order to achieve this ideal Francis Trevithick's 1847 design for *Cornwall* had its boiler *below* the driving wheel axle, and T. R. Crampton reverted to the idea used on the American bogie locomotives of the early 1830s by putting the driving wheel behind the firebox.

Even with its small boiler the riding of A at speed was exceedingly unsteady, and, according to Daniel Gooch, 'she jumped about so much' that he refused to ride on her for the return trip during the gauge trials. (96) The outside cylinders and short wheelbase did not help but, from his evidence to the Gauge Commission in 1845, Robert was starting to appreciate that the 'yawing' motion of locomotives was caused by their unbalanced reciprocating masses: '…if we could contrive to balance the pistons by a weight upon the wheel, we should get rid of that very much.' (97) Since 1844 Robert had been Engineer-in-Chief of the Eastern Counties, and William Fernihough, the locomotive superintendent of that railway, stated in his evidence: '…we now balance our engines by a small weight placed at the periphery of the wheel'. G. P. Bidder confirmed in 1849: 'Several engines having six wheels, four of which were coupled, were unsteady until the weight of the connecting rods was perfectly balanced, when they immediately became steady.' **(98)** On the London and Birmingham Edward Bury had brought the mass of the tender into play to help damp the oscillations by connecting it to the engine with a screw coupling flanked by side buffers. (99)

Two years before his death George Stephenson made his first foray into locomotive construction for a number of years by taking out a patent with William Howe in 1846 for a long-boiler locomotive with three cylinders. Howe had left Robert Stephenson & Co. and was now engineer to Stephenson's Clay Cross Collieries, six miles from George's home at Tapton House, Chesterfield. The more even torque produced by the three cylinders eliminated the yawing at speed, and the ride quality was further helped by using Bury's method of coupling the tender. Two 2-2-2-0s emerged from Robert Stephenson

& Co. with two sets of link motion working the valves on the three cylinders. A trial run by one of these locomotives, on 7 May 1847 between Wolverton and Birmingham produced a top speed of 75 mph and an average speed of 60 mph; 'the motion at the highest velocity being perfectly steady.' There must have been some disadvantages as these were the only two locomotives of this type; both were purchased by the York, Newcastle and Berwick Railway in 1848. **(100)**

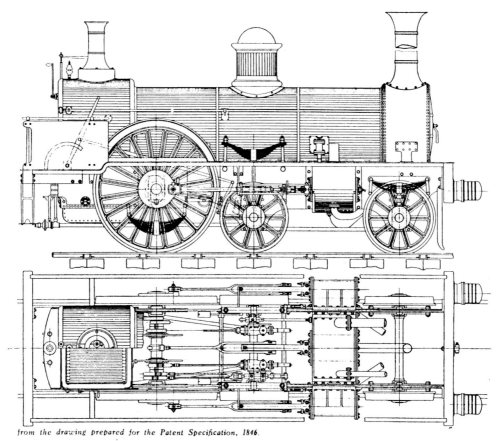

from the drawing prepared for the Patent Specification, 1846.

Figure 3.19: the 3-cylinder locomotive incorporating George Stephenson and William Howe's patent. In 1839 Isaac Dodds had patented a 3-cylinder 0-4-2 locomotive with the two cylinders outside the firebox driving the front axle and the inside one, under the smokebox, driving the rear. J.G.H. Warren.

The three-cylinder locomotive was one of the more sound developments in the mania produced by the 'battle of the gauges'. Freak locomotives were being produced just to exceed the broad gauge maximum speeds, and little of lasting value accrued from their designs. **(101)** The simultaneous improvements in permanent way, with cross sleepers instead of longitudinal bearers or stone blocks, heavier rails and fishplated joints were to have far more effect on the immediate progress of railways.

When Robert Stephenson & Co. had not been allowed to supply locomotives to the London and Birmingham, Edward Bury had been given the job. He remained aloof from competing with the broad gauge and insisted on keeping to outdated, small, four-wheeled locomotives against the wishes of his directors. After the London and Birmingham became part of the London and North Western Railway (LNWR) in July 1846 Bury had to 'go'. **(102)** He was replaced on the Southern Division of the LNWR in 1847 by his former foreman, J. E. McConnell (1815-1883), who immediately ordered larger locomotives from six contractors including Robert Stephenson & Co. Soon, as Locke and others had already discovered, he found that he was unable to cannibalise parts from different makers' locomotives to keep his fleet in steam; standard designs were needed.

The days of individual manufacturers selling their own designs to most British companies were coming to an end. Many railways set up their own workshops and only ordered locomotives, to their individual designs, from contractors when their own shops could not meet the demand. From the 1850s Robert Stephenson & Co. had to look abroad for much of their work, where their designs had considerable influence (colour plate 7). 'On the continent thousands of long-boiler engines have been put into service since the 'Mammoth' was supplied to the Paris-Orleans Railway [1846], and the Stephenson long-boiler engine remains the standard six-coupled locomotive today [1923].' **(103)** Some of the early long-boiler types supplied to Spain had working lives of 100 years. The output of the

Company was such that from 1825 until 1937, when the firm amalgamated with Hawthorn, Leslie & Co., they had produced nearly 3,900 locomotives; an average of one every one-and-a-half weeks.

Former rival, George Rennie, who in partnership with his younger brother, Sir John, had built 16 locomotives between 1838 and 1843, proclaimed at a meeting of the Institution of Civil Engineers in April 1849: 'Mr Stephenson had brought his engines to such perfection in construction, that all questions appeared now mere matters of detail in arrangements, which revealed themselves in the results of actual working.' (104) If we are to assess Robert's contribution to locomotive design, the gradual development of the boiler and firebox between 1828 and 1842 was outstanding, but his simplification of the mechanism and his acceptance and advancement of others' ideas in his pursuit of excellence had considerable merit. When *Evening Star*, the last steam locomotive built for British Railways, was turned out in 1960 it incorporated ideas and improvements by hundreds of engineers and mechanics, but its firebox and boiler were based on principles established in *Rocket* and *Northumbrian*. Few will object to the statement that *Evening Star* was one of 999 standard steam engines *designed* for British Railways by R. A. Riddles, even though he only chaired a committee which lifted their specifications from established practice. Strangely, Robert Stephenson, who had a much more 'hands-on' approach to really pioneering locomotive design, is often denied his pre-eminent input with his credit being generally ignored or transferred to his father and others. **(105)** However, it must be admitted that his own outstanding achievements in other fields tend to overshadow his locomotive work. It is worth remembering that in the same period as his major locomotive developments he had engineered over 300 miles of railway.

It is difficult to assess how much the provision of stationary engines on the L&M would have affected the progress of railways. Whether the introduction of locomotives on main line railways would have been delayed by several months or several years, if Robert had not been involved, will never be known. He won battles for the locomotive and against the broad gauge and atmospheric railways, but was unable to achieve his desire for sound legislation to promote a sensible, competition-free railway network as outlined by William James and others.

If George Stephenson has hardly figured in this account of the later development of the locomotive, it is worth recalling that he gave Robert the start in life essential to his success – a fact acknowledged in Robert's presidential address to the Institution of Civil Engineers in January 1856: -

> 'For it is my great pride to remember, that whatever may have been done, and however
> extensive may have been my own connexion with railway development, all I know and
> all I have done, is primarily due to the Parent whose memory I cherish and revere.' (106)

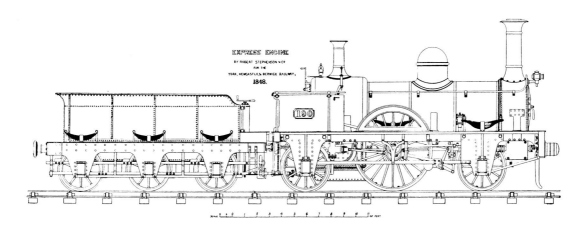

Figure 3.20: a 2-2-2 express passenger locomotive built for the York Newcastle and Berwick Railway in 1848 by Robert Stephenson & Co. J. G. H. Warren.

ENDNOTES

1. *Newcastle Chronicle,* advertisement 22 October 1803.
2. Francis Trevithick, *The Life of Richard Trevithick,* (1872) Vol. 1 pp. 184-9.
3. Jeaff. Vol. 1 p. 28.
4. John Blenkinsop's patent No.3431, 10 April 1811.
5. Tomlinson, p. 21 quotes a letter from J. Watson to J. Birtley 11 October 1813.
6. Ibid. p. 22.
7. T. H. Hair, *Views of the Collieries,* (1844) quoted on p. 23. Original in unspecified local newspaper.
8. St Nicholas Church, Newcastle, Parish Register. Information supplied by R. S. Roper.
9. *Newcastle Chronicle,* letter dated 17 December 1836.
10. L. G. Charlton, *The First Locomotive Engineers,* (1974) pp. 10, 12 & 44 gives drawings of these locos.
11. Samuel Smiles, *Lives of the Engineers,* (1862 edition) pp. 98-9, also Wood (1825) pp. 136-7.
12. J. G. H. Warren, *A Century of Locomotive Building,* (1923 reprinted 1970) p. 23. James G. H. Warren (1875-1935) became chief draughtsman at R. S. & Co. in 1904. The results of his painstaking research into, and his analysis of, the original records at R. S. & Co., helped by his first rate knowledge of steam locomotive design, is shown in the quality of his book on their locomotives. In order to allow the reader who wishes to obtain more detailed explanations, of the many developments, footnote references are given to Warren, which is easily obtainable, rather than to the primary sources that he quotes and the authors have explored.
13. N. Wood, (1825) p.143. In order to promote G. S's image Wood's manuscript was subjected to censorship to give more credit to George. A letter from Longridge in Jan. 1825 to Pease; '… George has an extraordinary field for the display of his peculiar talents and that if he manage well he may easily distance his competitors. We must however assist him much. **Wood's book must undergo strict censorship before it is published.**'
14. Ibid. pp. 141, 151.
15. A major disadvantage was that the pistons of the steam springs could be moving either in sympathy or direct opposition to the pistons driving the locomotive, and would require large clearance volumes in the cylinders in order to prevent damage.
16. Wood, (1838) pp. 506, 521.
17. Wood, (1825) p. 147.
18. Ibid. p. 293.
19. Jeaff. Vol. 1, p. 70.
20. Warren, pp. 113-4.
21. Charlton, pp. 60-1. This loco was later rebuilt by Hackworth to become *Chittapratt.* See also T. R. Pearce, *Locomotives of the Stockton and Darlington Railway* (1996) pp. 34-8.
22. Warren, p. 261.
23. Ibid. p. 143.
24. Ibid. pp. 140-4. Another experimental locomotive, the 'Liverpool Coke Engine', which was certainly not in accord with Robert's ideas, was built in 1828. It had two vertical boilers carried on six wheels. It was later referred to as the 'Twin Sisters', ibid. pp.155-7. Coke has a similar calorific value per lb to all but the best Welsh steam coals. Surprisingly, in the 1850s, when railways decided to revert to coal, problems were encountered and it was the introduction of the brick arch in the firebox and the blower in the smokebox that overcame them.
25. Ibid. p. 147.
26. PRO/RAIL 371/1 L&M minute 26 July 1827. Walker and Rastrick later estimated the cost of the winding engines and their equipment as £10,000 each. (Wood (1838) p. 631)
27. W. O. Skeat, *George Stephenson. The Engineer and his Letters.* (1973), pp. 103-4.
28. Warren, pp. 165-70. Significantly 'George's report' in favour of locomotives is in Robert's handwriting.
29. Neither of these engineers was against locomotives per se. Walker had modified a scheme of G. S. to avoid the use of inclines and stationary engines on the Leeds and Selby Railway (L&S) in 1825. In July 1829, shortly after the L&M report, he recommended *against* the use of stationary engines throughout the L&S as the traffic 'would not be sufficient to keep the engines constantly at work.' (Tomlinson p. 203) Rastrick had charge of the construction of Trevithick's *Catch-me-who-can,* which was demonstrated at Euston in 1808, and was building his own locomotives including *Agenoria* and *Stourbridge Lion* in 1828 and 1829. (B. D. of Civil Engineers p. 545) Confidence in the use of locomotives for main lines was generally not very high as, for example, the 1830 scheme for the London & Birmingham was for a horse-worked railway.
30. Wood (1838) p. 625 stresses that the Walker and Rastrick reports were 'made *previous* [it. sic] to the improvements in the locomotive engines, induced by the Liverpool experiments; while the estimates of Messrs. Stephenson and Locke, contrasted with them, were made *subsequent* [it. sic] to those improvements.' The first report estimated a saving of 0.0651 of a penny per ton mile in favour of stationary engines while the latter 0.105 in favour of locomotives on figures of around 0.25d per ton mile.
31. Robert Stephenson and Joseph Locke, *Observations on the Comparative Merits of Locomotives & Fixed Engines as Applied to Railways,* (printed 1830). The title page of the printed version claimed it was 'Compiled from the Reports of Mr. George Stephenson', and the text was updated from the original hand-written version. Many years later, Robert told Smiles; 'I believe I furnished the facts and arguments, and Locke put them into shape. Locke was a very flowery writer, whereas my style was rather bald and unattractive; so he was editor of the pamphlet'. (Smiles p 259)
32. Warren, p. 172.

33. Jeaff. Vol. 1, pp. 125-6.
34. Victoria Haworth, *Perceptions of Great Engineers*. (1994) p. 68 endnotes 225-228.
35. *The Engineer,* Vol. 9, (1880) p. 217.
36. R. S's own notes, now in Devon County Record Office, state that it was Ralph Hutchinson that assisted with *Rocket*. A series of reports on the progress of *Rocket* written by R. S. to Booth appear as Appendix II in H. Booth *Henry Booth* (1980).
37. John Cox Stevens' patent No. 2855 of 31 May 1805 for a 'boiler of [water] tubes for high-pressure steam' would have expired by 1820, and any future patents, to be allowed, would have to be of different designs. The problem with water tubes was that they rapidly became furred up due to impurities in the water.
38. E. Galloway, *History and Progress of the Steam Engine* (1835) pp. 311-99 details various early boilers. H. Booth, *Henry Booth*, p. 60, gives details of Neville's somewhat impractical boiler.
39. Warren, p. 138. R. S & Co. had supplied two early 'S&D type'0-4-0 locomotives to Séguin's order in March and April 1828, and it is thought that one was rebuilt with his new boiler, for which Séguin is said to have already *applied* for a patent in England in December 1827 (he was granted a French patent on 22 Feb. 1828). Séguin met G. S during his stay in England between 9 Dec. 1827 and 3 Feb. 1828, and the bellows used on the 'Liverpool Travelling Engine' almost certainly came from their discussions.
40. Ibid. p. 295, suggests that there was concern about boiler patent infringements when, in 1831, R.S. & Co. advised Hackworth that a design of one of his infringed a marine boiler patent by Napier of Glasgow.
41. M. R. Bailey and J. P. Glithero, *The Engineering and History of* Rocket (2000) p. 18 concludes; 'The evidence indicates that, even allowing for George Stephenson's strong interest in the boiler, it was very much the work of Robert Stephenson and his Newcastle team that brought about its successful implementation.'
42. Wood (1838), pp. 524-5.
43. Warren, pp. 211-222.
44. Letter from R. S. to Henry Booth dated 5 September 1829. Jeaff. Vol. 1, p. 141, is quite wrong when he says that *Rocket* was shipped from the Tyne to Liverpool and was much delayed en route. It was the Liverpool stationary engine that was shipwrecked and delayed. See p.30, footnote 3.
45. Warren, pp. 185-210. There is no mention in the contemporary reports the trials of the failure of *San Pareil's* cylinder, which had been cast by R. S & Co.; there are remarks about the leaking boiler and other problems. A letter from Hackworth, to the L&M directors soon after the trials, stated that its poor steaming was a direct result of the defective cylinder casting, and as soon as it was replaced the loco performed well. The L&M minutes for 26 Oct 1829 state that it was to work on the Bolton & Leigh as soon as it was repaired in place of *Lancashire Witch* now on the L&M.
46. Warren, p. 202.
47. Ibid. pp. 180, 227.
48. Ibid. p. 236.
49. Ibid. p. 268. The ratio of the volume to heating surface of a given length of a 3" tube on *Rocket* was 54% of that of *Northumbria's* 1⅝" ones, and, of course, many more of the smaller tubes could be accommodated within the boiler.
50. Ibid. pp. 242-3.
51. RAIL 371/1, 26 October 1829. (Sir) Goldsworthy Gurney (1793-1875) had managed to run one of his ingenious steam road carriages from London to Bath at a speed of 15 mph in 1829.
52. Warren, p. 237.
53. *Proc. I. C. E. Vol. 16*, pp. 22-5. James Kennedy claimed, at an I. C. E. meeting when R. S. was presiding, that his partner, Bury, had been the first to come up with the idea of a crank axle on a locomotive in 1830 even though *Novelty* of 1829 had one! R. S's letter of 1 January 1828 (q.v.) shows he was already considering inside cylinders as used on Gurney's steam carriages. Robert explained the need for retaining as much heat as possible to prevent condensation within the cylinders had been impressed on him from his conversations with Trevithick, and placing them under the smokebox helped this aim. Cylinder condensation was to remain a problem even with high-pressure, high-superheat steam so much so that André Chapelon (1892-1978) decided to apply live steam jackets around the high-pressure cylinders some of his later compound locomotives as part of his unending quest for efficiency.
54. Warren, pp. 252-3. Deceptively Stephenson and Locke's report had claimed a very modest 30 tons at 12 mph.
55. Warren, pp. 256-7. The L&M board meeting of 25 October had agreed the trial.
56. Ibid. p. 243.
57. It was not possible to fit 5ft diameter coupled wheels under the short boilers originally used on the Planets.
58. Warren, p. 266
59. Ibid. p. 229.
60. Ibid. p. 269.
61. Ibid. pp. 150-2. This was originally named *Pride of Newcastle*, and was intended for the L&M.
62. There were two *John Bulls* supplied by R. S. & Co. in 1831. One supplied to the Mohawk & Hudson and the other to Stevens' specification with a Bury-type circular firebox.
63. The American railroad pioneers that met both Stephensons were: Horatio Allen, J. B. Jarvis, J Knight, W. G. McNeill, R. L. Stevens and G. W. Whistler. Whistler, who had ordered the first American locomotive from R. S. & Co., is reputed to 'have liked the elder man. A clever man he was, to rise from common digging [sic] in the Newcastle pits to engineering – observe how highly! But his son Robert was another matter. Whistler did not prize this young man who had been educated at the University of Edinburgh and talked in highfalutin' terms because he felt the necessity of impressing people.' (A. Parry, *Whistler's Father* 1936)

64. There was an early British bogie-tank locomotive, built by J. Carmichael & Co., for the Dundee & Newtyle Railway in 1833.
65. Warren, pp. 299-310.
66. Ibid. pp. 76-7.
67. Ibid. pp. 320-1.
68. Ibid. pp. 85-6.
69. There had been 26 locomotives supplied to the L&M by R. S. & Co. since *Rocket.*
70. Warren, pp. 311-9.
71. Ibid. pp. 312-3. R. S. did not achieve these aims with the *Patentee* hence the need for the long-boiler type.
72. Ibid. p. 314.
73. Stephenson and Locke, p. 4, para. 2.
74. Warren, pp. 89.
75. E. T. MacDermot, *History of the Great Western Railway*, Vol. 1 (1964 edition) p. 373.
76. Ibid. p. 272
77. Ibid. pp. 392-4.
78. Warren, pp. 340-2.
79. Ibid. p. 441.
80. MacDermot, p. 398.
81. Ibid. p. 399. R. S. & Co. was much too busy to supply any locos to the GWR in 1840; the next that the Company supplied to the GWR were in 1855 when Swindon Works could not meet its demand.
82. Ibid. pp. 117-8.
83. T. H. Shields, *The Evolution of Locomotive Valve Gears,* (1943 reprinted 1999) p. 3.
84. William Murdock (1754-1839) had produced a working model of a steam locomotive, introduced the eccentric, sun-and-planet gear and patented the slide valve between 1784 and 1799. The slide valve achieved its final form by Matthew Murray in 1802.
85. Wood, (1825), pp. 148-9.
86. Warren, pp. 359-70.
87. *Proc. I. C. E. Vol. 11,* p.401.
88. Warren, p. 346.
89. S. C. Brees, *Railway Practice,* (1838-40) shows turnplates of only 12'-6" to 15'-0" diameter, whereas. *Dempsey's Practical Railway Engineer,* (1847) shows loco turntables 30 feet diameter. The first locomotive turntable to work using the annular outer rail was introduced on the North Midland Railway by Isaac Dodds in the early 1840s. The turntable problem recurred every time designers added another pair of wheels to increase the power of their locomotives.
90. Brian Reed, *Loco Profile 5,* (1971) p.98-9.
91. *Proc. I. C. E. Vol. 17*, p. 192.
92. Warren, p. 353.
93. Ibid. p. 402, states that a bogie 4-4-0 was designed by R. S. & Co. in 1844 but not built.
94. Ibid. pp. 381, 387.
95. *Locomotives of the LNER: Part 2A,* p. 10. The Pacific being superheated would affect its performance.
96. R. B. Wilson (Editor) *Sir Daniel Gooch Memoirs and Diary* (1972) pp. 50-1.
97. *Gauge Evidence,* p. 18.
98. *Proc. I. C. E. Vol. 8,* T. R. Crampton, 'The Construction of Locomotive Engines.' p. 251. This paper produced a lively discussion on locomotive stability with length of wheelbase, positioning of the driving wheels and cylinders and other features being considered.
99. Warren pp. 377-8, 393.
100. Ibid. pp. 391-3. During the first half of the twentieth century a large number of three and four-cylinder British locomotives were built for the more arduous duties, but to simplify maintenance only one of the 999 British Railways standard locomotives, produced after 1950, had the complication of more than two cylinders.
101. Trevithick Vol. 1 p. 216. Francis Trevithick admitted: 'An exceptional engine was built in 1847 to refute a dogma of broad gauge advocates that the narrow gauge reached its limit in speed because the driving wheels could not be safely increased in diameter.' His driving wheels, with their axle above the boiler, were 6" larger than the largest broad gauge ones.
102. E.L. Ahrons *The British Steam railway Locomotive 1825-1925* (1927), p. 66 tables. By the mid 1840s the average coke consumption per ton mile for the Bury locos was over 50% greater than those of other major railways, which indicates that by then they had to be 'flogged' to do their duties; their repairs cost twice as much per mile as R. S. & Co's locos. The figures given by Ahrons are more generous than those quoted in Bury's March 1840 paper to the I. C. E. (Vol. 3) where, for example, his maintenance costs are even higher. The 'superior' evaporation rates that he boasted about achieving were actually worse than *Rocket's*!
103. Warren, pp. 357, 96. The first German loco *Adler* was supplied in 1835, and by 1843 81 out of the first 180 locos in Germany had been supplied by R. S. & Co.
104. *Proc. I. C. E. Vol. 8,* p. 245.
105. A typical example is Col. H. C. B. Rogers in *Chapelon* (1972) when, like many others, he is misled by Smiles and credits *Rocket* to George Stephenson (p. 140), and then goes on to argue that Chapelon was 'the most outstanding locomotive engineer in the whole history of the steam engine'.
106. *Proc. I. C. E. Vol. 15,* p. 153.

CHAPTER FOUR: LONDON TO BIRMINGHAM BUT NOT TO BRIGHTON

The London and Birmingham Railway

The London & Birmingham Railway (L&B) was described as, '...an undertaking of high historic interest, both on account of the gigantic difficulties which were encountered in its construction, and of it being the first public iron [trunk] road into London.' (1) It opened in 1838, and together with the Grand Junction Railway, opened the previous year, it completed the two hundred miles of railway needed to link London to Liverpool and Manchester, and became the springboard for many of the lines that serve Northern Britain.

The end of the eighteenth century had seen some improvement in communications with the completion of a network of canals linking London with Birmingham. (2) The idea of combining a railway and a canal followed 20 years later, and this came about when William James was surveying his railway from Stratford upon Avon to Moreton-in-the-Marsh (Incorporated 28 May 1821). He realised that by using the canals between Stratford and Birmingham and extending his railway southwards via Oxford and Thame he could give a much faster route to London than the woefully wandering canals. This scheme was ahead of its time and remained unsupported. (3)

In May 1824, just before Robert's departure to South America, George was asked to survey a 'Birmingham line'. On 11 July 1824 George wrote to Michael Longridge to say, 'I have now got four sets of Surveyors upon the Birmingham line and shall have 8 or 10 sets more when I return from the north'. He wrote again on 8 August to say that subscriptions of £700,000 had been promised. (4) Earlier, in January 1824, (Sir) John Rennie had also been asked to prepare a survey, but by the time he had completed his report for a line via Oxford and Banbury, in April 1826, interest had waned. Francis Giles then proposed a line through Coventry, and, in a resurgence of interest in 1829, rival companies supporting the Giles and Rennie lines issued prospectuses. However, common sense prevailed, and these groups decided to combine their efforts to promote whichever was the better line in order to avoid the expense of a parliamentary contest. (5)

The impending opening of the Liverpool and Manchester brought the firm of George Stephenson and Son to eminence in railway matters, so George was asked to arbitrate, and he gave his opinion in favour of the Coventry route. (6) At this stage Giles and Rennie reluctantly had to drop out of the picture, and an agreement between the London and Birmingham Railway Committee and George Stephenson and Son was signed, on 18 September 1830, but *only for the work necessary to get Parliamentary approval.* (7)

Even before the parliamentary survey was started, George was eased out, and Robert took complete control of the L&B. How this was achieved is not known, but George certainly had enough work with his colliery interests, the Grand Junction and other railways to keep him fully occupied.

The agreement was reached far too late to allow the Parliamentary plans to be prepared for deposit by the end of November to enable the Bill to be considered in the 1831 Session. The first survey by Robert Stephenson was completed in the autumn of 1830, and in 1831 a second line was staked out almost identical to the final route. (8) The stories about the local opposition, and even violence, to the surveyors, and the ploys used by the engineers to complete their work need not be retold here. Robert knew, in order to avoid the embarrassment caused, for example, on the Liverpool and Manchester, it was crucial that absolute accuracy of levelling and setting out be achieved regardless of these obstacles and obstructions. In the 1830s there were no conveniently placed Ordnance Survey benchmarks, to verify the accuracy of their levels, so it was essential that, at least, the difference in level between the ends of each relatively short section was double-checked. Where there was strenuous opposition, and having completed the first levelling by subterfuge, it may only have been possible to do this check by a circuitous route remote from the line of the railway. Parliament insisted on accurate surveys but afforded no powers to the railway promoters to help to achieve them. For more details of surveying see Appendix 1.

George had eventually weathered the storm caused by the inaccurate survey on the L&M, but it is likely that Robert might not have acceded to be Engineer-in-Chief of the L&B if the opposition found errors in the surveys during the searching Parliamentary inquiry. His ability as a witness was also to be crucial. In 1839, S. C. Brees wrote; 'One of the principal exhibits of a Civil Engineer's talent and resources is displayed in the Committee Rooms of the Houses of Parliament, in his examination as a Witness to prove the practicality or the contrary of proposed Public Works'. (9) It was surely the quality of Robert's survey and the clarity and weight of his evidence given for the Bill that gained the confidence of the directors, and led to him being made solely responsible for the building of the railway.

The swathe of country explored for the various railway schemes extended as far west as Banbury and east of the present East Coast main line at Baldock. For example, Francis Giles' route out of London ran north-eastwards to Barnet before swinging west to join the alignment finally built near Hemel Hempstead. Reasons for these wide variations were partly to explore the commercial implications, but, more significantly, to provide the best possible gradients, at the least cost, over the five ranges of hills and the intervening river valleys that cut across the route to Birmingham. (10) Another factor, that of avoiding the prime estates of major opposing landowners, had to enter into the equation of route selection with sometimes damaging and expensive results. The opposition of the Earls of Essex and Clarendon led to the construction of Watford tunnel and other extensive earthworks in the vicinity that could have been avoided with their co-operation. (11) It was originally intended that the line should go through Northampton, but it was said that opposition in the vicinity led to the town being bypassed, and the troublesome Kilsby tunnel having to be built. **(12)**

In order to avoid upsetting a major landowner, Lord Southampton, the original remit was for the railway to start no nearer the centre of London than Camden Town. Robert insisted that the line be designed and built without gradients steeper than 1 in 330; this was achieved even though it climbed 300 feet between Camden and Tring summit on the Chiltern Hills. (13) After the first Act was passed, Lord Southampton had become a railway supporter, and, with his blessing, it was decided to extend the line over his land as far as Euston Square. **(14)** This additional mile included a stretch of 1 in 66 that was long enough to need to be worked by winding engines until more powerful locomotives were introduced in 1844. When the Euston extension was proposed it was hoped that it should end in a station to be used jointly by the Great Western as its terminus from Bristol. **(15)** The logic of this proposal is demonstrated by the fact that little more than a quarter-of-a-mile separates the two lines, at their closest point, near I. K. Brunel's last resting place, Kensal Green Cemetery. The cosy idea of the joint station was finally dropped when Brunel decided to opt for the broad gauge; this resulted, after some debate, in the Paddington site being chosen for the GWR terminus. The advantage of the two additional tracks that had been provided on the Euston extension, to accommodate the GWR, was to be appreciated very soon by the L&B.

Nowadays with electronically recorded survey data and computer-aided design it is easy to forget that, even thirty years ago, it was a long and difficult process to plan a new route. Now with the survey data stored in the computer it is possible, with a little time at the keyboard, to produce plots of alternative alignments and their cross-sections, together with the volumes of earthworks to suit any circumstances, and thus to achieve the best possible solution. On the L&B possibly around 100,000 levels had to be taken, reduced and plotted. Also a lot of tedious trial and error work was needed to find the best levels and alignments to fulfil not only the essential but as many of the desirable parameters as possible before the plans were completed.

T. L. Gooch, Frank Forster and T. E. Harrison were amongst those who assisted in preparing the surveys, deposited plans and cross-sections for the railway. Amazingly, it took only six weeks to complete the basic levelling for the whole 112-mile line. This may have been due to the intuitive choice of the best route by Giles and the Stephensons in limiting the breadth of country to be investigated in detail. T. E. Harrison and Tom Gooch's worst task came in November 1831, at the end of which the plans, or parts of them, had to be deposited with Government offices, clerks of the county councils, parishes and individual landowners. Nine or ten totally accurate copies of each plan were wanted, and, as no process for copying the plans was available then, each had to be drawn separately. The pair undertook this task by tracing the original drawing by means of a light table devised by using glass plates with powerful lights underneath. Whilst doing this tedious work neither had much sleep for a week. The drawings were completed by 25 November, and all the assistants gathered at Stony Stratford, halfway along the route, where the plans, sections and books of reference were finished and thoroughly checked to enable them to be lodged on 30 November as required by Parliamentary Standing Orders.

Estimating the quantities and costs of the work was done in Newcastle by mid February 1832. In March, Robert Stephenson and Tom Gooch closely explored a more direct route, from Tring via Banbury and Warwick, as it was rumoured that they would be cross-examined on it by the counsel representing some of the opposing interests. (16) The saving in distance by this route was four or five miles, but it would be much more expensive or require steeper gradients than 1 in 330. (17)

The quantities for the L&B were estimated at 12,081,116 cubic yards for excavations and 10,698,315 for the embankments. Robert's total cost, which J. U. Rastrick and J. Locke considered *too high*, was estimated at £2,500,000. **(18)** All the roads then in use were crossed by bridges; an intelligent provision that was avoided by many later railways even after the Board of Trade was given powers to insist on bridges rather than level crossings. Their price varied from £2,500 each for turnpike roads to

£300 for farm accommodation bridges. The bridges over the canals were estimated to cost between £3,200 and £3,500. (19)

Traffic counts are carried out, manually or automatically, all over our present-day road network to provide government statistics, but one hardly imagines them being done in the early 1830s on many of the roads and canals between London and Birmingham. No less than 32 persons were employed by the railway to count the numbers and types of conveyances used and passengers carried in one year. Peter Lecount, later to write an account of the line, used the statistics to evaluate the traffic that could be gained for the railway. He allowed 5½ hours (20 mph) for the railway journey against 12½ to 72 hours by other means; he also estimated that the railway would charge only 60% of their average fare. **(20)** Small wonder that the road and canal people were concerned when these figures were given in evidence. Captain C. R. Moorsom R.N., one of the secretaries of the railway, calculated 30,000,000 passenger miles per annum for the line; this was soon to be exceeded. (21)

The L&B Bill went into committee from 5 to 13 April and 21 May to 5 June 1832, when it passed in the Commons after a very hard fight. (22) At one stage the opposing counsel ridiculed Robert's assurances about the safety of the steep angle of the cutting slopes that he proposed to use at Tring. If he could not prove them wrong they would have argued the need for significant increases in the quantities and expenses throughout the line, and his reputation as a reliable witness would have suffered. After leaving the committee room he remembered Thomas Telford's cutting for the Holyhead road (A5) through the same chalk formation, near Dunstable. Although he had endured three days cross-examination and had had little sleep for four nights he roused Tom Gooch, after midnight, and the pair took a post-chaise to Dunstable. In the cold light of dawn they found Telford's angle of repose to be the same as Robert intended to use, and they were back at the hearing, tired but triumphant, by ten o'clock. The point was won. (23)

However, all the valiant efforts were brought to nought in the House of Lords when on 10 July 1832 Lord Brownlow resolved, '...that they have not made out such a case as would warrant the forcing of the proposed railway through the land and property of so great a proportion of dissentient landowners and proprietors.' Thomas Roscoe summed up the affect of this crass decision relatively mildly: -

> 'Thus a great public Company was stopped for twelve months from pursuing a project of such vast importance to the country at large, in almost every relationship of social life; and the proprietors, some of whom had been laying years out of their money [sic], were put to the expense of no less than £72,869 before they were allowed to benefit the country by establishing one of the greatest public works ever achieved by man.' **(24)**

After spending a year-and-a-half of outstanding effort, to overcome every possible obstacle and objection, Robert was, not unnaturally, mortified, and utterly dejected by the outcome. The kindly Lord Wharncliffe, the chairman of the Committee, said prophetically, 'My young friend, don't take this to heart. The decision is against you; but you have made such a display of power that your fortune is made for life.' **(25)**

The opposition to the railway came from numerous sources. The most potent, not unnaturally, came from major landowners, some of whom had diverted or closed roads and even re-sited villages to enhance their views and increase their privacy; to them even the hint of a distant railway would destroy this illusion. These plutocrats also thought that their elite status would be eroded by the provision of transport for the masses. People with a vested interest in canals or roads rightly saw their livelihood disappearing, but many ordinary residents and tradesmen of the district also felt this innovation would somehow adversely affect their way of life. How much some of these views were to change, after the success of the L&B and other early trunk railways, was to be demonstrated by the 'railway mania' of the next decade.

On Friday 13 July 1832, three days after its rejection, the projectors of the L&B held a meeting, at the Thatched House Tavern in St. James's Street, for those in favour of the railway. Sixteen peers and thirty-three members of parliament attended the meeting, which was chaired by Lord Wharncliffe. The second resolution, which was carried unanimously, included: '...it must be presumed that its failure in the House of Lords has arisen from apprehensions on the part of landowners and proprietors respecting its probable effect on their estates, which this meeting firmly and conscientiously believes to be ill-founded.' The 'apprehensions' were removed by the payment of enormous sums of money, almost bribes, for relatively small and worthless pieces of land. (26) In 1831, the railway's valuers had considered that £250,000 would be a generous figure for almost 1,400 acres of land; by 1839 £706,152 had been paid out for nearly 2,000 acres. **(27)**

Some slight modifications were made to the plans that were deposited in November 1832, but without the 'bribes', there was nothing in the revisions to justify the changed opinions of the dissenting landowners. The Bill passed the Commons' Committee on 15 March 1833, and the Lords' on 22 April;

Royal Assent was given on 6 May. (28) The directors were empowered to raise £2,500,000 in shares and £835,000 by loan. **(29)** The other link between London and the North West, the 78-mile long Grand Junction Railway, was authorised on the same day, initially with George Stephenson and Joseph Locke as engineers.

Richard Creed, one of the secretaries of the L&B, wrote to Robert, three weeks after the Act was passed, to say there had been no appointment of the Engineer-in-Chief 'but I think you may be easy on that head. You have friends here and in Birmingham who appreciate your merits and services' (30). The fact that he was not quite thirty, and the presence of an anti-Stephenson lobby, delayed by four months both his appointment, and the commencement of the railway. It is not known exactly what happened during these four anxious months but the opposition would have found it very difficult to find an engineer of the same calibre with suitable experience who was prepared to devote most of his time to their railway.

Henry Robinson Palmer (1795-1844), the founder of the Institution of Civil Engineers, and J. U. Rastrick, who had both already certified the quantities for the line prior to the Parliamentary hearings, were asked to prepare a report for the directors. Their long and favourable report was presented on 13 May 1833, and Rastrick concluded: -

> 'Let nothing deter you from executing the work in the most substantial manner and on the most scientific principals so that it may serve as a model for all other railways and become the wonder and admiration of Posterity. There is not anything but what a Large Spirited Company like yours can accomplish. Remember that faint heart never won fair lady. Therefore let me conclude with the advice of Queen Elizabeth to one of her courtiers: Climb Boldly Then'

In spite of this the directors did not agree Robert's appointment until 7 September 1833, and they informed the shareholders, on the 19th, that, '...considering it indispensable that one engineer should have the entire direction, and that his time and services should be devoted exclusively to the Company, they had, under these conditions, appointed Mr. Robert Stephenson Engineer-in-Chief for the whole line; and were persuaded that to no one could that charge be more properly or safely confided. He has received instructions to stake out the line without delay, and the directors have reasons to expect that the railway will be completed in about four years from the commencement of the work.' He signed his contract with the company on 20 September 1833. His salary was to be £1,500 with an additional £200 for expenses, but when the directors heard that the GWR was to pay I. K. Brunel £2,000 they made his the same. (31)

From 1500 to 1830 there had been only 335 major engineering works carried out in Britain, and 155 of these projects had been completed since 1790. The latter included over 2,000 miles of canals, several docks and harbours, drainage works, roads, large bridges, lighthouses and even a few railways. (32) During their construction came an inevitable vast gain in knowledge and expertise. In 1830 Robert joined the 12-year-old Institution of Civil Engineers, which had been '...established for the general advancement of Mechanical Science and more particularly for promoting the acquisition of that species of knowledge which constitutes the profession of a Civil Engineer...'. There had never been a project approaching the size and complexity of the London and Birmingham Railway, and Robert had to draw on the experience of other civil engineers, as well as his own, to evolve his grand design to bring about the successful completion of the huge work. A very junior engineer on the railway, F. R. Conder, was to write later: -

> 'Here lay the good fortune of Mr. Robert Stephenson, who possessed the signal advantage of a practical acquaintance, from childhood, with the details of mechanical work of all kinds, together with that of a regular education expressly intended to qualify for the profession of a civil Engineer. He thus stood almost alone, and owed, no doubt, to this favourable conjunction of circumstances, even more than to his practical and his scientific acquirements, or to his knowledge of the world, the eminence which he so rapidly attained. In this respect he had the advantage of his great rival Brunel, who, possessed alike of hereditary constructive genius, of bold and courageous originality, and of the results of the most scientific training then attainable, had in some measure to make his acquaintance with the practical details of actual work, and with the best method of dealing with master workmen, at the cost of his supporters.' **(33)**

When George had started work on the Liverpool and Manchester, even though he had a lot of practical experience, he had no real appreciation of the amount of work required or how to organise labour. **(34)** On the other hand Robert tried to eliminate as many difficulties as possible by anticipation and sensible pre-planning.

Robert's attitude towards delegation is worth considering at this juncture. It was impossible for one man, however capable, to control in detail such a large civil engineering project, and he shrewdly chose a group of exceptionally competent assistants. His basis was to decide how *he* wanted to carry out the work and set up a sound management structure using these carefully chosen assistants to achieve *his* concept. Francis Conder contrasted Stephenson and Brunel's ways of working: -

> 'The staff of Mr. Stephenson, although it cannot be said to have had a military organization, yet to some extent resembled an army corps in division and subordination of duty. Each officer was the servant of the Company. Each had his own limit of function and responsibility; and although Mr. Stephenson well knew how to show, from time to time, that not the smallest detail would escape his attention, if it involved what was wrong, the order of his office was not such as to overburden the Engineer-in-Chief with details that fell properly within the competence of the Residents, or even the Subs. But the Engineers on the broad-gauge lines appeared to regard themselves less as officers of the Company than as a channel of the will of Mr. Brunel. His Residents no more ventured to act without his direct authorization, *ad hoc,* than did any inspector on the line.' (35)

G. P. Bidder elaborated on Stephenson's method and the advantages of it, shortly after Robert's death:-

> 'His habit, with those who enjoyed his confidence, was to leave with them the utmost amount of responsibility, which he could possibly lay upon them; and never to interfere, except in cases of emergency, or where his moral influence was required, to prevent undue interference from superior authorities. The consequence has been, that over the whole face of the globe, there are men of his school, who have risen to competency and eminence, and who live to extol and respect the memory of their revered chief.' (36)

To delegate properly requires considerable strength of character. 'In estimating Robert Stephenson's conduct to his professional brethren, it should be remembered that he always took all the responsibilities of works on his own shoulders. Whatever mistakes might be made, he always took all the blame of errors to himself, and shielded his assistants from criticism.' (37) If he took the blame for his subordinates' errors he had the right to take the credit for their achievements, but, in contrast to his father, he did not seek adulation and was happy to share the credit with others.

He divided the line into five engineering districts. The first nine miles from London were under his personal control, with John Cass Birkinshaw (1811-67) as his principal assistant. The oldest, George Watson Buck (1789-1854), took charge of the 23 miles from Harrow to Tring with (Sir) Charles Fox (1810-74) as one of his assistants. William Crosley looked after the next 22 miles including Tring cutting and Wolverton viaduct. Kilsby tunnel, with Charles Lean as its sub-engineer, came into District No. 4 under Frank Forster (1800-52). Thomas Longridge Gooch (1808-82) was given the last 24 miles, and had amongst his assistants Robert Benson Dockray (1813-71), who had worked on the S&D and later became a chief engineer of the LNWR, and Peter Lecount (1794-1852), a former naval officer. This changed after Tom Gooch's appointment as joint engineer, with George Stephenson, of the Manchester & Leeds Railway; Frank Forster took over District 5 and *Rocket's* draughtsman, George Henry Phipps, took District 4. Charles Fox was later given the Euston Extension. (38)

The first drawing office was a small cottage that the railway had acquired with a piece of land near Edgeware Road, but it was much too small for any permanent use. The company rented the vacant Eyre Arms Hotel, in St. John's Wood, which was ideal for the purpose of the Engineer-in-Chief's office. The main lounge was adapted as the drawing office in which twenty or thirty draughtsmen were employed to produce the average of 30 engineering drawings per week that were needed to keep the engineers happy. Forty years later, the Institution of Civil Engineers said: 'The great drawing office at the Eyre Arms tavern, … has become classic in the history of modern engineering; for within its bare walls was located a staff of clever engineers, such as was probably never before, nor has been since, assembled at one time.' (39)

On his appointment, Robert insisted on the preparation of most accurate and detailed plans together with longitudinal and cross-sections of the whole line, within the limits of deviation permitted by the Act. The sections not only allowed the volumes of cuttings and embankments to be worked out to give, where possible, an economical balance of cut and fill, but also enabled the sizes of the bridges and viaducts to be determined. The exact number of farm occupation bridges could not be determined until the land agents had finished their negotiations. When all the drawings, specifications and quantities were finalised the work was ready to be put out to tender; these documents were so good as to set the standard for those to be used in future railway construction. **(40)**

Robert's diary for 1834 gives some indication of his tasks during the preparation of the contracts: -

> *11 February:* At Kilburn Office writing specifications and sketching bridges.
>
> *19 April:* At Weedon gave further instructions to Mr. Forster.
>
> *15 May:* At St John's Wood all day writing letter and designing Bridges for Birmingham end.

20 June: At meeting of Board. At Birmingham for the purpose of explaining contract and specifications.
15 August: At Kilsby – gave Forster instructions to proceed with survey.
30 September: At St John's Wood … calculating Kilsby Tunnel … Wolverton Viaduct.
5 December: Wolverton Viaduct … considered abutment [design] too weak. (41)

In the early 1830s there were few contractors with the capabilities and resources to complete more than a relatively small length of the railway. Even so, at least one of the directors, Henry Rowles, an architect, considered the line should be let as a single contract. Wisely, 30 contracts were let, including the London Extension. However, some firms were awarded more than one contract; W. and L. Cubitt won and completed four. Each contractor submitted his tender 'accompanied by a "Schedule of Prices" upon which his estimate is founded.' **(42)** The contracts had been advertised in London and provincial newspapers, and competition was keen with a dozen tenders being submitted for some contracts.

The table gives the contract details, but *not* the final costs. **(43)**

Contract	Length (miles)	Original Contractor	Date Awarded	Contract Price £	Second Contractor	Revised Estimate £
Euston Extension	1	W. & L. Cubitt	Dec 1835	76,860		91,528
Primrose Hill	5¾	Jackson & Sheddon	May 1834	119,987	The Company, (i.e. the L&B) Nov 1834	280,014
Harrow	9½	Jos. Nowell & Sons	May 1834	110,227		144,574
Watford	5	Copeland & Harding	May 1834	117,000		138,219
King's Langley	2½	W. & L. Cubitt	Sep 1835	38,900		57,386
Berkhampstead	4½	W. & L. Cubitt	Sep 1835	54,660		65,002
Aldbury	2½	W. & L. Cubitt	Sep 1835	16,694		25,134
Tring	3	T. Townshend	Sep 1834	104,496	Assignees of Townshend, Oct 1837	144,657
Leighton Buzzard	7½	James Nowell	Sep 1835	38,000		43,162
Stoke Hammond	3⅞	E.W. Morris	Sep 1835	39,303		42,345
Bletchley	3⅜	John Burge	Sep 1835	54,500		61,071
Wolverton	5	William Soars	Oct 1834	67,732	The Company, June 1837	107,765
Wolverton Viad.	⅛	James Nowell	Feb 1835	25,226		28,964
Castlethorpe	4½	William Soars	Oct 1834	49,735	Craven & Sons, July 1837	71,873
Blisworth	5	William Hughes	Feb 1835	112,950	The Company, Dec 1836	184,301
Bugbrook	5	John Chapman	Feb 1835	53,400		65,013
Stowe Hill	1¼	John Chapman	Feb 1835	23,050		31,536
Weedon	1⅛	Edward Boddington	May 1835	26,150	W. & J. Simmons, May 1836	31,442
Brockhall	3⅛	J. & G. Thornton	May 1835	34,157		50,583
Long Buckby	3⅝	J. & G. Thornton	May 1835	42,582		48,256
Kilsby	1⅜	Jos. Nowell & Sons	May 1835	98,988	The Company, Feb 1836	291,030
Rugby	5⅛	Samuel Hemming	Nov 1835	59,283	The Company, Oct 1837	93,384
Long Lawford	3¼	W. & J. Simmons	Feb 1835	20,330		25,893
Brandon	4¼	Samuel Hemming	Feb 1835	40,000	The Company, Jan 1838	55,090
Avon Viaduct	1/16	Samuel Hemming	Nov 1835	7,979		8,621
Coventry	7¾	Greenshields & Cudd	Nov 1834	101,700	The Company, May 1837	150,496
Berkswell	4½	Daniel Pritchard	Nov 1834	53,248		62,738
Yardley	7½	Joseph Thornton	Aug 1834	68,032		78,131
Saltley	1⅞	James Diggle	Aug 1834	32,878		38,707
Rea Viaduct	⅛	James Nowell	Aug 1834	13,644		15,505

Many practices that were to become standard contracting procedure were already in use. The tenders submitted by the hopeful contractors were formally opened, and Robert Stephenson was present at the opening. The directors accepted the lowest tender 'if the parties are respectable and are able to give [10%] security'. The signed Form of Agreement required the successful contractor to provide a bond, and if he failed to execute either the contract or the bond, it specified, '…nor shall they [the company] in any case be liable to any claim by [the contractor] in respect of the work then already done by [the contractor] on the said Railway.' The contractor was to be paid monthly on the agreed measure of the work done with an initial retention of 20% later reduced to 10%, when the contract was half-complete. He was also responsible for the maintenance of the completed works for a year, after which the retention was released. (44) All the material and plant had to be provided by the contractor with one notable exception - the permanent way. The entire temporary tracks used during the construction were provided by the contractor, but the company supplied the final permanent material for him to lay. This practice became general as later companies either manufactured their own material or bought it on highly competitive annual tenders.

During the hearing in June 1835 for the GWR Bill, supporting evidence was given by some of those involved in the L&B, namely: a director, a secretary, R. Stephenson, G. W. Buck and one of the contractors. Although the works had only been going for a year, some interesting information was presented. The first L&B contracts were let in May 1834, and in June 1835 the prospects looked good as eighty miles of the line had been let for £1.3 million, which was slightly below the Engineer's estimate. One contractor, Jackson and Sheddon, on the Primrose Hill or Willesden contract, had failed by November 1834. At the time, this did not bode ill and Robert's explanation was, '…want of capital occasioned it in some degree, and it was likewise grossly mismanaged.' (44) It was difficult to let a contract after a failure so the company took it over with J. C. Birkinshaw as the engineer. Ultimately ten contracts failed. Of these eight were taken over by the company, one was let to a contractor already working on the line, and one to a newcomer. In all but one case the size and difficulties of the task were beyond the contractors' capabilities; in this single case it was '…from the supineness and incapacity of the contractor.' (45) The director, Mr. Henry Rowles, thought the unavoidable practice of the company taking over failed contracts was more expensive as their superintendents 'have not the intelligence, ingenuity, or personal interest of a contractor'. (46) So much for having faith in your staff! At least the company secretary was happy; Richard Creed stated that the shares in the L&B, for which £35 had been paid, were now selling for £50. (47)

Francis Conder gives a coeval description of the Engineer-in-Chief: -

'Robert Stephenson, in those days, almost lived on the line, and the first occasion on which he visited the portion in question [Watford], after the contracts were let, accompanied by the secretary and by four or five of the Directors, was the twelfth time that he had walked the whole distance from London to Birmingham. The personal appearance of that fortunate engineer is unfamiliar to many of those, whose eyes never rested on his energetic countenance, frank bearing, and falcon-like glance. It is rarely that a civilian has so free and almost martial address; it is still more rare for such features to be seen in any man who has not inherited them from a line of gently-nurtured ancestors. In the earlier days of Robert Stephenson, he charmed all who came in contact with him. Kind and considerate to his subordinates, he was not without occasional outbursts of fierce northern passion, nor always superior to prejudice. He knew how to attach people to him: he also knew how to be a firm and persistent hater. During the whole construction of the London and Birmingham line, his anxiety was so great as to lead him to very frequent recourse to the fatal aid of calomel. **(48)** At the same time the sacrifice of his own rest, and indeed the necessary care of his health, was such as would have soon destroyed a less originally fine constitution. He has been known to start on the outside of the mail, from London to Birmingham, without a great coat, and that on a cold night; and there can be little doubt that his early and lamented death was hastened by this ill-considered devotion to the service of his employers, and the establishment of his own fame. **(49)**

The contractors often let a large proportion of their work to sub-contractors who in turn sub-let to gangs of navvies, who split between themselves the work of excavating and moving the vast quantities of material necessary to build the railway. Assistant engineer, G. W. Buck, described the method of working. 'There are 2 gangs, or shifts, employed upon the Watford Cutting, and 80 men in each; they work 20 hours out of the 24, each Shift working 10 hours.' (50) The true navvies on the L&B were paid around three shillings (15p.) a day, with the locally recruited agricultural labourers being paid a few pence less.

Both the contractors and the engineers knew that the profit margins, given by the prices quoted in the tenders, were small. The average price per cubic yard of excavation, in reasonable soils to be moved about 1½ miles, was 1s. 2d. (5.83p.); an extra of around one penny per mile was added for increasing the lead distance to tip. Significantly Jackson and Sheddon, the first contractor to fail, had only allowed 11½d. (4.8p.) for working in the notorious London clay. (51)

The resident engineers agreed the quantities of all the work done each month, and the contractors submitted their claims for payment based on these figures. When the prices were checked against the tender documents, in Robert's office, he found that the contractors were attempting to claim at higher rates than they had submitted. He said, 'I endeavour to make them agree with the Tender; and frequently have them altered in consequence of the discrepancy.' (52) This statement suggests a certain amount of leeway rather than rigid enforcement, and allowances were made for difficult conditions. There was absolutely no advantage to be gained from forcing a good contractor out of business.

When the railway was opened the still-bare faces of the cuttings gave an object lesson in the geology of the country that it crossed. Clay, sand, gravel, marl, chalk, limestone and sandstone of variable qualities were encountered; **(53)** some had presented little difficulty but others had caused enormous delays and expense.

The maintenance of easy curves and gradients meant that a number of long tunnels had to be bored through uncertain materials. The engineers and the contractors were on a steep learning curve. The canal builders had taken a very long time to accomplish anything approaching the magnitude of these railway tunnels. One of the longest, the 3,076-yard Blisworth tunnel on the Grand Junction (later Union) Canal, a mile to the west of the L&B, was begun in 1793, and not opened to traffic until 1805. The Brunels' tunnel under the Thames was started in 1825, and not completed until 1843!

Robert knew of the difficulties encountered in the past, **(54)** especially when attempting to tunnel in London clay, and he hoped that he had made reasonable provisions in his estimate and in the design of the first tunnel on the railway. This was Primrose Hill, 1,164 yards long, just north of Camden depot. **(55)** The original designs for all the L&B tunnels included an inverted arch below the tracks, which was of a less substantial thickness than the tunnel arch. (Fig. 4.2) Where the chalk was solid as in Watford tunnel the invert was found to be unnecessary, and ordinary footings were built under the side walls. According to Conder this was tried at Primrose Hill, where the clay at first needed a pickaxe to cut it. A large saving could have been made had it worked, but as soon as the clay became moist it oozed to fill the whole of the excavation. (56) The original plan was then reverted to, but this was inadequate to resist the enormous pressure of the clay; the mortar was squeezed out of the joints, and even the bricks were crushed. The hardest possible bricks had to be used with the much more costly Roman cement substituted for mortar. It was found that the thickness of the brickwork had to be increased from the 18 inches of the original design thickness to 30 inches in some places, and that the maximum length of clay that could be safely exposed, before the brickwork was put in place, was around nine feet. Included in this contract was the 322-yard cut-and-cover tunnel to carry Harrow Road over the railway, at a very oblique angle, at Kensal Green. (57) The original tender for the 5¾ miles section was £120,000, but the Primrose Hill tunnel alone came to £160,000 with the whole contract's estimated cost escalating to £280,000. (58)

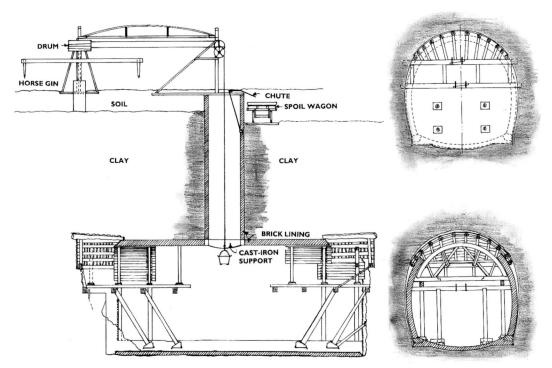

Figure 4.1. Method used for excavating, supporting and lining a tunnel in London clay. J. F. Addyman

The 1,792-yard long Watford tunnel would have been straightforward had there not been treacherous pockets of gravel and running sand within the chalk, which could burst into the workings without warning. An inrush of sand at the bottom of one of the six working shafts caused ten men to be buried alive. Francis Conder, who was there, considered that the disaster only happened because the mode of working had been changed by a new resident engineer, but, from Richard Creed's description, so great was the collapse that it could have occurred with any method. **(59)** The revised cost of this contract, which also included substantial cuttings and embankments, worked out at about 20% over the tender price.

Northchurch tunnel, 345 yards long, was included in a stretch of 9½ miles comprising three contacts that had been won by W. & L. Cubitt. The total cost averaged out at a reasonable £16,000 per mile, which, nevertheless, was a third above the tender price. There were also short tunnels at Linslade (285yds), Stowe Hill (484yds), and Beechwood (292yds).

Even before the Parliamentary hearings, boreholes had been made along the line of the railway, and quarries and wells in its vicinity had been examined to find out as much as possible about the subsoil conditions. A borehole had been made to a depth of over 45 feet near each end of the proposed, 1⅜-mile-long, Kilsby tunnel and neither had indicated the presence of sand or water. (60) As often happens, when boreholes are taken, Murphy's Law had prevailed, and an extensive basin of waterlogged sand had been missed by only a few feet.

Joseph Nowell and his sons John and Jonathan had won two contracts, one at Harrow and the other at Kilsby. They started work at Kilsby in June 1835, and it was not until the second working shaft was being excavated that the waterlogged stratum was discovered. Additional borings were taken and it was found that the quicksand extended about 450 yards along the tunnel, and was shaped like a flat-bottomed basin that dipped to about six feet below its arch. **(61)** When Robert assessed the situation, at the end of the year, he considered that it was impossible for the contractor to complete the work, and that the company should take over. When the ailing Joseph Nowell was informed of the decision, instead of being relieved, he fell ill and died on 12 January 1836. **(62)** The company formally took over the work in February 1836, and became responsible for the most difficult and expensive feature on the whole line. The contract had been for £99,000, and the revised estimate came to £291,000, but the total cost was around £320,000. **(63)**

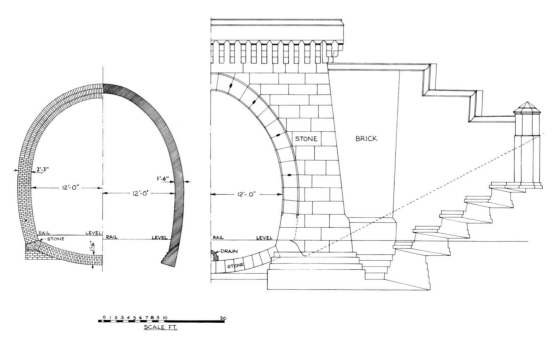

Figure 4.2. Left: a comparison of typical cross-sections of Primrose Hill and North Church Tunnels showing the invert necessary in London clay and the reduced thickness of brickwork and normal footings needed in the chalk. Right: half-elevation of an entrance to Kilsby Tunnel. J. F. Addyman

If when carrying out a simple DIY job, like fastening something to a wall, one finds that the wall is unsound, or, worse still, the drill goes through a water pipe 'that should not have been there', it can be humiliating, frustrating, time-consuming and costly. How much worse, it must have felt, to be in charge of the largest engineering project yet undertaken, when virtually every unforeseen thing that could go wrong did go expensively wrong. However, not only did the gods appear to conspire against him, but there was also a critical faction within the railway committee, most particularly Messrs. Rathbone and Cropper, who took every opportunity to get at their young engineer. As well as overcoming the physical difficulties, and explaining to the directors the reasons for the ever-increasing costs, Robert also had to face this continual sniping. Rathbone and Cropper had become enemies of George when the Liverpool and Manchester was being built. Cropper was a supporter of fixed engines rather than locomotives and both, like their ally, C. B. Vignoles, had not approved of some of George's business ethics and his pursuit of a monopoly in the railway industry.

A year before the problems at Kilsby emerged, they had attacked Robert for being a locomotive manufacturer as well as Engineer-in-Chief of the railway. Just how dispiriting this was is shown in a typical letter, dated 26 January 1835, from a series to Michael Longridge: -

'Our enemies, viz. Rathbone & Cropper, are raising a hue and cry about our having an Engine to build [for the L&B] at Newcastle – they say another article will be brought out by Lardner on the subject. They half intimate that I shall withdraw either from the Railway or Engine building. The revenge of these people is quite insatiable. This distresses me very much. Can I withdraw temporarily from the Engine building? I wish you would think this over for the above named parties are annoying me all they can by advancing Vignoles and his opposite opinions. The Directors support me, but it makes it sad uphill work.'

An undertaking that no locomotives should be supplied by Robert Stephenson & Co. to the L&B resolved the matter, but, as will be explained later, left the company with a serious difficulty. **(64)**

When the problem at Kilsby was discovered the directors were very concerned, and the anti-Stephenson lobby found in it a great opportunity for sniping. No doubt the diversion of the line, or altering the gradients, must have been considered. However, the directors were persuaded that their own engineer might be out of his depth, and the opinions of other engineers could be helpful in solving their problem. Captain C. R. Moorsom R.N., **(65)** as secretary and business adviser to the company, was sent to Kilsby to make their decision known. The story goes that when he arrived at the site office he found Robert holding a meeting with Frank Forster, Charles Lean, and the other sub-engineers. Stephenson, Forster and Lean all had coal mining experience and knew what must be done. (66) At this time Captain Moorsom knew little about Robert Stephenson. He '…had heard him spoken of by friends as a young man fortunate in the possession of extraordinary intellects – spoken of by enemies as a young man fortunate in the possession of an extraordinary father.'! With some trepidation he put to Robert the directors' proposal about calling in other engineers. He was told quite calmly that the time had not come yet, '…I have decided what to do. I mean to pump the water all out, and then drive the tunnel under the dry sand. Tell the directors not to be frightened, and say that all I ask is time and fair play. If I can't get rid of the water, I'll then think about going to other engineers for help.' Moorsom was sufficiently impressed to return to the directors and stave off the criticisms. (67)

The sand at Kilsby outcropped on a spring line at one side of the hill, and it was worth exploring whether a drainage adit near this point would solve the problem. George Stephenson thought that it would not work, but Robert considered it worth a try during the time that the preparatory work for installing the pumps was being carried out. When the excavations were very close to the quicksand, and the men had withdrawn to the entrance to the adit, they heard a roar and hoped that the water had burst in. Only a trickle of water appeared, and it was found that an immense quantity of sand had blocked the passage and prevented any drainage. Even when pumping was started it was found the water only percolated through the sand at a relatively slow rate, and a number of well points, averaging 120ft deep, were required to be pumped out continuously to achieve reasonable progress. (68)

A lithograph by J. C. Bourne (Fig. 4.3) shows the rather substantial engine houses that were built for the pumping engines, which indicates that it was expected to be a long job. It actually took between eight and nine months to pump the water out at an average of around 2,000 gallons per minute. **(69)** At this rate over three million cubic metres of water must have been removed, and discharged to nearby watercourses, before it was safe to commence tunnelling in the critical section. The quicksand only affected about one quarter of the tunnel's length, and 18 working shafts were eventually used in order to speed the excavation. In November 1836, water burst into the tunnel, where there were no pumps, and to prevent a collapse it was decided to complete the brickwork by using rafts for the men to work on. Just how dangerous this was, was shown when the water rose so high that the men were nearly jammed against the tunnel roof. According to Jeaffreson, '…Mr. Charles Lean, sub-assistant engineer, jumped into the water, and, swimming with a tow-line between his teeth, tugged his men to the foot of the nearest working shaft, through which they were drawn from their perilous position "to bank".' (70)

Figure 4.3: a lithograph by J. C. Bourne showing the activity above Kilsby Tunnel with steam engines working the pumps and horse gins still used to remove spoil and supply material to the tunnellers.

The length of the tunnel was 2,442 yards, and two immense ventilation shafts, 60 feet in diameter, were considered necessary. The largest was 130 feet deep and used one million bricks. Again, in the tunnel, the thickness of the brickwork was 50% greater than the original design. A passage written by John Britton in 1839, when Kilsby was already taken for granted, is worth quoting: -

> 'The quantity of soil taken from the whole tunnel was upwards of 177,000 cubic yards; the total number of bricks employed, 30,000,000. From the time the execution of it was undertaken by the Company until its completion, 1,300 men were constantly employed, and twelve steam-engines were worked day and night. Nothing but great engineering ability and perseverance, assisted by ample funds, could have surmounted the difficulties of carrying the railway through this hill; but they have been effectually employed, and thousands of persons have since daily passed through its great duct, without experiencing the least inconvenience from the surrounding water and sand, and unconscious of the amount of labour spent in its formation.' (71)

Even the formation of the cuttings and embankments posed their own problems, but this was not surprising as up to 16,000,000 cubic yards of material had to be excavated, transported to form embankments or disposed of to tips. **(72)** The rate of excavation, of four million cubic yards per annum, was not even doubled when the adjacent M1 motorway was built, with specialist earthmoving plant, 120 years later. (73) The navvies on the L&B were each capable of excavating up to 9 cubic yards, or around 20 tons, of material a day. The spoil was taken out of the cutting by means of barrow or horse-runs, formed of timber planks, located about every twenty-five yards. The horse moved above the top of the cutting and by means of a pulley and a rope drew the barrow of earth together with the labourer who controlled it up the slope: -

> 'This is a dangerous occupation, [!] for the man rather hangs to, than supports the barrow, which is rendered unmanageable by the least irregularity in the horse's motion. If he finds himself unable to govern it, he endeavours, by a sudden jerk, to raise himself erect; then, throwing the barrow over one side of the boards, or "run," he swings himself round and runs down the other. Should both fall on the same side, his best speed is necessary to escape the barrow, which, with its contents, comes bounding down after him. Although there were thirty to forty horse-runs in the Tring cutting constantly working, during many months, and each labourer was precipitated down the slopes several times; such, from

continual practice, was their sure-footedness, that only one fatal accident occurred. A moving platform was invented by the engineer to supersede the necessity of thus risking life and limb, but the workmen, who considered it was designed to lessen their labour and wages, broke it.'! (74)

The material from the barrows was loaded into wagons, which were hauled by horses or locomotives either to form a nearby embankment or to be tipped as unusable.

Figure 4.4: a wood engraving showing the barrow runs, which could be used either to remove material from cuttings or from adjacent borrow pits to form embankments (from Roscoe & Lecount).

About 1,000 cubic yards of material were excavated in a large cutting on a good day, but an average of only 700 cubic yards of embankment could be tipped. (75) The disparity arose from the large number of barrow runs being available along the sides of the excavation, whereas the maximum number of tipping points was limited by the width of the end of the embankment. Fewer wagons were tipped when the excavation was clay as it stuck to the wagons and had to be shovelled out. If favourable circumstances allowed the embankment to be worked equally at both ends, then obviously the rate of progress could double. However, from engineering evidence given at the 1836 London & Brighton inquiry, it was best to programme a maximum of 250,000 cubic yards per annum rather than the optimum of 350,000, theoretically achievable in 250 working days.

In order to allow extra tipping points, to speed the work, the top of the embankment was made wider than necessary and the base correspondingly narrower. On completion of the earth moving, it was trimmed to size at the top, and the surplus was used to extend the base to its correct width. (76) It would have been ideal if the embankments could have been built up and compacted in layers, about three feet thick, but, with them already timed on the critical path, this would have extended the completion of the works beyond reasonable limits. Unfortunately mechanical scrapers and large vibratory rollers were a long way in the future. However, a horse drawn plough or scraper was used to good effect on broken rock and other friable material on the L&B. Not only did it help with the excavation but 'actually dispensed with the labour of several men who were formerly employed to break up the lumps at the foot of the embankment.' (77)

The most difficult embankment was immediately south of Wolverton Viaduct where some of the available imported material turned out to be black, soapy clay, which, even when dry material was mixed with it, slipped outwards up to 170 feet from the top of the embankment. The embankment had to be 48 feet high. In order to continue tipping beyond the slip, during the winter, a temporary timber viaduct was built. However the summer brought little improvement, 'It was only after incredible labour and patience that it was conquered, and this was done by barrowing as much earth to the outer part of the slip as would balance the weight on the top.' (78) In some cases there was not sufficient excavated material available nearby to form an embankment, and borrow pits had to be opened alongside to make good the deficiency; the work at Boxmoor was a good example. (Fig. 4.3)

The largest cutting was at Tring; two-and-a-half miles long, averaging 40 feet deep. Nearly all the 1,400,000 cubic yards of material that was excavated had to be disposed of in tips adjacent to the line, as it could not be used to form embankments within economical distances. Thomas Townshend, the contractor, was declared bankrupt in October 1837, mainly due to problems with his contracts on the Grand Junction Railway. The L&B completed the outstanding work at Tring with his nephew, Richard Townshend, supervising it. **(79)**

At Blisworth the Grand Junction Canal had used a tunnel to get through the ridge of high ground, but the railway decided on a mile-and-a-half long cutting, up to 60 feet deep. It was to be a far more difficult proposition than Tring. The boreholes, taken to a depth of 32 feet, had found limestone between 4 and 25 feet below the surface. **(80)** As usual, nothing could be taken at face value, and, during the progress of the work, it was found that the rock did not extend to the full depth of the cutting, but it overlaid a treacherous band of waterlogged clay or shale over 20 feet thick. After almost two years' work the (not very energetic) contractor had to be replaced by the company, and a new specification was drawn up to solve the problems of underpinning the rock and retaining the clay. Retaining walls were designed to support each side of the cutting, where the rail level had to be some depth below the base of the rock. Buttresses were made on the walls at 20 feet centres, and these were connected with six-feet-wide inverted arches. Wisely, drains were provided behind the walls to prevent the build up of water pressure. (Fig. 4.5)

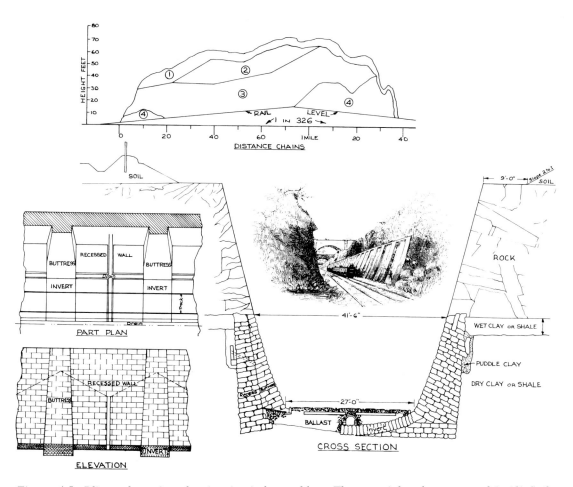

Figure 4.5: Blisworth cutting showing (top) the problem. The material to be excavated is (1) Soil, stones and clay. (2) Marl and clay. (3) Limestone rock of variable hardness, in beds one to four feet thick. (4) Blue shale or clay. The solution (bottom) shows how the unstable material was removed and sloped back above the limestone, and how this rock was underpinned by retaining walls with inverted arches. The vignette from Roscoe and Lecount shows the work almost completed. J. F. Addyman

Where there was some thickness of soil or clay above the rock a level bench, or shelf, nine feet wide, was provided, and the material was sloped back at two to one, to reduce the possibility of landslips. The extra work increased the amount to be excavated by 25% over the estimated 800,000 cubic yards. The rock needed to be removed by blasting. According to Roscoe and Lecount, when the company took over 700 to 800 men were employed and: -

> 'In fact, the whole cutting seemed alive; and the busy hum of labour, resounding from one end to the other, gave ample testimony to the zealous exertions of the engineer. Of course, the expense was considerable. The article of gunpowder alone was, in many cases, twenty-five barrels, of 100 lbs. each, per week; enormous quantities being used before the rock could be removed.' (81)

It is surprising, in the circumstances, that the final cost of Blisworth was only 60% over the original tender. *Rocket's* draughtsman, G. H. Phipps, had supervised the successful completion of the work.

Until the middle of the nineteenth century the building of bridges was largely based on empirical principles. The theory of structures was developing quite slowly, and major breakthroughs permitting the precise calculation of stresses, to allow safe and economical designs, were not to appear until the latter half of the century. The Romans had built some very successful, and still extant, masonry structures; also they had developed the use of cofferdams and piling for foundation work. The late eighteenth and early nineteenth centuries had seen the very competent use of masonry for bridges in this country for spans up to 200 feet. The use of cast iron for bridges had pre-dated the building of the L&B by 55 years, and confidence and expertise in the use and manufacture of this, not totally satisfactory, material was increasing rapidly.

There were almost 400 culverts, bridges and viaducts on the L&B **(82)**. Never before had anyone had to construct this number of bridges within a four-year period. Some required the ingenious use of iron to overcome site problems, but the vast majority were built of brick with elegant stone facings and other details. Semi-circular, semi-elliptical and segmental arches were used in their construction. The main spans for the viaducts varied between 24 and 60 feet, and the abutments were usually pierced with three small arches. Details of the viaducts appear in Appendix 2, and Figs. 4.6 and 4.7.

Figure 4.6: vignettes from Roscoe and Lecount showing: (top left) Colne Viaduct, near Watford, (top right) the Ouse Viaduct at Wolverton, (bottom left) Weedon Viaduct over a road (the River Nene flows through culverts a few hundred yards to the north), (bottom right) Sherbourne Viaduct, Coventry.

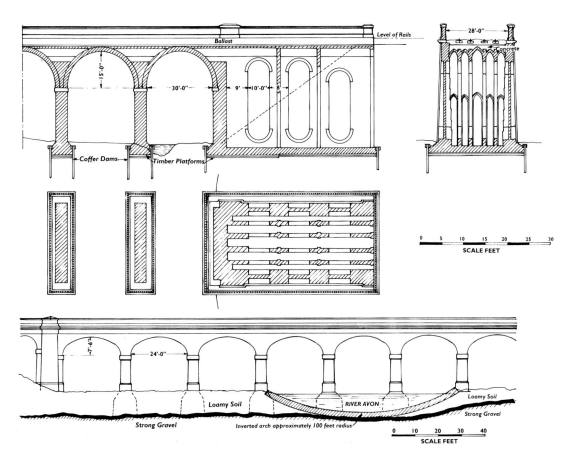

Fig.4.7: (top) sections, plans and elevations of the viaduct over the River Colne. The abutments and piers are supported on timber platforms and protected from scour by permanent coffer-dams. The weight relieving cavities within the abutments and above the piers are based on an idea used by John Smeaton in his bridge over the River Tay at Perth in 1769. (Bottom) part elevation of the nine-arch Avon Viaduct showing the large invert spanning the three river arches. Inverted arches were widely used on the L&B even for under-track structures as small as cattle creeps. J. F. Addyman

Although road builders were often prepared to put steep gradients and sharp curves in their highways, to give them the shortest possible bridge spans, the turnpike trustees had clauses inserted in the railway Act preventing the company from altering their alignments, or levels, even to a lesser extent. This meant it was often necessary for the railway to cross a highway and, of course, a canal at an oblique angle. The expensive cut-and-cover tunnel at Kensal Green has already been mentioned, but in other cases skew brick or iron under-bridges were used.

A number of erroneous claims have been made about railway engineers originating the construction of oblique or skew bridges in brick or masonry. According to Vasari (1511-74) one was completed in Florence in 1530, three hundred years before the railway age! Canal builders such as William Chapman and Thomas Telford had used them; the former had built some over the Grand Canal of Ireland around 1787. In 1827 author and architect, Peter Nicholson (1765-1844), had given some limited guidance on oblique bridges in his treatise on masonry and stone cutting. (83) By 1830, there were single examples on the Stockton and Darlington and Canterbury and Whitstable, and, according to Henry Booth, 15 had been completed on the Liverpool and Manchester Railway. (84) Oddly, after 1834, when G. W. Buck had to build some oblique masonry arches on his section of the L&B, Charles Fox, his assistant, gave the impression that he (Fox) had actually developed the idea of skew arches. This was inferred in an article in the *London and Edinburgh Philosophical Magazine* of April 1836, and later, when he gave a paper to the Royal Institution in 1838. During 1839 G. W. Buck published *A Practical and Theoretical Essay on Oblique Bridges,* and P. Nicholson penned his *Guide to Railway Masonry.* (85)

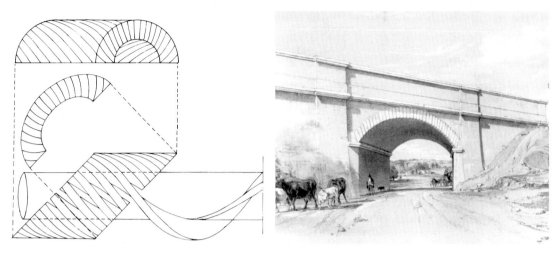

Figure 4.8 (left) Charles Fox's diagram showing the formation of the spirals for the masonry and (right) a Bourne lithograph of the skew bridge at Boxmoor.

Both Watford and Lawley Street viaducts include brick skew arches, but the site that attracted most attention at the time was Boxmoor, where a bridge crosses the London road at an angle of 32 degrees. In order to achieve the accurate spirals of the brickwork the centring of a skew span was covered in sheeting on which the lines to be followed by the bricks were scribed. G. W. Buck made a number of practical innovations during the construction of the L&B, and 'The perfect manner in which the whole of the stone work, and the spiral courses of the bricks, are executed, reflects great credit on the builders, Messrs. Cubitt, of London.' (86) (Fig. 4.8)

Figure 4.9: the Hampstead Road Bridge on the London extension showing the massive retaining walls necessary to retain the London clay.

All the early cast-iron bridges followed the obvious precedent of masonry structures, and supported their decks above a series of arch ribs. This was only satisfactory as long as the deck and its approaches could be constructed high enough to give the necessary clearance between the arch and the road or watercourse below. With the need to maintain easy gradients, on the railway, the construction depth, or the dimension between the underside of the bridge and the top of the rails, often needed to be as small as possible. The problem also occurred with bridges over the railway, on the Euston Extension, where the highway levels could not be raised. Some of the two-span bridges on the Euston Extension used shallow segmental cast-iron arches with a rise of 2ft. 6in. on a spans of 25 feet to support the jack arches carrying the road, while others achieved the same dimensions simply in masonry. (See colour plate 3)

Crossing the canals could provide problems not only in design but also in execution. In its 112-mile journey it was necessary for the railway to cross canals several times. The fact that a tunnel, bridge or viaduct could not be completed quickly meant that spoil could not easily be taken beyond the obstacle to form embankments. A physical and, later, legal battle occurred when the railway company tried to build a temporary bridge on the authorised line of the railway near Wolverton, over the Grand Junction Canal. This was to carry the 600,000 cubic yards of fill needed beyond the canal. When it was obvious that trouble was brewing, Robert decided to complete the temporary bridge on Christmas Eve and Christmas Day 1834, in the hope that a fait accompli might forestall further trouble in the New Year. The navvies toiled to build the bridge, whilst the canal people enjoyed their Christmas. However, farce intervened, and on 30 December the indignant canal company sent their body of navvies to destroy the bridge! The railway company had to apply for an injunction against the canal people, and in January, 'the Master of the Rolls in a lucid and admirable judgement granted the injunction.' (87)

The permanent canal bridge at Wolverton was constructed of flat cast-iron girders and gave a clearance of 14 feet above the water. A similar bridge was built at Crick (Welton) to cross the Leicester branch of the Grand Junction Canal. (Fig. 4.10) At other locations, where there was ample clearance above the water, spandrel-braced cast-iron arch ribs were used, resembling those developed by Telford. (Fig. 4.11)

Figure 4.10: the cast-iron girder bridges over the canals at Wolverton station (left) and Crick.

Figure 4.11: a Bourne lithograph of the spandrel-braced cast-iron arch skew bridge over the Grand Junction Canal at Nash Mill near King's Langley

There were two locations on the railway where clearances were critical and the spans were too long for the ordinary cast-iron girders then in use. The first was over the Grand Junction Canal, at Long Buckby in, then, remote Northamptonshire, and the second, and much better known, was over the Regent's Canal, on the Euston Extension. **(88)** These employed, for the first time, the ingenious combination of the tied or bowstring arch, with the deck suspended from the arch ribs. Flat segmental arches produce, under the same loading, far greater horizontal thrusts on the abutments, or piers, than do semi-circular ones. The first known tied iron arch in Britain was completed in 1820 for a short-lived road bridge over the River Chelmer, near Chelmsford, to the designs of Ralph Dodd (c. 1756-1822). A description of it in *The European Magazine* for September 1820 appreciated that the tied arch 'has no lateral thrust or pressure and … is certainly of the greatest importance in saving of expense where there is difficulty in getting a foundation.' Telford gave the credit for solving the arch clearance problem to George Leather (1786-1870) of Leeds. Leather's concept was to suspend the deck below the cast-iron arch ribs by wrought-iron ties, an idea he had first used for bridges over the River Aire, which he had completed between 1827 and 1832. (89) The design of the canal bridges, combining the two ideas, as used by Robert and, later, George Stephenson is shown in Fig. 4.12.

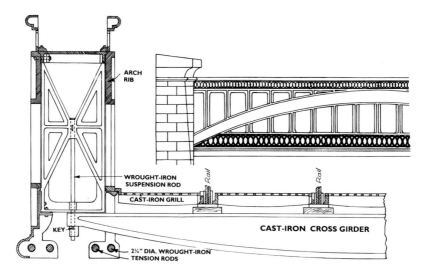

Figure 4.12: a part section and elevation of the tied arch cast-iron bridge with its deck suspended from the arch as used at Long Buckby and over the Regent's Canal in London. The original coloured drawing of the former is shown on the rear cover and the abutment of the latter is shown in colour plate 3. J. F. Addyman.

There was also another bowstring bridge formed by a flat parabolic cast-iron arch, tied with wrought-iron rods, to give an elegant lenticular shape. This carried the Lutterworth to Banbury road over the line with a skew span of 64 feet. Other skew bridges worth mentioning are the iron bridges over Watling Street (A5) at Denbigh Hall and over the Holyhead road immediately west of the Sherbourne viaduct, near Coventry. Although the angle of skew at Watling Street was less than 30 degrees, very flat segmental cast-iron ribs had to be used to get the smallest possible construction depth; the square span of the girders is 26 ft. 9 in. The maximum angle for a skew bridge in masonry was considered to be 40 degrees, but the angle of the crossing near Coventry, which could not be altered, was said to be 60 degrees. Again a flat iron bridge had to be used; the span was 24 feet over the carriageway, to the stone piers, which separate the road from the arches over the footway. (90)

Where bridges had to span cuttings in solid rock, the abutments were dispensed with, and flying arches were used. An elegant masonry example, also near Coventry, has a span of 76 feet. (91) There was certainly no lack of variety or ingenuity in the design or detailing of the L&B bridges. The monotony of standard segmental brick arch or plate girder bridges was a long way in the future.

The Act required a movable iron bridge where the railway had to cross, with a clearance of only two feet, a short branch of the canal, which served the important military depot at Weedon. The width of the canal was 8 feet. Fortunately, it was only necessary to move the bridge infrequently; it weighed about 20 tons, and took three minutes to slide across. **(92)**

Track and drainage only make the headlines if faults in their maintenance are the cause of a major disaster. Failure to provide, or maintain, adequate drainage is still the most frequent cause of landslides on railway earthworks. Francis Whishaw described the L&B drainage as 'of the best description; no expense has been spared to make it in every respect complete.' (93) The use of cast-iron tubes to carry the water under the railway, at some locations, tempts one to ponder if the idea of the iron tubular bridges germinated here. The provision of good drainage did not entirely eliminate slips in the raw earthworks, soon after the opening of the railway, but these were inevitable after major disturbances of the landscape. All new railways, even the Great Western (e.g. Sonning and Dawlish), had some fairly spectacular examples in their early years.

The use of stone blocks to carry the rails and chairs was acceptable on the earlier horse drawn railways, but their continued use, on lines to be worked entirely by locomotives, has been questioned. The attitude on many of the railways, built in the 1830s, was summed up by Nicholas Wood: -

'On all the excavations where stone blocks can be had at a moderate cost, and on embankments which are sufficiently consolidated, stone blocks are, decidedly, the best support for the rails; but, upon high embankments made of clay, and which are constantly settling down, it is found most advisable, in the first instance, to lay down wooden sleepers, stretched across from one rail to the other.' **(94)**

In spite of the use of Kyan's process to protect the wooden sleepers, the life of some on the L&B was reported to be as little as three years. **(95)** However, the difficulties of maintaining alignment and gauge, with the increasing weight and speed of traffic, led to the eventual replacement of the blocks by durable types of softwood sleepers. **(96)**

The first rails to be used, at the southern end, were the ubiquitous fish-bellied type, and weighed 50 lbs per yard. Following reports, commissioned by the directors, including ones from Peter Barlow FRS (1776-1862), double-headed rails, 15 feet long weighing 65 or 75 lbs per yard, were used to complete the rest of the railway. Lecount states that the company used nearly 35,000 tons of rails, costing £460,000. However, simple arithmetic shows either about one third of these totals must have been for rails used in the temporary tracks, on the contracts that the company had to take over, or, more probably, they must include the weight and cost of the chairs used in the permanent way. It was estimated that 152,000 tons of stone blocks were used, costing £180,000. **(97)**

George Aitchison (1792-1861) designed the stations between Euston and Birmingham, and the railway's locomotive workshops at Wolverton. The stations were categorised either as 'principal' or 'intermediate'; the distinction was not based on the immediate population being served, but more on their use as an interchange point with other forms of transport. **(98)** Wolverton was chosen for the works, as it was almost at the mid point of the line, where it was intended to change the locomotives on the trains. As a locomotive manufacturer, Robert knew exactly what was needed, at Wolverton, to carry out anything from minor running repairs to complete overhauls, and the facilities were very comprehensive. **(99)** In order to provide an interchange point with the Grand Junction Canal, a transit shed and wharf were built beside it, and livestock handling was catered for. The total cost, including the passenger station, and housing accommodation for the anticipated workers, was £110,000.

Camden depot was near the site intended for the original terminus of the railway; about a mile north of Euston.

> 'Not without difficulty did Mr. Robert Stephenson succeed in inducing the directors to purchase thirty acres of land here; it was only by urging, that, if unused, the surplus could be sold at a profit, that he carried out his views. Genius can foresee results which, to ordinary capacities, are dark and incomprehensible. Since 1845 it has been found necessary to take an additional plot of three more acres, all now fully occupied.' (100)

Figure 4.13: a vignette showing part of the extensive facilities built at Camden

The depot was to the east of the line, and housed the goods sheds, loading and cattle docks, stables, offices, locomotive shed, coke ovens, wagon building and repair shops, also the stationary engines needed to haul the trains up the gradient from Euston. (101) The stationary engines, which together with their apparatus and ropes cost £25,000, were only in use from 14 October 1837 until 14 July 1844. (102) If Messrs. Rathbone and Cropper had not insinuated Edward Bury (1794-1858), as locomotive supplier and superintendent to the L&B, the expense of the fixed engines would not have been necessary. The Bury 0-4-0s were somewhat deficient in power. **(103)** It is certain that if Robert Stephenson & Co. had been allowed to provide the locomotives, a design capable of hauling trains up the gradient would have been forthcoming in 1837 rather than 1844. The cost of the whole of the facilities at Camden was £114,385. (104)

Initially a pneumatic telegraph was used to sound a whistle to signal the working of the trains between the winding house and the station. On 25 July 1837, Robert introduced Wheatstone and Cooke's electric telegraph, which had only been patented the previous month, 'for business purposes' between Euston and Camden, and later for signalling on the incline. (105) The very first of the thousands of railway telegraphs, so necessary for safe working, had come into in use.

Great care was taken at Euston and Birmingham, not only in the provision of adequate amenities for efficiently handling the passengers, but also in the appearance of the two stations. Even Francis Whishaw who was '...far from advocating extravagant expenditure in any of the buildings connected with railways,' condescended, 'that the grand Doric entrance to Euston station, from the design of Mr. Hardwick, which is … the key to all the railways north of London, is perfectly allowable.' (106) A modern architectural dictionary, when lamenting the 1962 demolition of this majestic Greek Doric propylaeum, goes further: 'The station building was quite independent of the propylaeum, whose spiritual function was that of a worthy introduction to that miracle of human ingenuity, the London to Birmingham railway.' (107) The carriage road beyond the propylaeum led to the waiting rooms and ticket offices. On the east side of the ticket office was the train shed, with four tracks; the nearest track served the departure platform, and the far one the arrivals. The two intermediate tracks were for storing carriages, which were moved to or from the adjacent lines by means of small turntables. (Fig. 4.15)

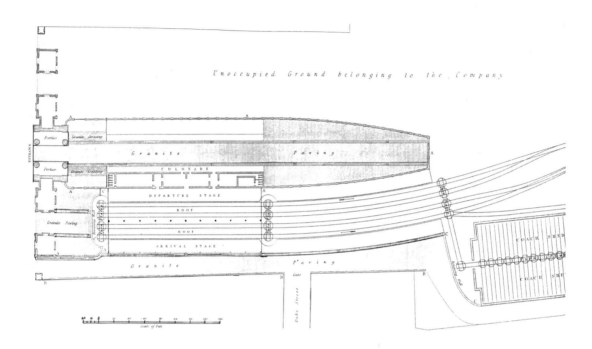

Figure 4.14: an original plan of Euston Station. The 'unoccupied ground' at the top would have been the site of the GWR terminus. From F. W. Simms Public Works of Great Britain *(1838).*

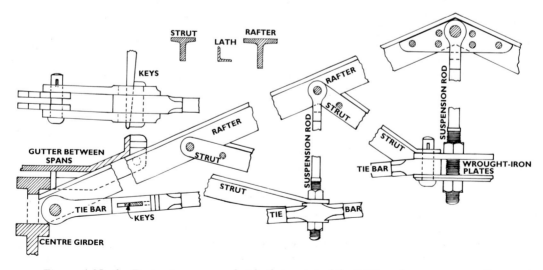

Figure 4.15: the Euston truss as used at both termini of the L&B and on numerous other Stephenson lines. Based on F. W. Simms Public Works of Great Britain *(1838) J. F. A.*

The train shed, 'a beautifully constructed and elegant iron roof, supported on iron columns,' was 200 feet long with two 40 feet spans. (108) The light wrought-iron roof truss that was adopted for the train sheds at London and Birmingham, by Robert Stephenson, became known as the 'Euston truss', and was subsequently used for numerous railway roofs throughout the country. **(109)** (Fig. 4.15) The propylaeum cost £35,000 out of the total figure for the station of £81,532. (110)

Figure 4.16: Philip Hardwick's termini buildings; Euston (top) Curzon Street (below). J. C. Bourne

The station at Birmingham, which was originally intended to serve both the Grand Junction (GJR) and London and Birmingham railways, was called Curzon Street. The railways should have met at an end-on junction there, but, rather surprisingly, the GJR ran into insuperable difficulties when trying to purchase land leased to the son of James Watt. The Grand Junction had to change its route, and eventually entered Curzon Street parallel to the L&B. Relations between the GJR and the L&B became strained, and the latter built its station to occupy most of the restricted site south of Curzon Street. When the GJR officially opened, through from Warrington, on 4 July 1837 it used a temporary station, at Vauxhall, about a mile short of Curzon Street. (111)

The L&B also had land difficulties, and had to pay £3,736 for the acre-and-a-half of land needed to squeeze in its station frontage. The purchase was not finalised until 25 July 1837. (112) The frontage was again designed by Philip Hardwick (1792-1870), and, being less flamboyant than Euston, cost only £26,000. (Fig. 4.16) The train shed roof's design probably pre-dated the one at London by being, unlike Euston, on the original authorised railway. It may possibly have been a re-use of the plans for the proposed joint through station. It was 217 feet long, with two wrought-iron spans of 56 feet 6 inches;

the extra width was needed to cover six tracks. It was divided into thirty-three bays, and supported by cast-iron columns and a linking arcade. (113) The provision of two more tracks under this train shed than at Euston may indicate that the engineers, if not the directors, were still considering the possibility of a joint station. In the event the GJR squeezed an independent station into a corner of the Curzon Street site. The L&B termini saw the introduction of Robert Stephenson's practice of the Engineer designing the track layout and train shed but leaving the rest to the architect.

The first, almost 25-mile-long, section of the L&B to open was from Camden to Boxmoor, on 20 July 1837. The Euston extension together with another 7 miles northwards to Tring were opened on 16 October. A temporary station at Denbigh Hall, where the line crossed Watling Street, 50 miles from London, and the 30-mile stretch from Rugby to Birmingham were ready for traffic on 9 April 1838. Until the final length, including Kilsby Tunnel, was opened a coach service operated between Denbigh Hall and Rugby or Birmingham. This service soon needed every available horse-drawn conveyance in the area to carry the vast number of passengers that had been attracted to the incomplete railway. **(114)**

Kilsby Tunnel and Blisworth cutting were the last works on the railway to be completed, and the line was fully opened on 15 September 1838, only three-and-a-half months over the anticipated four years. The official opening was on 17 September, and Robert preferred the footplate of *Harvey Combe* to the upholstered luxury of the carriages crammed with now mainly sycophantic shareholders and directors. From the locomotive he had an uninterrupted view of his great work unfolding, but, no doubt, his pride was mixed with some self-reproach. Memories of men that had died on the works, criticisms of things that could have been improved with the benefit of hindsight, and a feeling of regret that a project that occupied the prime years of his life was now over, must have engaged his mind during that journey. Some critical remarks in that morning's newspapers, about his father, by one of the directors, also clouded his day, and the banquet in the evening 'passed off heavily'. Robert tackled the director, on the following morning, and 'expressed in the strongest terms his opinion', so much so that the director appealed to the chairman for protection! He did not get any sympathy. **(115)**

On 23 December 1837, with many of the contracts either complete or nearly so, and the imminent break up of his team of engineers, a celebration dinner had been held in the Dun Cow inn at Dunchurch, in Warwickshire. Unlike the later Birmingham banquet, it was a relaxed occasion amongst respected colleagues. Frank Forster chaired the celebration, with Peter Lecount, the 'historian of the works', as vice-chairman. Robert was presented with a large silver soup tureen for which the engineering staff of the company had subscribed 130 guineas. The inscription read: - 'To Robert Stephenson, Esquire, Engineer-in-Chief of the London and Birmingham Railway, a tribute of respect and esteem from the members of the Engineering Department who were employed under him in the execution of that great work. Presented on the eve of their gradual separation.' As the contracts were either not complete, or retentions were still being held, it was unethical, at this stage, for any contractor to make a contribution. In November 1839 'gentlemen who had been engaged as contractors for the construction of the railways, or the supplying of permanent materials' presented him with a candelabrum and service of plate costing £1250. As each individual's subscription was limited to £5 this demonstrated 'the expression of a general and widespread sentiment.' **(116)**

In spite of all the problems, the railway had been completed at an average rate of exactly half a mile per week. Even today this would be a remarkable performance. An average of twelve thousand men, or 107 to each mile, was needed to achieve this; stories of their behaviour and its impact on the communities surrounding the line have been retold many times. **(117)**

The original Act authorised £2,500,000 capital plus £835,000 loans; the Euston Extension Act (3 July 1835) permitted another £165,000; two further acts, in 1837 and 1839, each authorised £1,000,000. This made the total of £5,500,000, which included £350,000 for the manufacture or purchase of locomotives and rolling stock. The cost of the earthworks and track came to almost double the original estimate, which, it must be remembered, expert witnesses, at the committee stage, considered *30% too high*. The directors do not seem to have been too concerned by the overspend as the far more extensive station and depot facilities, that they approved throughout the line, added considerably to its cost. The original estimate for the 'depots' was only £16,000 whereas nearly £400,000 was spent, including the luxury of the Euston propylaeum and its equivalent at Birmingham. **(118)** However, unlike the Scottish Parliament building, which opened in September 2004 at *ten times* its original estimate, and is to be a constant drain on the taxpayers, **(119)** the L&B was very soon making a return of 10% per annum for its investors.

The railway could have been completed at a lot less cost had the Engineer-in-Chief been prepared to accept lower standards. When the L&B was conceived other railways were still being built to 'waggonway standards' with sharp curves, steep gradients, inadequate spacing between adjacent tracks, and limited clearances between the tracks and structures. The tighter clearances were accepted, with some lack of foresight, by the older generation of engineers. According to Whishaw, the Liverpool and

Manchester was built with an interval between the tracks of 5 ft 2 in, and on the Newcastle and Carlisle it varied from 4 ft 8½ in to 5 ft 3 in. Robert adopted, for the L&B, what later became the standard 'sixfoot' of 6ft. 0in. between the outside of the rails, which gave 6ft. 5in. between gauge faces. **(120)**

The widths of the bridges on the L&B were generally 28 feet with some exceptions of 25 feet. The tunnels varied from 22 to 26 feet. **(121)** The smaller dimension, which was typical of many early tunnels, was used for Primrose Hill, and was based on the logic that if two trains could pass each other with ample clearance, with an interval of six feet or less, only three feet were necessary on the outsides of the tracks, for them to pass fixed objects. Robert had considered the provision of recesses or refuges at intervals, in the tunnel walls, for the use of platelayers working in the smaller bores. But, 'when I became more conversant with the difficulties of constructing even plain tunnels, I gave up the idea of complicating them with recesses.' When trains approached the men were expected to lie down on the outside of the rail next to the wall. **(122)**

Vast amounts of ink have been used in arguing the merits of broad or standard gauge, but the most restrictive thing in the development of the railways of this country, the relatively small dimensions of the bridges and tunnels, is rarely mentioned. These limit the size of the locomotives and rolling stock and the loads that can be carried. Just compare the size of standard gauge American locomotives and trains with those in this country. Robert had taken a step forward when he adopted the standard sixfoot, but, as far as vertical clearances were concerned it is fortunate that early locomotives had tall chimneys, and that the stagecoach idea of sitting the guards atop the carriages was followed, or all our trains may have been like those on the London Underground. In 1853 the Railway Clearing House issued a crude booklet entitled *The Minimum Dimensions of Railway Bridges and Tunnels* purporting to show the diverse loading or structure gauges of most British railways. However, the first stipulations on clearances, by the Board of Trade, were not issued until 29 April 1858. They specified the standard sixfoot, as the L&B's, and a clearance between the rails and structures of 3 ft 6 in, 'where the carriages are not above 7 feet 4 inches in width', but made no mention of vertical clearances. **(123)**

The alignment chosen by Robert Stephenson now permits 100 mph running with very few exceptions, where short speed restrictions of 80 or 90 mph apply. (124) When commenting about the curvature of the contemporary Newcastle and Carlisle Railway Whishaw said 'unless it had been laid out for a railway or tram-road to be worked by horses, no engineer would have ventured to recommend a plan which exhibits on the face of it almost one continuous series of curves from end to end.'! (125) With its numerous speed restrictions and steeper gradients, its best pre-war average speed was only 70% of the fairly sedate speeds from London to Birmingham. However, even though it had some large earthworks and numerous river crossings, its cost, per mile, was one third of that of the L&B.

Was the expense of the extensive earthworks and tunnels needed to maintain 1 in 330 gradients justified on the L&B? At the other extreme Joseph Locke has been praised for his lower construction costs. These were arrived at by his avoidance of tunnels and extensive earthworks even though this resulted in sharper curves and long 1 in 75 gradients. These not only gave lower average speeds, **(126)** but also brought to the West Coast route the high cost of double heading trains and maintaining banking engines at Shap and Beattock, throughout steam days. The total expense of providing extra locomotives and crews, for nearly 130 years, must have far outweighed the initial savings in construction costs. Robert's vision of establishing the best possible standards for trunk lines, at this stage of railway development is, surely, far more commendable.

Many writers mention that Robert walked the L&B up to 20 times during its construction, as if this was tangible evidence of the amount of effort that he put into it. Actually it works out at less than a mile per day over the whole period that he was involved in building the railway! It gives no indication of the hundreds of problems that had to be solved, on a scale that had never been encountered before, and the nagging doubts and frustration that must have assailed him when a totally unexpected major difficulty appeared. Robert's choice of extremely reliable assistants enabled him to delegate most of the routine responsibilities to them, but he alone was answerable to the directors for the general progress and for anything that went wrong. When things did go wrong, as at Kilsby, he had to choose the solution that *he* felt would be most likely to succeed, and take the blame if it did not. No matter how great was the problem he never let it beat him, but waiting for the pumps to start winning at Kilsby, the embankment to stabilise at Wolverton, or the cutting at Blisworth to be completed must have produced a lot of sleepless nights.

Even today the completion of a project of the size and difficulty of the London and Birmingham would be regarded internationally as an outstanding achievement, but it is unthinkable that its design and construction would be the responsibility of a single individual.

The London and Brighton Railway

Robert usually only got involved in railways that were to act as feeder lines to the L&B during the time that he was building it. However, an exception was the London & Brighton Railway (LBR) into which he put a great deal of effort to no avail. Schemes for various different routes for a railway between London and Brighton had been receiving consideration from 1820. William James, the Rennies, Francis Giles, H. R. Palmer, J. Gibbs, C. B. Vignoles and N. W. Cundy had all become involved in schemes by 1833. **(127)** The LBR committee first asked Robert Stephenson's opinion on their options in November 1833. By 1834 he considered that the main contenders were down to Sir John Rennie's direct route and Nicholas Wilcox Cundy's (1778-1837) Dorking route. Around October 1834 the LBR committee, apparently without Rennie's knowledge, made his plans available, together with Cundy's, for detailed examination by Robert Stephenson. **(128)** In January 1835, Robert asked G. P. Bidder to check these plans and calculations for him. During the previous year, Robert had asked this old friend, from Edinburgh University, to join him on the L&B, where his phenomenal arithmetical talents would be of considerable assistance in the thousands of calculations needed for the earthwork quantities. **(129)**

On the LBR, Bidder found, with Cundy's line being based only on the two-inch to the mile Ordnance Survey maps prepared during the Napoleonic Wars, it contained significant errors. However, Robert thought that the country through which it passed gave the opportunity for better alignment and gradients, with reduced earthworks and tunnelling, at the expense of greater length. (130) The committee resolved, on 9 March 1835, that further surveys, including one by Stephenson, should be made before adopting a line. Although he was under contractual obligations to the L&B Robert was permitted to accept the role as consulting engineer. He delegated G. P. Bidder to do the survey work for a line, via Dorking, with a ruling gradient of 1 in 330 and a minimum radius of 1½ miles. (131)

The Stephensons, Cundy and Joseph Gibbs all preferred longer routes to the west of Rennie's. Select Committees considered all in the spring of 1836, and this resulted in an epic battle between the supporters of the Stephenson and Rennie routes. The Rennie line proposed to start along the Greenwich and embryonic Croydon Railways and then follow the present-day route to Brighton, whereas the Stephenson route was to use the much faster London and Southampton Railway from Nine Elms to Wimbledon, and proceed via Dorking eventually into the Adur valley, passing Shoreham to enter Brighton from the west. The total length of the Stephenson line from Nine Elms to Brunswick Square in Brighton was five miles longer than the 'Direct Line'. A second, more northerly, terminus at Brighton was requested by the residents, which would have added a single line branch 1 mile 33 chains long. (132)

The engineering arguments at the Parliamentary inquiries ranged over many subjects including; gradients, lengths of the lines, earthwork quantities, construction costs and the suitability of the starting and finishing points of the routes. Sir John Rennie's earlier line, which Robert had reported on in January 1835, had gradients as steep as 1 in 180 to reduce the length of tunnelling; these were amended to 1 in 264 in his final plans, with the inevitable increase in earthworks. Although it was never stated directly, in the evidence, 25% more power was required to take the same train at the same speed up a 1 in 264 gradient than was needed on a 1 in 330. The Stephensons considered the potential for heavier trains or greater speeds justified more circuitous routes, in this case a mere increase of 8% on the mileage. Oddly, when the London & Birmingham was being contemplated Rennie and Giles, as well as the Stephensons, had all proposed much longer routes, than the most direct one, without question. Robert believed that his line to Brighton had better commercial prospects, and would not give any longer journey times. The Rennie route, although needing less new railway, had its earthwork quantities estimated at 8,000,000 cubic yards, whereas the Dorking line total was only 6,000,000. It was also at a disadvantage in the length of tunnelling required. (133)

The main engineering evidence was given by Robert Stephenson and G. P. Bidder in favour of the Dorking line, and Sir John Rennie and Joseph Locke for the direct line. Some indication of its extent and depth is shown when one finds that it fills a 456-page A5 size book, using a small typeface. It has often been assumed that after Joseph Locke ousted George from the GJR that he and Robert ceased to be friends until reconciliation after the Dee Bridge disaster of 1847. Although 'George Stephenson and Son' was officially at war with Locke there are no grounds to suggest that Robert ever ceased to be his friend. **(134)** Towards the end of Locke's evidence in support of the Rennie route, he refused to be drawn to condemn Robert Stephenson's line: -

> 'You have stated that you think that Sir John Rennie's line is the best line to Brighton, superior to Mr. Stephenson's?
>
> 'No; I have stated that I have not seen any other line but that of Sir John Rennie's. I have examined that upon the points of which I have given evidence here; but I have answered the questions put hypothetically to me.

'You stated that you considered it a better line than Mr. Stephenson's, did you not?

'I stated in answer to a question, giving me the length of the inclinations of the two lines which I would prefer; but I have not stated, because I do not know, all the circumstances to enable me to say which of the two is the best line.'

At the very end of his questioning he also admitted, inevitably, that he would prefer a line without tunnels to one with them. (135)

Later during his penetrating cross-examination for the Lords Committee it became obvious that George Stephenson was claiming to have had more influence on the Dorking route than was actually the case. Counsel, Mr. Harrison, got illuminating answers to two of his questions: -

'Your name was put to it as principal Engineer, and you signed the estimate, and it was always talked of on the Stock Exchange as Mr. Stephenson's line?

'Surely you will allow the Father and Son to go together.

'But the Father should not put his Name upon the Credit of the Son unless he has done it?

'I have brought him up since a Child to be an Engineer, and I ought to have some Benefit from it now.' **(136)**

Incredibly, with all the evidence, Parliament was still unable to reach a decision. A year later, on 13 May 1837, it was proposed that an army engineer be appointed to examine all the routes, and report his recommendations. Captain Robert C. Alderson, R. E. was given the task, on 2 June, and he reported back on 27th. Although he admitted that the Stephenson scheme was the best from the engineering point of view, he felt that the advantages of the direct line outweighed its construction costs. **(137)** Ironically, after the promoters had spent a total of £194,000 on the Parliamentary contest they got the outcome decided on the recommendation of a junior army officer. (138)

The Act was rushed through by 15 July 1837, just six weeks after Captain Alderson's appointment. To say that Robert was not very pleased would be an understatement, and he responded to Captain Alderson's report in a 16-page pamphlet that was published on 24 October 1837. His arguments stated that there were some serious inaccuracies and omissions in the report that made the case unfairly more favourable to the direct line, and that the logic was sometimes flawed. The use of the Greenwich Railway, with its admitted defects, for the start of the direct line was questioned with some justification. This railway was built entirely on a viaduct, and had cost £171,000 per mile to build. With the additional traffic from the Croydon and Brighton lines it would need an additional two tracks, at an estimated £300,000. Also the difficulty of getting the space for a larger depot at London Bridge, and the problems of more congested roads to central London were mentioned. The London & Southampton, which Stephenson intended to use, already had plans to extend from Nine Elms to Waterloo, thereby bringing it equally near to the centre of the city. (139)

Five years after Robert's pamphlet Francis Whishaw still felt 'the *direct* line has been chosen; but a more difficult and expensive one could not have been selected.' (140) John Urpeth Rastrick, and not the Rennies, was entrusted with the construction of the line, which was modified to reduce the earthworks and to improve the alignment. **(141)** It was undoubtedly this extremely capable engineer's masterpiece. Modern express trains can average over 70mph between Croydon and Brighton, but might they not have averaged 90-100mph over the Stephenson line?

NOTES AND REFERENCES

1. *Proc. I. C. E. Vol. 19*, p. 177.
2. S. C. Brees, *Appendix to Railway Practice containing a copious abstract of the whole of the Evidence given upon the London and Birmingham and Great Western Railway Bills,* (1839) (The book, in fact, only gives a summary of the House of Lords evidence in favour of the L&B Bill) p. 39. There were three canal routes available between London and Birmingham; according to the evidence the shortest was 152-miles long, and had 173 locks to negotiate. The time taken for the journey was between three and six days. The canals could be interrupted in winter by ice and in summer by shortage of water.
3. E. M. S. Paine, *The Two James's & the Two Stephensons,* (1861 reprinted 1961) inside rear covers; 'Plan of Central Junction Railway or Tram-Road'. William James had just completed the canal immediately north of Stratford upon Avon.
4. W. O. Skeat, *George Stephenson,* (1973) pp. 70-74 quotes original letters, and states that they apply specifically to the L&B and not to a line from the Mersey to Birmingham.
5. J. C. Bourne and John Britton, *Drawings of the London and Birmingham Railway,* (1839 reprinted 1970) p. 9. Sir J. Rennie's report appeared in Vols. 1 and 2 of the *Railway Magazine.* (Later *Herapath's Railway Magazine*) Peter Lecount, writing for the seventh edition of the *Encyclopaedia Britannica,* c. 1838, says, 'In the year 1830 when the L&B was projected, the expense of construction was stated at £6,000 per mile with one line of rails, which were to be worked by horses,'

6. Thomas Roscoe and Peter Lecount, *The London and Birmingham Railway,* (1839) p. 6. Oddly, in a letter to the *Civil Engineer & Architect's Journal,* in Feb 1841, Lecount claimed to have little or nothing to do with this book, but the publisher was able to disprove this in the March issue.

7. Jeaff. Vol. 1, pp. 167-8. Jeaffreson gets quite worked up about the credit for building the L&B being given to George Stephenson, George Stephenson and Son, or even Messrs. Stephenson. '*This line was, however, constructed by Robert Stephenson alone, and to him is due the entire merit of overcoming all the gigantic obstacles to its construction.*' Out of the blue, the agreement named William Brunton (1777-1857) as 'the resident engineer for the London end'. Brunton, who is well known to students of early railways for his design of a locomotive propelled by legs, had set up a civil engineering practice in London in 1825, but his involvement with the L&B, and later the GWR, was only for survey work.

8. S. C. Brees, page v.

9. Jeaff. Vol. 1, p. 168.

10. Roscoe and Lecount, pp. 9-11.

11. Bourne and Britton, p. 19.

12. Roscoe and Lecount, p. 90. This has been denied in *Northampton Vindicated,* (1935) by Joan Wake, and in other essays. The maintenance of the ruling gradient of 1 in 330 may have been difficult as Northampton lies over 100 ft. below the L&B. The 'Northampton Loop' from Roade to Rugby is over two miles longer than the L&B, and is graded mostly at 1 in 200-230, and includes three tunnels one of which is 1,152-yard long. Jeaff. Vol. 1 pp. 200-1, lays all the blame for his hero's problems at Kilsby tunnel on the inhabitants of Northampton.

13. Roscoe and Lecount, p. 12.

14. Brees, p.128. At the end of 1834, R. S. had considered extending the L&B as far as the Thames, but he had not been sufficiently bold to put it to the board. Eventually when Charles Parker, the L&B solicitor, had encouraged him to approach the board, he had been told to concentrate on engineering rather than policy. (See Jeaff. Vol. 1 p. 207.) In 1845 the L&B did ask R. S. to prepare a scheme for a line to the river, mainly in tunnels, from Camden Town to Farringdon Street, near the site of the Fleet prison. It was never taken beyond the planning stage. (See *Builder* 31 Jan. 1846, p. 56. Deposited plans, PRO RAIL 384/199.)

15. E. T. MacDermot, *Great Western Railway,* (1964 edition) p. 9. Also PRO RAIL 384/257. The junction was to be at Kensal Green.

16. *Proc. I. C. E. Vol. 72* 1882, pp. 303-4.

17. Roscoe and Lecount, p. 29.

18. Brees, pp. 17 & 19. Rastrick said, 'In the course of my experience, I have had pass through my hands, the estimates of all the Engineers of the day that have come before Parliament, and I think Mr. Stephenson's is 30 per cent. higher than any I remember.'

19. Ibid. p. 5.

20. Ibid. p. 43. John Francis, *A History of the English Railway,* Vol. 1 (1851) p. 40 states that by 1846 the Grand Junction Canal was only paying 6% whereas four other canals are still giving between 16 and 30% dividend.

21. Brees p. 41.

22. Roscoe and Lecount, pp. 15, 16.

23. Jeaff. Vol. 1, pp. 177, 8.

24. Roscoe and Lecount, p. 28. It is not fair to assume that all this money was wasted, as the surveys and details of land ownership would have to have been done in any case.

25. Jeaff. Vol. 1, p 178. Lord Wharncliffe was one of the 'Grand Allies' who had aided G. S. earlier.

26. Ibid. p. 178-9.

27. Brees, pp.21-2. Roscoe and Lecount, p. 96, give the final figure for the railway and stations as nearly 2,000 acres, or almost 18 acres to the mile. This figure also includes the land purchased for severance, borrow pits and tipping surplus material. The original average width of nearly 105 ft gives some idea of the cuttings and embankments involved when the track formation itself was only 30 ft. wide. See also Whishaw, p. 252.

28. Roscoe and Lecount, p. 30.

29. Bourne and Britton, p. 11. One third of the authorised capital had already been absorbed by the cost of the land and the Parliamentary expenses.

30. Jeaff. Vol. 1, p. 181.

31. Ibid. p. 185-6.

32. Prof. Sir A. Skempton, (Editor) *Biographical Dictionary of Civil Engineers, Vol. 1,* (2002) p. xviii.

33. F. R. Conder, *Personal Recollections of English Engineers,* first published 1868, reprinted as *The Men Who Built Railways* with notes by Professor Simmons (1983), p. 27. Francis Roubiliac Conder (1815-89) had served on the L&B under R. S., and eventually he set up as a contractor for railways in Europe, where, 'through the treachery of the Neapolitan Government', he became penniless. He returned to England in 1864, and took up writing. For his obituary see *Proc. I. C. E. Vol. 100,* 1890, pp. 379-83.

34. It was George's lack of organisation that led to him being replaced by Joseph Locke on the Grand Junction Railway.

35. Conder, p. 118

36. *Proc. I. C. E. Vol. 19,* p. 217.

37. Jeaff. Vol. 2, p. 165.

38. Jeaff. Vol. 1, pp. 190-1. Jeaffreson incorrectly gives John Crossley (1812-79) instead of William Crosley (fl. 1802-38)

39. *Proc. I. C. E. Vol. 57,* p. 297.

40. Jeaff. Vol. 1, pp. 191-2. P. 213 elaborates that when I. K. B. started the construction of the GWR he borrowed R. S's plans, 'and used them as the best possible system of draughting.'

41. R. Stephenson, *Diary 1834,* Science Museum.

42. Brees, pp. 113-5. J. Smeaton, T. Telford and J. Rennie Snr. had gone a long way towards establishing sound contracting procedures.

43. Jeaff. Vol. 1 p. 192, and Roscoe and Lecount, op. cit. p. 193. The total for the revised estimate comes to £2.5 million, to which a further 1¼ million should be added for permanent way, stations and depots. This makes a shortfall of over £½ million on the final cost of the infrastructure, which was £4,287,647. See Francis Whishaw, *Railways of Great Britain and Ireland,* (1842 reprinted 1969), pp. 223, 227, 252-3.

44. Brees, 113, 4, 7. The first turf on the L&B had been cut at Chalk Farm on 1 June 1834.

45. Roscoe and Lecount, p. 123.

46. Brees, pp. 156-7.

47. Ibid. p. 154.

48. Calomel was used as a fairly nasty purgative, and has no addictive effects, and is obviously a misprint. Conder could have written 'chloral' (chloral hydrate) which is an addictive sleep-inducing drug, whose use was in vogue, with some eminent Victorians e. g. Dante Gabriel Rossetti.

49. Conder, pp. 14-15. Some of these statements emphatically give the lie to the dubious legend about Robert's delicate health.

50. Brees, p. 103.

51. Ibid. pp. 116-7.

52. Ibid. p. 116.

53. S. H. Beaver, 'Geography from a Railway Train', *Geography,* Dec. 1936, p. 275 gives a geological section of the line from Euston to Rugby, as do O'Dell and Richards, *Railways and Geography,* (1971) p. 48. The latter gentlemen state (p. 24) that because of problems at Kilsby the engineer committed suicide!!

54. A road tunnel had been proposed at Highgate in 1808, in similar ground conditions. Initially it was to be about a mile long, but when it failed in 1811 it had been reduced to 211 yards, and then only one third of the reduced length had been completed. Brees p. 156 states it was designed by John Rennie, but he was only consulted after the work got into difficulties, and his recommendations were ignored. Robert Vazie was the engineer. (See Skempton op. cit. p. 738)

55. The lengths of the tunnels are quoted with variations of up to 60 yards. Bourne and Britton's figures supplied by R. Creed are used throughout.

56. Conder p. 25.

57. Bourne and Britton, p. 18. Whishaw, p. 226.

58. Jeaff. Vol. 1. p. 194.

59. Conder, p. 17. Conder differs from the contemporary accounts by saying there were three working shafts, not six, and that there were nine men killed. The shaft was enlarged to form a huge ventilator. A report by R. Creed (PRO RAIL 384/261) gives no grounds to believe that the collapse was anything but a totally unavoidable accident. The original specification by R. S. said the tunnel 'was to be worked with six shafts, not less than 8 feet diameter within the brickwork, and 9 inches thick; the brickwork moulded to fit the circumference of the shaft, and laid in two half-brick rings; an air shaft at a distance of 50 yards on each side of each working shaft, and not less than 3 feet 6 inches diameter inside; the arch and side walls of the tunnel, usually two bricks thick, and the invert, one and a half-brick, except in places where the stratum passed through seemed to require an increased, or admit a diminished thickness. The form of the top of the tunnel is nearly semicircular, supported by curved side walls standing on stone footings or skew backs, which rest on the invert forming the base of the tunnel. The ends of the tunnel are formed with wing walls. The brickwork at the ends of the tunnel is bound by wrought iron rods 100 feet long, secured at each end in a cast iron rim or plate built into the brickwork.' (Quoted in *Dempsey's Practical Railway Engineer,* (1847) p. 110)

60. Brees, pp. 11, 12. Frank Forster's evidence.

61. Roscoe and Lecount, pp. 106-7. Crick Tunnel on the Grand Junction (later Union) Canal, over a mile to the north east of Kilsby, had been re-routed when quicksand and poor strata had been discovered in 1811.

62. Prof. Sir A. Skempton, pp. 490-1. Joseph Nowell's sons completed the Harrow contact with the help of their uncle, who accomplished three other contracts on the line.

63. Jeaff. Vol. 1, p. 201. Bourne and Britton, p. 23, state that the cost was between £300,000 and £400,000. See also note 43.

64. J. G. H. Warren, *A Century of Locomotive Building,* (1923, reprinted 1970) pp. 85-7, quotes some of the original correspondence. Dionysius Lardner (1793-1859) was a paper tiger who made all sorts of rash pronouncements about the dangers of railways, but nevertheless had a strong following amongst the feeble-minded and frequently targeted R. S. and I. K. B. Other engineers had problems with their directors. As a result of more general criticism, in Dec. 1838, the GWR directors very nearly replaced I. K. B. by J. Locke. (See MacDermot, pp. 44-5). C. B. Vignoles was replaced on several railways because of fallouts with the boards. K. H. Vignoles, (*Charles Blacker Vignoles* (1982), pp. 107, 115,) suggests by 1844 R. S. enjoyed a cordial relationship with Vignoles and they offered to combine efforts on the London and Chatham line, and in 1845 R. S. employed Vignoles' eldest son as an assistant on the Leeds and Bradford Railway.

65. Constantine Richard Moorsom (1792-1861), later vice-admiral, elder brother of the civil engineer, William Scarth, was director of the C&HR, and later chairman of the LNWR. He became a firm friend and supporter of R. S. especially during the building of the C&HR bridges. Capt. Moorsom shared the secretarial duties of the L&B with Richard Creed.

66. Sir Francis Head, *Stokers and Pokers,* (1849) p. 30.

67. Jeaff. Vol. 1, p. 203-4.

68. S. Smiles, *Lives of the Engineers.* (1862) pp. 316-8.

69. Roscoe and Lecount, pp. 106-7. Smiles (1874) p.249, states that the water level was only lowered at the rate of 2½ to 3 inches per week, and pumping had to continue for 19 months until the brickwork was completed.

70. Jeaff. Vol. 1, pp. 204-5.

71. Bourne and Britton, pp. 23-4.

72. G. D. Dempsey, *The Practical Railway Engineer,* (1847) p. 64 gives an average of 142,000 cu. yds. per mile, which makes it 30% above the original estimate. The paper quoted below (73) gives 115,000 which is only 7% above the estimate. Probably the truth lies somewhere in between. Whishaw, writing in 1842 (p. 225), was unable to find the final quantities.

73. M. Chrimes, (Editor), *The Civil Engineering of Canals and Railways before 1850,* (1997). Prof. A. W. Skempton, 'Embankments and cuttings on early railways', pp. 290-307. A most valuable account of a neglected subject.

74. Bourne and Britton, p. 20.

75. Brees, p. 103.

76. Dempsey, p.54.

77. Ibid. pp. 57-8. Dempsey in Plate 9 Fig. 9 illustrates a two-horse plough that was being used in the United States at the same time. See also *C. E. & A. J.* June and July 1839, pp. 224-5, 252.

78. Roscoe and Lecount, pp. 85-6. The well-known illustration by Bourne exaggerates the embankment's height.

79. Bourne and Britton, p.21. Skempton, p. 713. *Proc. I. C. E. Vol. 93*, pp. 492-3. In 1833-4 R. Townshend had been employed to survey Rennie's rival London to Brighton line, and a high-level canal between London and Birmingham. This did not seem to blot his copybook as R. S. sent him to Italy to do the preliminary survey for the railway between Leghorn and Florence, in 1838.

80. Dempsey, p. 10. Contemporary accounts refer to Blisworth cutting, but today it is usually called Roade.

81. Roscoe and Lecount, pp. 91-4.

82. The contract documents number 375 bridges.

83. Henry Booth, *An Account of the Liverpool and Manchester Railway,* (1830), pp. 98-9. Only three of these 15 were under the railway. The total number of bridges on the line was 63. The famous, still extant example, carrying the main road across the railway at Rainhill, with a skew of 33 degrees, reputedly was pre-assembled in a field beside the railway to ensure it could be built correctly.

84. Peter Nicholson, *The Guide to Railway Masonry; comprising a complete treatise on the oblique arch,* (1839) pp. iv-v. In 1836 Charles Fox had claimed to be the first who had 'turned his attention to the subject'. Nicholson remarks 'Mr. Fox is either chargeable with ignorance of the subject on which he treats, or with want of that candour which induces men of science to allow their predecessors the honour and credit of what they have written on the same subject.' G.W. Buck, *A Practical and Theoretical Essay on Oblique Bridges,* (1839) p. iii, 'This work was announced about three years back, [i.e. at the time of the first Fox article] the author being then urged to do so, but it was afterwards postponed in consequence of finding that his knowledge of the subject was daily increasing by the experience afforded in the construction of a variety of bridges.' He added, 'he would have regretted if the work had appeared earlier.' Copies of the relevant information kindly supplied by James Armstrong of Edinburgh.

85. *Proc. I. C. E. Vol. 14*, 1854, pp. 129-30, states G. W. Buck was asked to write his treatise by his friends. R.S. was always considered one of his friends, and when Buck was afflicted with total deafness in 1846 and needed financial support, 'Mr. Robert Stephenson's name was, as usual, first and largest on the list, and his kindness and munificence are continued to the family to the present time [1854].' His son, Joseph, became the resident engineer for the widening of some of the railway that his father built, within the first 28 miles of the L&B, as far as King's Langley, for two additional tracks, in 1877-9.

86. Roscoe and Lecount, pp. 62-3. Conder, pp. 15-16.

87. Jeaff. Vol. 1, pp. 196-200.

88. Some authors, starting with Whishaw, have given the credit for the Regent's Canal design, as the prototype, to Charles Fox. The contract, including the design for Long Buckby, was let a month before the Euston extension had even received its Act of Parliament. Jeaff. Vol. 2, p. 47 states; 'The earliest railway bridge on this plan was designed by Mr. Robert Stephenson in 1834, and erected in 1835 or 1836, to carry the London and Birmingham Railway over the Grand Junction Canal near Weedon [Long Buckby].' Fox had probably been delegated to adapt the Long Buckby design to suit the Euston site. When R.S. and G. W. Buck had assisted F. W. Simms to produce his *Public Works of Great Britain,* in 1838, Fox had been asked to provide the drawing of the Regent's Canal design from which the engravings for the book were prepared. This may have given rise to the misunderstanding. Also writing on 'Bridges' for the *Encyclopaedia Britannica,* in 1856, R. S. had obviously forgotten about the Weedon or Long Buckby Bridge when he described the Regent's Canal as the first of its type, and has misled a number of authors including this one (JFA).

89. Skempton, p. 399, and *The Annals and History of Leeds,* (1860), p. 346.

90. Roscoe and Lecount, pp. 77 and 123, also E. A. Labrum, *Civil engineering Heritage Eastern and Central England,* (1994), p. 181.

91. Ibid. p. 123.

92. Ibid. p. 99. PRO RAIL 384/122 gives details of R. S's report for amending the Act to alter the alignment at Weedon to avoid a sharp curve. A copy of Capt. Jebb R.E.'s contemporary description of the sliding bridge was kindly provided by the Weedon Bec History Society

93. Whishaw, p. 224.
94. Nicholas Wood, *A Practical Treatise on Rail-roads,* (1838) pp. 150-1. By 1852 R. S. had decided, '…that if traffic was small and the speed was slow, stone blocks sufficed for a railway for the conveyance of heavy minerals, at a speed of about ten, or twelve miles per hour.' (*Proc. I. C. E. Vol. 11*, p. 296.)
95. Dempsey, pp. 80-1. The Kyanising process for preserving wood by 'bichloride of mercury' had been patented on 31 March 1832, but it was not particularly effective until the Hull and Selby Railway made improvements on its method of application in 1839. After WW2 British Railways could not get good quality sleepers, and those they did get were protected by Tanalising, rather than creosoting, and many had a life of less than 10 years. The 1960s saw the rapid re-introduction of 'stone' in the form of pre-stressed concrete ones which not only were much more durable, but had a slight advantage in cost over the chaired wooden sleepers.
96. P. Lecount, *A Practical Treatise on Railways,* (1839), states to get the new railway to a high standard, as soon as possible, financial awards for the 'best lengths' of track were being made to the L&B permanent way staff.
97. Whishaw, pp. 219-220, 223. Roscoe and Lecount, p. 40. The quantity of stone blocks quoted was sufficient for just over 80 miles of double track railway.
98. The principal stations were: - Watford, Tring, Leighton Buzzard, Wolverton, Roade, Weedon, Rugby and Coventry. The intermediate ones were: - Harrow, Boxmoor (Hemel Hempstead), Berkhamsted, Bletchley, Blisworth, Crick, Brandon and Hampton in Arden. The number of important towns that did not have stations, and that the principal stations of Roade and Weedon have closed long ago shows how much things have changed. There was a temporary station at Denbigh Hall, whilst Kilsby tunnel was being completed.
99. Whishaw, pp. 234-8 gives a full description of the facilities. He thought 50-60 miles was too far between engine changes, and preferred 30-mile stages. Other railway towns that sprung up, on the workshops near their mid-point principle, were Crewe on the GJR, and Swindon on the GWR.
100. Samuel Sidney, *Rides on Railways* 1851, pp. 16-7.
101. Ibid. p. 229.
102. Jeaff. Vol. 1, p. 208.
103. The Bury locomotives lack of power made double heading necessary on the heavier trains, and the L&B speeds were generally slow. After Bury 'resigned' in 1846 things improved significantly. Whishaw, p. 249, in a footnote, quotes Bury's reasons for his preference for small locomotives. The GJR purchased locos from a number of companies, and J. Locke recounted; 'At an early period the Grand Junction Company bought all their locomotives from manufacturers, and it was only justice to admit, that those of Messrs R. Stephenson & Co. were the best.' Six out of the first twenty locos delivered to the GJR were from Robert Stephenson & Co.
104. Whishaw, p. 227 footnote.
105. Jeaff. Vol. 1 pp. 235-6.
106. Whishaw, pp. 227-8.
107. *Penguin Dictionary of Architecture,* (1999 edition) p. 252.
108. Roscoe and Lecount, pp.38-9.
109. The origin of the Euston truss, which pre-dated the railway, is again wrongly credited to Fox. The Fox camp never mentions the problem with the movement of the retaining walls on the Euston Extension, which was obvious to Fox and Conder even when they were setting out their footings. R. S. later had to rebuild parts of the walls and provide cast-iron arches to span between the walls in order to stabilise them.
110. Whishaw, p. 227. Roscoe and Lecount, p. 39.
111. Richard Foster, *Birmingham New Street, Vol. 1. The Years up to 1860.* (1990) pp. 37-54.
112. Ibid. p. 40.
113. Roscoe and Lecount, p. 161.
114. Ibid. p. 79. *The Railway Magazine,* Aug. 1921, p. 137 gives details of the coach operators co-operating with the L&B and acting as ticket agents for the company. See also *Drake's Railway Sheet,* 1839.
115. Jeaff. Vol. 1, pp. 210-1. The *Harvey Combe* was a Patentee which R. S. & Co. had supplied to the contractor, William Cubitt, in 1835. (Warren, p. 320)
116. Ibid. pp. 211-2, also (*Proc. I. C. E. Vol. 19*, p. 179). The subscription list gives 268 names.
117. Ibid. p. 209. For more details of the navvies' work and behaviour see *The Railway Navvies,* (1965) by Terry Coleman.
118. Whishaw, pp. 219, 227, 253. The average cost per mile for *all* railways built in Britain by 1880 was almost £41,000, making the L&B £8,000 above par; Brunel's London to Bristol cost over £52,000 per mile. In 1842 R. S. produced a report for the board of the South Eastern Railway, on 'French Lines', which included; '…the excess of the actual over the calculated cost does not arise so much from errors in estimate, properly so called, as from the entire omission of items which either do not come within the scope of precise calculation, or are regarded as foreign to a simple estimate of construction.' Locomotives and rolling stock, as well as buildings, which have nothing to do with the construction, are included in the final costs. (J. Weale, *Ensamples of Railway Making* (1843), p. iii)
119. The incomplete building was opened three years behind schedule.
120. Whishaw, pp. 191, 339, 222. The 6'-5½" (1970mm) dimension now used, between gauge faces, is arrived from the use of a 2¾" wide rail head, instead of the 2½" of earlier days.
121. Alan Blower, *British Railway Tunnels,* (1964). The contemporary drawings all give a width of 24 feet, but this was obviously varied during construction.
122. *Extracts from Gauge Evidence, 1845.* p. 103.
123. L. T. C. Rolt, *Red for Danger,* (1955), pp. 219-220. This gives a width between walls, piers or abutments of 22ft-10in for double and 11ft- 8½in for single track.

124. *British Railways, London Midland Region, Sectional Appendix, Southern Section,* (1980).

125. Whishaw, p. 335.

126. The significance of lower uphill speeds was explained by Sir Nigel Gresley in his presidential address to the Institution of Mechanical Engineers (*Proc. I. Mech. E.,* Oct. 1936, p.259) '...to run a distance of 15 miles at 30 mph occupies 30 minutes, a similar distance at 60 mph takes 15 minutes, and at 90 mph takes 10 minutes. To increase the downhill running speed from 60 to 90 mph therefore only saves 5 minutes, but to increase the uphill running speeds from 30 to 60 mph saves 15 minutes.' Dionysius Lardner had come up with similar arguments in the 1830s, but with faulty arithmetic. Only the use of extremely powerful locomotives or lightweight trains can provide 60 mph averages up long 1 in 75 gradients.

127. Gurney's shorthand notes published as *Minutes of Evidence taken before the Committee of the London and Brighton Railway Bills; Engineering Evidence.* (1836) pp. 171-3. Recent works i.e. J. T. H. Turner's *The London, Brighton & South Coast Railway,* Vol. 1, (1977) and E. F. Clark's *George Parker Bidder,* (1983) give good accounts of the LBR struggle. Information kindly supplied by Alan Bowman.

128. Gurney, p. 16. Also pp. 104-6, Rennie had agreed to supply the plans to R. S. in Oct. 1833, but did not.

129. *Proc. I. C. E. Vol. 57* pp. 297-8. It must have been at this time that Bidder produced his first sets of tables to aid the calculation of earthworks, which are mentioned Nicholas Wood's 1838 *Treatise.* (p. 146)

130. Gurney, p. 26-7.

131. Ibid. p. 2.

132. Ibid. pp. 5-9.

133. Ibid. pp. 66, 80, 103, 190.

134. See *Proc. I. C. E. Vol. 19*, p. 2, for Locke's remarks about R. S. being his life-long friend.

135. Gurney, op. cit. pp. 450, 454.

136. *Brighton Railway Bill. Minutes of Evidence taken before the Lords Committees.* (1836) p. 162. A little later in the cross-examination Harrison got quite insulting and twice referred to George's 'weak mind'. Harrison had represented the opposition at the L&M inquiries.

137. Turner, p. 113. Capt. (later Col.) Alderson became Commissioner of Railways in 1848, a year before he died.

138. Whishaw, pp. 269-70.

139. *Mr. Robert Stephenson's reply to Captain Alderson,* (1837) I. C. E. Archives.

140. Whishaw, p. 270.

141. Turner, pp. 114-5. The earthwork quantities ended up 1,000,000 cubic yards below Rennie's estimate.

Figure 4.17: activity near Park Street Bridge on the London Extension on 17 September 1836 showing the vast amount of work that had been completed in a little over a year: '... the yet unfinished and unopened Railroad was in progress; and, from the very core of this dire disorder, trailed smoothly away, upon its mighty course of civilisation and improvement.' (Dickens, Dombey and Son, Chapter 6) All the J. C. Bourne lithographs reproduced in this chapter are from photographs by Ron Prattley.

CHAPTER FIVE; MAIN LINES TO THE NORTH EAST AND DISPUTES

Through the Midlands to York.

With the London and Birmingham and Grand Junction Railways being projected to serve Birmingham and the North West, it was inevitable that Yorkshire and the North East would also need rail links to the Midlands and London. The York and North Midland Railway (Y&NMR) arose as a result of schemes in 1833 for a railway from York to Leeds, and in 1834 for three lines from London to York. Significantly, it saw the 'Railway King's', George Hudson (1800-71), debut in railway promotion. In 1834 George Rennie (1791-1866) was asked to prepare a survey for the York to Leeds line, but, by the time that he had completed his report, Nicholas Wilcox Cundy and Joseph Gibbs (1798-1864) had each proposed lines from London to York. (1) The plans for Cundy's line were deposited in November 1834, (2) and he had aroused sufficient interest for James Walker, now the president of the Institution of Civil Engineers, to be brought in to do a detailed investigation. On 30 June 1835, when Walker reported that his own London route, through lightly populated agricultural districts, would cost £4,000,000 questions started to be asked. In April 1835 the *Athenaeum* had already suggested that a railway from Leeds to connect to the London & Birmingham, north of Northampton, might profitably serve a series of important manufacturing towns. The Midland Counties Railway was soon to be projected from the L&B at Rugby to Derby and Nottingham, with C. B. Vignoles as engineer (opened 1840). The Stephensons were considering the shorter rival Birmingham and Derby Junction Railway which left the L&B at Hampton-in-Arden (authorised 19 May 1836; opened August 1839). 'On a beautiful morning in the autumn of 1835' George Stephenson was to commence a survey for the next section northwards from Derby to Leeds. This became known as the North Midland Railway (NMR). At this stage the supporters of the York and London line realised that a Midland route to the capital would open the way to a cheap solution. (3)

It was appreciated that 25 miles of railway from York to the NMR would serve the dual purpose of connecting the city to Leeds and London. On 13 October 1835 the Y&NMR was formed. George Stephenson and Son were appointed the engineers for the railway, which was to run from York to a junction with the NMR at Altofts, near Normanton. A loop left the main line between Castleford and Altofts to allow trains to run directly to Leeds over NMR metals. James Walker's Leeds and Selby Railway, which had been opened in 1834, crossed over the Y&NMR at South Milford. Here it was proposed to have four connecting loops, but, because of politics on the part of George Hudson, only the eastern two, towards Selby, were built.

With Robert being busy with the L&B, his input into the building of the NMR and the first stage of the Y&NMR has been generally ignored. Robert was officially the Engineer-in-Chief of both railways, together with the essential Birmingham and Derby Junction link to the L&B. (4) His workload on the L&B was declining even before its first section opened in July 1837. According to Jeaffreson, 'As soon as he was able to give his attention to the matter, the North Midland line from Derby to Leeds was in his hands.' (5) George usually gets all the credit for the NMR but, after his fiasco on the Grand Junction, it is probable that Robert and his assistant engineers had a considerable input to this well-engineered 73-mile line from an early stage. On the L&B and GJR Robert and Joseph Locke had easily mastered all the design and contracting procedures needed to build a railway, but George, already in his mid-fifties when the GJR was being built, could not. This makes his contribution to the NMR considerably less than the total mastery that he is usually credited with. Samuel Smiles gives all the credit to George, but Whishaw at least shares the honours: 'During the execution of the works, Messrs. G. and R. Stephenson were the principal engineers.' However, F. S. Williams states that Robert had total control of the line at its completion. George may have pursued his interest in forming the Clay Cross Company, rather than the railway, after coal was discovered during the boring of the tunnel at the summit of the line in 1837.

Royal Assent was given for the North Midland Railway on 4 July 1836. In September 1836 Frederick Swanwick (1810-1885) was appointed the assistant engineer for the NMR and the Sheffield and Rotherham Railway; in December he was reported to be based in Chesterfield and working on the plans, estimates and alterations to the line. (6) The first contract for Clay Cross Tunnel was let in February 1837, and Alexander M. Ross (1805-62) and Thomas Dyson (1771-1852) were appointed the resident engineers for the construction of the line. (7)

The Y&NMR was authorised on 21 June 1836, and opened from York to its junction with the Leeds and Selby on 29 May 1839. The NMR reached Leeds on 30 June 1840; the Y&NMR was opened to Altofts on the next day, and its link towards Leeds followed on 27 July. (8) George officially pulled out from the engineering of the Y&NMR in August 1840. (9) As the Y&NMR empire extended, under Hudson's leadership, Robert was involved in its future lines although he delegated much of the work to his assistants, John Cass Birkinshaw and Thomas Cabry, often with himself acting more as a consultant.

The next Y&NMR line to be built was from York to Scarborough, with a branch to connect with George's horse-worked Whitby and Pickering Railway of 1836. It was to be yet another project in which both the Stephensons and Rennies emerged as rivals. When giving evidence to the London and Brighton inquiry, on 14 April 1836, Sir John Rennie said that he had already explored a line from York to Scarborough. George Stephenson and G. and J. Rennie first deposited their rival plans for railways between York and Scarborough, with a Pickering branch, on 1 March 1841. Both these schemes, which intended to tunnel under the Howardian Hills near Whitwell, were not pursued. (10) Robert, with J. C. Birkinshaw as his assistant, deposited their plan on 30 November 1843. (11) With George Hudson at the helm cost cutting had become the order of the day, and only a single line was planned; however, it had to be doubled immediately after the opening. There were only 25 bridges on the 42 miles long main line as level crossings were substituted on all the roads but three; timber under-bridges replaced some intended to be iron or masonry. At least £30,000 was saved by avoiding the tunnel and following the sinuous course of the River Derwent. The proposed line had an objectionable approach into York, and the Act was granted on 4 July 1844, without giving compulsory purchase powers at the York end. A year later Royal Assent was given for a revised and shorter route into the city, with the acceptance that trains would now need to reverse to get into the original York station. (12)

The most interesting structure was the bridge over the Ouse on the revised approach to York. This was a continuous two-span trussed girder bridge with piled foundations for the pier and abutments; the pier, in the centre of the river, is supported on cast-iron friction piles. **(13)** The bridge over the River Derwent was intended to be similar, but a timber structure was substituted, and the need for two other bridges over the Derwent near Malton was avoided by a short diversion of the river. (14) The earthworks through the Vales of York and Pickering were extremely light. J. C. Birkinshaw and Alfred Dickens, the younger brother of the famous novelist, supervised the works. (15) The cost of the almost 50 miles of railway was estimated at only £280,000. One of the many myths about Robert Stephenson was that all his lines were expensive to construct but, even with the extra work of upgrading the 24-mile Whitby and Pickering Railway for locomotive use, the total expenditure, according to Hudson's accounting, only came to £342,000. **(16)** This was the same as the cost of Kilsby Tunnel on the L&B.

With the exception of the 31-arch Crimple Viaduct outside Harrogate, the engineering works on other Y&NMR routes were not particularly demanding. Most of the rivers were crossed with the, then fashionable, trussed-girder bridges. A departure was the river span of the brick viaduct over the Derwent at Stamford Bridge on the line from York to Market Weighton, where a spandrel-braced cast-iron arch was used. **(17)**

The bridge that was to give rise to the greatest controversy was over the River Aire, at Brotherton, on a branch that had been authorised on 9 July 1847. This three miles long line was initially intended only to give access from the Y&NMR to Knottingley, but eventually, by way of a Lancashire and Yorkshire branch, it tapped the Great Northern traffic from London and East Anglia. (18) As on the contemporary Chester and Holyhead, navigation requirements suggested a tubular bridge, and Robert Stephenson and Edwin Clark came up with a design that saved an amazing 300 tons when compared with a land span tube of the Britannia Bridge, which was only five feet longer (see Chapter 6). Dispensing with the cellular construction and reducing the cross section of the tubes achieved this saving of over 60%. The reduced cross section meant that the tubes, though 20 feet deep, were very narrow, and gave limited passing clearances for rolling stock. (Fig. 7.4c) Although it was only ten feet wide at carriage window level Captain Wynne R. E., for the Board of Trade, approved the first tube for traffic on 2 July 1851, but he formally refused the identical second tube, on 4 November, because of the limited clearances to Great Northern trains, which had begun to use it. **(19)**

Robert gives some details of the tubes, which were fabricated at his Newcastle works, and explains how the clearances were improved: -

'The weight of one tube is as follows: -

Between the bearings the wrought-iron	198 tons
On the bearings the wrought-iron	13 tons
Cast-iron on the bearings	14½ tons
Cast-iron in rollers and plates	9½ tons
Total weight	235 tons

'The rigidity of the tube exemplifies remarkably the advantage of solid or closed sides in diminishing deflection. A circumstance also occurred in the construction of this bridge which illustrates one of the great advantages peculiar to tubes, viz., their independent strength.

'The form given to these tubes is not rectangular, but the top was narrower than the bottom, so that their section was slightly pyramidal; their [outside] width at the bottom was 11 feet 10 inches, and at the top only 11 feet. Now, after the opening of the bridge, the width at the level of the carriage windows was objected to by the government inspectors, although they had previously sanctioned the width on the first tube erected. It became necessary, therefore to widen the tubes, and this was done in a very interesting manner, viz., by literally opening the top of the tube down a centre line throughout its length, and inserting in the opening a longitudinal plate, 10 inches broad, from end to end. In this manner the sides were evidently moved farther apart to a lesser extent at the level of the carriages. By these means, and the removal of a portion of the projecting rib of the T irons, the whole was sufficiently widened. No other form of beam could evidently have retained its form during so extraordinary an operation.' (20)

At the time that the bridge was built carriages were less than 7 feet 6 inches wide, but at the beginning of the twentieth century widths were approaching 9 feet, and the tubes were replaced between 1901 and 1903, by (less than satisfactory) Whipple Murphy trusses.

George Hudson had betrayed his Midland lines' interests by allowing the Great Northern trains to run over the line, and this contributed to his downfall in 1849. In 1853, when Robert's former assistant, T. E. Harrison, made his successful proposal for the amalgamation of three companies to form the North Eastern Railway, the Y&NMR had expanded, within Yorkshire, to control 225 miles of railway. It had absorbed the Whitby and Pickering, York to Knaresborough, Leeds to Selby, and leased the Selby to Hull; it had also built 130 miles of its own lines. (21)

York to Berwick

A satellite of the Stanhope & Tyne was a five-mile branch, which left it Washington, crossed the River Wear, and ran south in an attempt to tap further traffic. It was authorised on 16 June 1834 as the Durham Junction Railway, and completed to Rainton Meadows in August 1838. James Walker, then president of the Institution of Civil Engineers, had suggested that the design for the superb Victoria Bridge, with its 160-foot main span over the Wear, should be based on Trajan's Bridge at Alcantara, in Spain; T. E. Harrison was the engineer for the works. **(22)** In the story that will unfold it was destined to become a far more important part of the railway network than the projectors could have envisaged.

The 80-mile-long Great North of England Railway (GNER) had been projected from York to Newcastle. The shorter section, north of Darlington, had been authorised on 4 July 1836, and the remainder on 12 July 1837, with a total capital of £1,330,000. When the directors were unable to obtain acceptable tenders for the northern end, they decided it was more sensible to build the much easier southern end first and get a connection with the lines from London. However, in 1841, when the still-rising cost exceeded £1 million, the company could not proceed north of Darlington. **(23)**

Robert became involved in the York to Darlington section soon after its delayed opening to freight traffic on 3 January 1841, when an overbridge collapsed. The engineer for the line, with the exception of the major bridges over the Ouse and Tees, had been Thomas Storey. **(24)** Extremely bad weather during construction, and an understandable, but unwise, decision to try to earn revenue as soon as possible, meant that a number of bridges and some earthworks were not ready to bear the weight of traffic. Following Storey's resignation on 18 January, the directors asked Robert to take over as Engineer-in-Chief, and complete the remedial works that were needed before the railway could be used safely. This work was speedily completed, allowing the line to be opened for all traffic on 30 March 1841. **(25)** Branches to the west of the main line were opened to Richmond, Boroughbridge and Leeming Bar on 10 September 1846, 17 June 1847, and 6 March 1848, respectively.

In 1841 a Parliamentary Commission was of the dubious opinion that the traffic between London and Scotland was only sufficient to justify one route, and it favoured a West Coast line via Carlisle. **(26)** This report certainly stiffened the resolve of the projectors on the East Coast, and fortunately the forceful George Hudson came into the picture. The Stephensons had always wanted to link the Thames to the Tyne, and eventually to Scotland, by rail, so here was a chance of furthering their aim, and improving the prospects of the Stanhope & Tyne in the process. In April 1841, Robert reviewed the proposed GNER route, north of Darlington; this was very similar to the present main line except that the most expensive central section veered to the east of Durham. He adopted the bones of a scheme suggested by Nicholas Wood and T. E. Harrison in 1838, for building the first 17 miles of the original GNER line, almost as far as Shincliffe, getting seven miles of new railway authorised, and then making use of the bankrupt, or almost bankrupt, existing lines at the north end. **(27)** The use of the Durham

Junction and parts of the S&T and Brandling Junction Railways, although making a longer and more easterly route, would, Robert envisaged, provide a line from Rainton to Gateshead. This would not only avoid the immediate construction of 13 miles of new railway but also improve the fortunes of these companies out of all recognition. A short branch could serve Durham, and connections already existed to Sunderland and South Shields.

Hudson skilfully arranged the finance, and the Act permitting this scheme, known as the Newcastle and Darlington Junction Railway (N&DJ), was authorised on 18 June 1842; the company was allowed to raise capital of £500,000 and loans of £166,000. Five miles north of Darlington, the N&DJ was still only one mile to the east of the S&D main line, but Hudson was adamant that he wanted an independent railway, and, despite some opposition, he got away with it. **(28)** This was fortunate, as the S&D alignment, through the later suburbs of Darlington, would not have allowed for high-speed running, though the Stephenson line, squeezing through the shallow valley of the River Skerne, at Aycliffe, would have benefited from easier curvature. **(29)**

In order to keep costs as low as possible, the expensive original GNER route continued to be reviewed, and the main deviations proposed by Robert Stephenson were, '...to avoid very heavy works through the high ground near Croxdale and a bank which would have been 100ft. high over Shincliffe valley, also a long tunnel under Gilligate [Gilesgate] Moor, near Durham.' **(30)** These were authorised by Parliament on 11 April 1843. Due to 'the unlimited energy of Mr. Hudson' this Act had been processed in just four weeks, an achievement for which 'there is no parallel in railway history.' (31) Initially a deviation near Aycliffe did not work out. It took the line through marshy areas known as Mordon, Bradbury and Preston Carrs in preference to the shorter GNER route which followed the Great North Road, to their west, and then skirted round the north of them. This resulted in the tighter curves at Aycliffe, and meant forming the embankment on a raft of 3-inch planks, which was far from successful. When the railway opened, it was reported that a train on this section, 'receives an undulatory motion distinctly felt by the passengers.' (32) A further report, in January 1846, said that the severe delay caused by the subsidence on Mordon Carr 'has now been obviated by a substantial deviation,' and repairs were being carried out with 'deep piling, driven to an immense depth, so that, when finished, this portion of the line will be as firm as any in the kingdom.' (33)

Overall, the deviations did allow far more economical and speedier construction, reducing the total costs to £18,000 from the estimated £20,000 per mile; '...the first time in the history of railways the actual expenditure would be less than the estimate.'(34) It had been intended to lease the Durham Junction, but these savings permitted its purchase in 1844 at a reasonable price of £88,500; the Victoria Bridge alone had cost £40,000 to build.

The excavation quantities averaged 80,000 cubic yards per mile, and all the contracts for this work and the structures were let between November 1842 and June 1843, for a total of £170,000. The length, including the branch to Durham, was 28 miles. In contrast, when the GNER sought tenders in 1837 for just nine miles near Durham, the lowest quote that they could get was £185,000. **(35)** The contract for the three-and-a-half-mile section north of Shincliffe was to boast three spectacular timber viaducts; this was unusual for a Stephenson line. These came about because the first mile-and-a-quarter of this contract crossed the valleys of the Shincliffe, Cassop and Sherburn Becks, with depths, below formation levels, of 63, 42 and 62 feet, respectively. The problem was that the total material excavated from the cuttings over this length was only 15,000 cubic yards, and five times this amount of fill was required to form an embankment just over the first valley. The spoil produced from the deeper cuttings at the north end of the contract, was already spoken for to cross another valley occupied by the Durham and Sunderland Railway. (36) The prospect of getting any fill from the works further south was dependent on the passing of the second Act, which meant a delay of at least six months. Rather than excavate extensive borrow pits or haul material long distances, it was decided that it would be cheaper and quicker to provide timber viaducts. T. E. Harrison is given the credit for designing them, and they were described in the *Railway Chronicle,* in 1844, as 'amongst the finest specimens of the adaptation of timber to bridge building, which, up to that time, had been designed'; their cost came to £18,700. (37) Enough land was purchased so that they could be replaced by embankments at a later date.

The opening of the railway on 18 June 1844 was exactly two years after the passing of the first Act; credit must be given to the skilful engineering, and to the very competent contractors who had achieved this. One of the major contracts was completed in only 44 weeks, and very tight schedules were imposed for the completion of all the station buildings. The board had only approved the architect, G. T. Andrews', plans for the substantial terminus at Gateshead on 14 February 1844, but the building was ready for the opening 17 weeks later. (38) A special train running the 303 miles from Euston to Gateshead in 12½ hours (stoppages accounted for 2¾ of these hours) triggered the celebrations of the opening day. This was the first time that anyone had covered a distance of over 300 miles in such a short time. (39)

It was inevitable that the roundabout route using part of the original S&T line and most of the Brandling Junction must soon cease. This happened on 1 October 1850 when a cut-off line, originally proposed by Wood and Harrison in 1838, between Washington and Pelaw, was opened to passengers, reducing the journey by three miles. During the late 1860s embankments replaced the timber viaducts. The present main line, serving Durham, was completed by 15 January 1872, and the original route, subsequently referred to as the 'Old Main Line', then served as an important secondary route. Six substantial viaducts carry the later line; four were purpose built and two were inherited from the 1857 Durham to Bishop Auckland branch. The large and prosperous North Eastern Railway Company, with an assured future, could easily afford these and the other expensive engineering of the new line.

The decision to terminate the 1844 main line on the south bank of the Tyne was a great disappointment to Newcastle, and, for a time, frustrated the long-term local ambitions for another bridge across the river. Robert Milne had replaced the medieval bridge at Newcastle, destroyed by the great flood of 1771, with a stone arch structure at a similar height. The torturous descent or ascent of around 90 feet between the town centres and the bridge was always a cause of great inconvenience and expense. Between 1771 and 1843 there were no less than 17 proposals for additional bridges at Newcastle. These included practical and impractical schemes for road or rail bridges at high and low levels; the majority favoured high-level crossings, upstream of the old bridge. In November 1843 three proposals for high-level road or rail bridges were deposited; two were by architects, J. & B. Green and John Dobson, and the third, and least practical, was by the Newcastle entrepreneur, Richard Grainger. In 1836 Grainger had proposed a main line railway crossing the river at a low level well upstream of Newcastle. He had only intended to serve the town centre with a steeply inclined branch. This provoked the Town Council into resolving on 9 November 1836 that the Tyne should be bridged at a height that would allow railway companies to run locomotives into the centre of town on any proposed route. (40)

The Greens had first proposed a bridge in 1839, but it remained in a state of flux with regard to the design, material to be used in its construction, and what it was to carry; only its position was fixed, on the site finally to be used for Robert's High Level Bridge. Financial support was forthcoming for a High Level Bridge Company, so Hudson backed the Greens' scheme for a *road* bridge with certain conditions; the main one being that the total cost would not exceed £100,000. (41) With the Newcastle Council's agreement, he had the proposal included in a Newcastle and Darlington Junction Act and this received Royal Assent on 4 July 1844. (On the same day the North British Railway had been authorised to build a far more positive contribution to the East Coast route - the 57-mile line from Edinburgh to Berwick!) A month later, at the N&DJ half-yearly meeting, on 5 August, Hudson reported the Stephensons estimated that the line from Newcastle to Berwick would cost the relatively low figure of £700,000, for the 66 miles, exclusive of the two major bridges. He added 'the subject of crossing the Tweed and Tyne was engaging the attention of the engineers; and he hoped that some feasible plan would be devised by which they could form a continuous railway through Newcastle.'

Although the Stephensons wanted very much a through trunk line to Scotland they backed the Greens' plan, and Robert even became designated as joint engineer for the high-level road bridge. They all must have realised that a railway bridge over the Tyne and a station in central Newcastle would be phenomenally expensive. A practical plan to cross the Tyne at Bill Quay, two miles downstream of Newcastle, had been suggested by T. E. Harrison in 1836. A railway bridge at this relatively narrow point on the river would achieve a shorter link between the line from the South and the proposed alignment of the Newcastle and Berwick much more economically. Newcastle could be served both from Gateshead, by the proposed road bridge and by a rail connection to the Newcastle and North Shields Railway on the north side of the river. In February 1844, a number of Newcastle councillors were quite happy for this to happen, and the Mayor, Sir John Fife, even said, 'It was in the interest of a large town like that [Newcastle] to have as many termini in or as near as possible; **and not that continuous lines should pass through it.**' (42) Less than twelve months later, when the Newcastle and Berwick Act was being projected, the council had a volte-face and insisted on a single station in Newcastle and a railway through the town!

I. K. Brunel's Northumberland Railway was put forward in opposition to the Stephensons' Newcastle and Berwick Railway (N&BR) by. This came about because the N&BR had offended a prominent landowner, Lord Howick. **(43)** Although the N&BR had amended its plans to avoid Lord Howick's property, Brunel had stepped in with what he hoped was a more acceptable westerly route, which was to use atmospheric propulsion. Brunel had intended to use Hudson's Gateshead station to start his 'Gateshead Branch', crossing the Tyne about half-a-mile upstream, and turning east to terminate at the site of the present Central Station. In order to continue north the trains would have to reverse and negotiate a very tight curve to plunge into a 2,400-yard long tunnel under central Newcastle. (44)

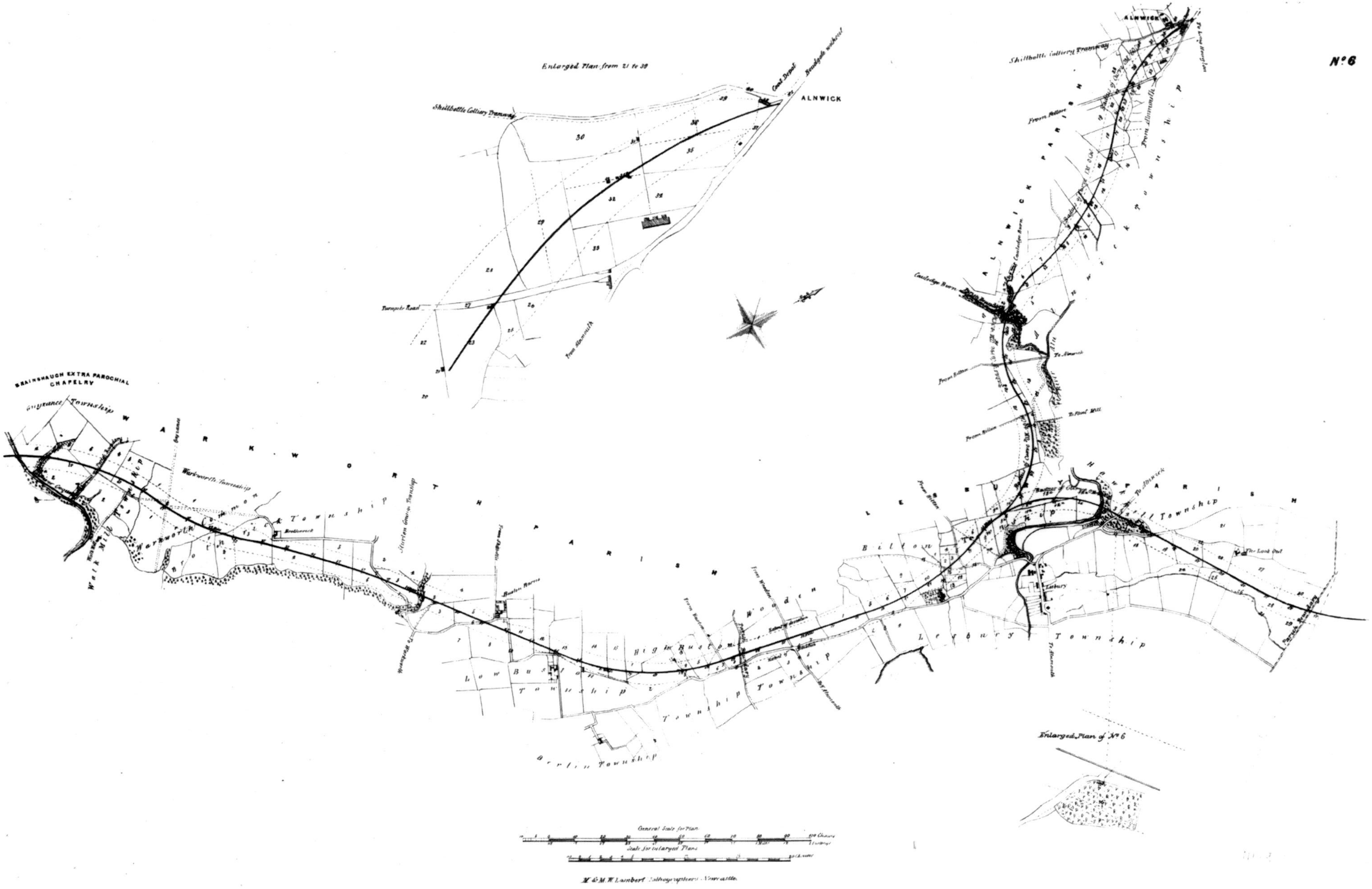

Figure 5.1: part of the deposited plan for the Newcastle and Berwick, showing the main line and the Alnwick branch. The sharp curve near the junction was caused by the deviation westwards needed to avoid Lord Howick's objections.

By November 1844 Hudson had apparently changed his mind as the deposited plans for the Stephensons' N&BR showed a high-level railway bridge over the Tyne, with its approach bypassing the brand new Gateshead station. However, the Councils of both Newcastle and Gateshead were suspicious that Hudson might not wish either to build the bridge, or subscribe to a joint station with the Newcastle and Carlisle Railway. They insisted that a clause be put in the Act depriving the railway '...of the power to take toll on any part of the line between Newcastle and Berwick, unless the bridge over the Tyne, and the line through the town, were completed [in accordance with the plan] within the term of five years from the passing of the Act'. A footway could be easily incorporated in the bridge but Newcastle also wanted a carriageway, and, after consulting Robert as to its feasibility, Hudson reluctantly had to acquiesce to this also. With the Brunel scheme and Joseph Locke's Caledonian Railway, to complete the West Coast route, from Carlisle to Edinburgh and Glasgow, also being proposed in the same parliamentary session, Hudson could not afford any delays. He got the Council's backing to the Newcastle and Berwick Bill at a very high price. The mile long link, including the High Level Bridge, the 'Grand Central Station' and their approaches, was to cost three times as much as the N&DJ and the Durham Junction together - over 30 miles of railway.

The rival East Coast Bills came before a Parliamentary Committee in May 1845, and Robert Stephenson successfully answered all objections regarding the design and position of the bridge, its approaches, and the rest of the line. He estimated that the road deck on the High Level Bridge would add between £15,000 and £20,000, and that the diversion to avoid Lord Howick's objection would cost another £30,000. (45) The Northumberland Railway supporters formally withdrew their opposition to the N&BR on 28 June 1845, and the Act was passed on 31 July 1845. The Act reduced the time for completion to only four years, and specified that the N&DJ should pay £100,000 towards the cost of the railway bridge, in order to be released of its commitment, under the previous Act, to build the road bridge. Included in the N&B Act were branches to Amble, Alnwick and Kelso, and powers to use a short section of the Newcastle and North Shields Railway immediately outside Newcastle. In all 95 miles of railway together with the High Level Bridge, 10 viaducts and 250 bridges had to be completed.

The first contract was let within a month of the Act being passed, and the main line was opened from the Manors (Newcastle) terminus of the Newcastle and North Shields Railway as far as Tweedmouth between 1 March and 1 July 1847. In order to permit this rapid opening all the viaducts, with the exception of the one at Alnmouth, were temporary timber structures of the same design as those used on the N&DJ. A temporary viaduct was opened over the Tyne on 29 August 1848, and over the Tweed on 10 October 1848, permitting through East Coast running to Scotland for the first time. All the temporary structures also aided the building of the permanent ones adjacent to them. The main lines north of York had become known as the York, Newcastle and Berwick Railway in August 1847, and the opening between Newcastle and Tweedmouth allowed the revenue of the system to rise rapidly to over £10,000 per week. Joseph Locke's steeply graded Caledonian Railway, which had been authorised on the same day as the N&BR, had reached Edinburgh on 15 February 1848, but this line had no really demanding engineering works.

The building of the High Level Bridge was to present the greatest challenge, and take the longest time to complete - it was, in fact, to take longer than the four years stipulated in the Act. The cause of the delays was the condition of the river bed, and the difficulty of getting sound foundations for the piers. The site chosen was just upstream of the old Tyne Bridge, and at this point the river had a maximum depth of only three feet at low tide, and a width at high tide of between 515 and 520 feet. Unfortunately there was 40 to 50 feet of sand, almost like quicksand, between the river bed and the bedrock. The engineers knew from their preliminary investigations that it would be necessary to drive long timber piles through the sand to the bedrock to obtain a sound base on which to build the masonry piers. The height from the bedrock to the superstructure was some 140 feet; 'Such a foundation for so lofty a structure rendered it necessary that the whole design should be as light as consistent with safety.' (46)

The height of the rails on the bridge had to be nearly 120 feet above ordnance datum to suit the levels of the existing Brandling Junction and Newcastle and North Shields railways on either side of the river. In order to avoid the expense of double width piers, and other complications, the road and the rails had to be at different levels; placing the road at the lower level fitted in well with both townscapes. A carriageway width of 20 feet and two six foot footways gave the exact width for a three-track railway on the top deck.

The Admiralty had specified in the Act that there should not be more than three piers in the river; this gave four spans of 125 feet. Robert added an extra span on each side of the river to tie back to the land arches, as it was too expensive to carry the masonry arches down to its edge. The piers were made as light as possible by means of large arched openings and voids in the ashlar on each side of them. The voids were only filled with rubble, set in mortar, from the bottom of the piers to about six feet above high tide to prevent the ingress of water. (Fig. 5.2) Even with these measures each pier was to weigh 5,000 tons and cost £11,000. It must be stressed that with any other design of superstructure than the one chosen, the figures would have been a lot higher.

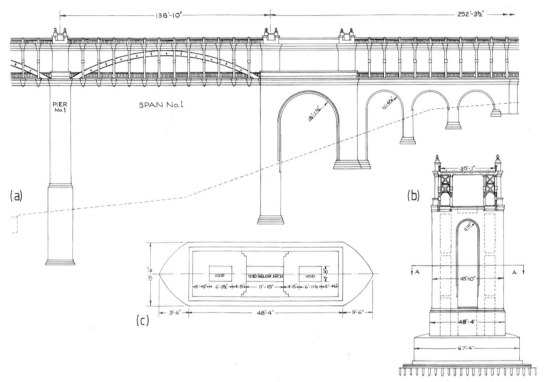

Figure 5.2: (a) elevation of span No. 1 and the Gateshead approach to the High Level Bridge (b) section through a main span (c) section of a pier. J. F. A. based on Network Rail originals.

Figure 5.3: an engraving from the Illustrated London News *for 1 September 1850 showing details of the High Level Bridge road deck.*

The prototype selected for the superstructure went back to canal bridges on the London and Birmingham, the first being at Long Buckby, and the second, and much better known, over the Regent's Canal in London. It should be recalled that these used tied or bowstring cast-iron arches, with their decks suspended from the arches by wrought-iron rods. (See Fig. 4.13) This form of construction was particularly valuable where the ground conditions were dubious as no sideways thrust was transmitted to the piers or abutments, and, if a little settlement did take place, the tied arch could accommodate it without the problems associated with ordinary arches. Little ingenuity was needed to modify and strengthen the L&B design for the High Level Bridge, and Robert Stephenson described how it was achieved in the eighth edition of the *Encyclopaedia Britannica*: -

'Each span is crossed by four main arched ribs with horizontal tie-bars to resist the thrust. The upper roadway rests upon the arches, the lower is suspended from them by wrought-iron suspension rods.

'Each arch is cast in five segments, strongly bolted together, and when entire is 125 feet in span, with a rise of 17 feet 6 inches from the centre of the tension bars, and 18 feet 1½ inch from the upper surface of the bed plates. The depth of the arch at the crown is 3 feet 6 inches, and at the haunches 3 feet 9 inches. The section is that of a double-flanged girder, the flanges being 12 inches wide, and 2 inches thick on the outer arches, and 3 inches thick in the internal arches, which have a greater weight to support. The vertical ribs are the same thickness as the flanges.

'The ties consist of flat wrought-iron bars, 7 inches by 1 inch of best scrap iron, with eyes of 3½ inches diameter, bored out of the solid, and pins turned and fitted closely.

'Each external [arch] rib is tied by four of these bars, and each internal by eight. The sectional area of each external tie is 28 [square] inches, and of each internal tie 56 [square] inches, giving a total area of 168 square inches. These bars were all tested to 9 tons per square inch.'

The drawings and specifications for the bridge were ready by June 1846, and the contracts for the masonry and ironwork were let in July and August. The main contractor for the ironwork was Hawks, Crawshay & Sons, of Gateshead, whose tender was accepted at £112,000. John Rush and Benjamin Lawton, of York, won the contract for the bridge piers and the land arches together with the long viaduct through Newcastle for a total of £176,500. The Gateshead approach viaduct was let to Wilson and Gibson, of Newcastle, for £9,861.

The demolition of property needed to build the bridge and its approaches, together with the viaduct from the proposed Central Station to join the Newcastle and North Shields at Manors, required 130 families in Gateshead and 650 in Newcastle to lose their homes. Most of them were tenants, and would only get small compensation, but the owners of the property expected a fair market price for their buildings. The amount paid out for land and compensation for the whole project was £135,000, over one quarter of the total cost.

Before any bearing piles could be driven, to support the piers within the river, substantial timber cofferdams had to be constructed. Their internal dimensions were 76ft 6in by 29ft, and they were formed by two rows of timber sheet piling set four feet apart, and strengthened by 12in square gauge piles also four feet apart. The inner row of gauge piles was driven down to the bedrock or as deep as the hand-worked pile drivers could get them; the outer row was driven 16 to 30ft. below low water level, and the timber sheeting a little less. The tops of the cofferdams were just above high water level, and the silt and sand between the two rows of sheeting was excavated and replaced by puddle clay to a depth of almost 30 feet to help to resist the ingress of water.

James Nasmyth (1808-1890) had designed a steam pile driver, which had first been employed at Devonport Docks in 1845. On 19 March 1846 the railway directors decided, on Robert's recommendation, 'to purchase a pile driving machine, including a small winding engine, for driving 48ft piles, from Nasmyth & Co. at £1,150 for the High Level Bridge foundations.' The machine had a 1½-ton ram that had a fall of 2 ft 9 ins and was capable of delivering 60 to 70 blows per minute to the head of the pile. The winding engine was used to haul the next pile upright whilst the previous pile was being driven. Prior to the invention of this machine the ram had to be laboriously raised by man, horse or, very occasionally, steam power prior to each blow on the pile. Samuel Smiles gives an amusing description; 'By the old system, the pile was driven by a comparatively small mass of iron descending with great velocity from a considerable height – the velocity being in excess and the mass deficient, like the momentum of a cannon-ball, rather for destructive than impulsive action.'!

This was the first use in bridge construction of the Nasmyth machine, although the hand-operated machines still had to be used for auxiliary work and for the cofferdams. The hand-operated machines were not quite as bad as Smiles described. Tests showed that an ordinary ram, weighing ¾-ton, when allowed to drop 16 feet, had the same driving power as the Nasmyth machine, under reasonable conditions. The difference was that it took four minutes to wind the ram up for the next blow, which compared unfavourably with the steam hammer's 70 blows per minute!

Clause 26 of the Act required the company to commence building the High Level Bridge within six months, and as the designs were still incomplete 'some show of work should be made', so a test pile was driven on 24 April 1846. Contemporary accounts vary, but at least 100-tons of pig iron were allowed to remain, on the head of the pile, for several days without any settlement being apparent. The first permanent bearing pile was driven on 1 October 1846, and it gave very optimistic results as 'a depth of 32ft. was attained in four minutes'. If it had all been as easy as this the work of driving 20,000 feet of piling could have been completed within a month. Because the ground became more resistant with every pile driven the technique was to drive the centre piles first, and then to work outwards. The piles were of Memel or the tougher American rock elm, and in several instances the heads of the latter burst into flames and burnt fiercely because of the heat generated by the rapid action of the machine. The problems were explained in Robert's own words: -

'Many difficulties occurred in driving the piles which considerably retarded the progress of the work, and, among others, the peculiar effect of ebb and flow during the operation is worthy of note. At flood tide the sand became so hard as almost totally to resist the utmost efforts of driving, while at ebb the sand was quite loose, allowing of doing so with facility. It was therefore found necessary to abandon the driving on many occasions during high water. Another difficulty arose from the quicksands beneath the foundations. Although the piles were driven to the rock bottom, the water forced its way up, baffling attempts to fill in between them; this however was remedied by using a concrete made of broken stone and Roman cement, which was continuously thrown in until the bottom was found secure.'

The piling problems delayed the completion of the bridge by about a year, and, when the cofferdams were eventually sealed from below and pumped out, work could start on the timber bases to support the masonry piers. When driven to their limit the battered and charred heads of the piles would not all be at the same level, and would need to be carefully cut off and mortised to take the 12in. square Memel crowns or sills. The space within the cofferdam, below the sills, was filled with Roman cement concrete to a depth of five feet. Two courses of 3in. planking were laid diagonally across the sills at right angles to each other, and the foundation course of the ashlar for the piers was built directly on top of them. The approaches and the piers were both ready by the middle of 1848, and the first ironwork was placed on the 10 July 1848. The average weight to be carried ultimately, by each of the bearing piles, varied between 50 and 80 tons.

Mixtures of iron from all over Britain were tested, and the best was selected in February 1847, allowing the first large casting for the bridge to be completed that month. Each casting was loaded with weights greater than those it was likely to carry in service to guard against hidden flaws. The first completed span was erected at the ironworks ready to be proof tested as a unit in July 1847. Confidence in iron bridges, and in Robert Stephenson, had declined since the collapse of the Dee Bridge, two months earlier. When Hudson turned up to view the completed span, already loaded with 700 tons, another 100 tons were added without the slightest ill effect being detected. By comparison when a 120ft.-span wrought-iron bowstring bridge, by Joseph Locke, was proof tested with only 240 tons at Fox Henderson's works, two months later, it deflected almost 3¾ inches, suggesting that, although it was adequate for its purpose, 800 tons would have irreparably damaged it. (47)

The first section of the arch ribs, which weighed about 10 tons, was placed on 10 July 1848, and the bridge was visually intact, from end to end, when a rib for the northern span was completed on 28 April 1849. The ironwork was finished when George Hawks J. P., of Hawks, Crawshay, and Mayor of Gateshead, ceremoniously drove the last key in the tension chain at the Newcastle end. Captain (Sir) Robert Laffan R. E. passed the bridge without any reservations, on behalf of the Board of Trade, on 11 August 1849, and the first passenger train crossed over it at 9.30 a.m. on Wednesday, 15 August. Queen Victoria formally opened it on her return from Scotland, on 28 September, in the presence of a crowd modestly estimated to be 60,000.

It had been decided to form the carriageway with specially shaped 4½-inch hardwood cubes laid on pitch. Around 200,000 of these were required and their slow supply may have been the reason for the road not opening until 4 February 1850. It had been intended that both entrances to the road deck should have magnificent triumphal masonry arches, and a statue of George Stephenson would surmount the one at the Newcastle end and one of Hudson at the Gateshead end. The economies following Hudson's downfall meant that they were never built.

The total cost of the bridge, its approaches and Newcastle Central Station exceeded £600,000, which suggests Hudson's initial reluctance to have been justified. The Gateshead approach included two state-of-the-art wrought-iron box girder skew bridges. The Newcastle viaduct has a still-extant cast-iron bridge, crossing the High Level Bridge approach road, similar to the attractive earlier London and Birmingham designs. A little to its east, the steeply-rising Dean Street is spanned by an elegant, and much-admired, stone arch incorporated in the viaduct.

The buildings of Central Station, together with its 1862 portico, were certainly designed by the Newcastle architect, John Dobson (1787-1865); but whether you consider that the train shed was also designed by him seems to depend on if your sympathies lie with the engineering or architectural profession. (48) **(49)** There is no *absolute* proof either way. **(50)** The engineering stance is Dobson did have some input for the roof design, but Harrison and Stephenson must have made all the basic structural decisions. The civil engineer is, after all, fully responsible for every structure below or above the tracks.

The other major structure on the N&BR, the Royal Border Bridge, crossed the valley of the River Tweed to link up with the North British Railway at Berwick. **(51)** Work did not start on it until 15 May 1847; possibly this late start was due to waiting for the pile driver being released from the High Level Bridge. The bridge was to be a conventional masonry structure with brick arch rings, and 28 spans each of 61ft 6in. Fortunately, only some of the piers in the river needed piling to support them, as, even with Nasmyth's machine, an average of 50 feet of bearing pile was all that could be driven in a day.

The resident engineer for the bridge was (Sir) George Barclay Bruce (1821-1908), the son of Robert's old tutor, presented a paper about it to the Institution of Civil Engineers on 25 February 1851. As major lithic viaducts were two a penny by that date, he concentrated on the more esoteric and original features of the design and construction, so much so that (Sir) John Hawkshaw, when leading the discussion, considered that the paper 'did not sufficiently describe the mode of putting the masonry together.'! (52)

A lesson had been learned from the frequent collapses of other lithic structures during construction, particularly the 1846 'domino collapse' of all 27 arches of Barentin Viaduct in France. As a precaution Robert Stephenson decided that the voids in the piers should be filled with rubble and that extra wide 'bastion piers' should be built; in the event only one was provided, at the mid-point of the viaduct, on the south bank of the Tweed. This bastion demonstrated its worth in preventing a more serious collapse when a pier failed due to the resident engineer not proving its foundations, as instructed. According to Robert: -

> '...the result was, that when six piers, forming one portion, were completed, and the arching was being proceeded with, the foundation of the third pier failed, and brought down the whole of the arching of that portion. The bastion piers [sic], which only increased the cost of the viaduct about £300, or £400, saved the remainder of the viaduct, thus preventing the additional loss of about £5,000, or £6,000. This instance showed that no dependence should be placed on the appearance of foundations, and proved the necessity of making borings.'

A number of features of the design, including the span of the arches, were subjected to critical comments during the discussion following Bruce's paper. Some methods of the mixing of ashlar and rubble in the construction of the piers were considered to be unsafe by experienced engineers. Robert explained that there was no such 'injudicious' mixture here, and gave his reasons for the choice of span:

> 'Now, in the Border Bridge, the piers were entirely faced with ashlar-work, with a hearting of rubble put in, but having no connexion whatever with the ashlar-work itself; in fact, the rubble might sink down through the ashlar without at all disturbing the latter, which really had the whole duty to perform. ... The bridge might be supposed to consist, in its original design, of a pier with two or three chimneys in the interior, and surmounted by an arch. In building a work of such magnitude, it was advantageous to give an additional amount of rigidity to the piers; centres would sometimes fail, and reliance had to be placed on the mass of the pier. He attached no importance whatever, as regarded the stability of the bridge, to the rubble in the piers; it was only like pouring so much sand down a chimney in order to add to its weight.
>
> 'The span of the arches had been well considered by him in arranging the design. The piers, as constructed, were exactly 70 feet apart, and that suited the foundations. He had a design made for the bridge, with larger spans over the Tweed itself, and smaller arches over the land; but he did not like to risk the erection of large centres, in a place where the foundations were decidedly bad, and he, therefore, preferred giving the work a uniform character throughout.' (Fig. 5.4)

The length of the bridge is 2,160 ft; it is built on a curve, and the maximum height of its rails, above the river bed, was quoted as 125 ft. The contractors were MacKay and Blackstock, and the total cost of the structure came to £120,000. This was exactly twice the cost, per foot run, of the 3,000 ft

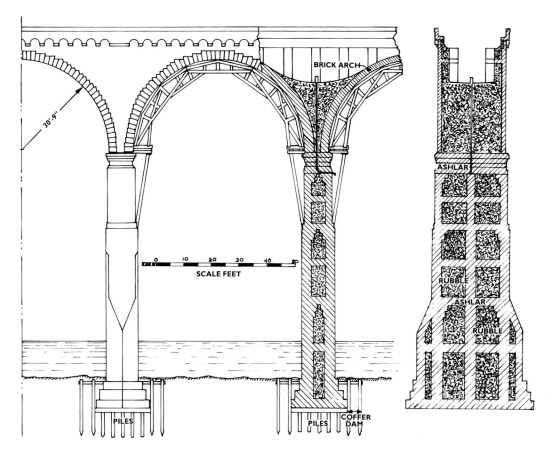

Figure 5.4: the construction details of the Royal Border Bridge. I. C. E./J. F. Addyman.

Figure 5.5: the Royal Border Bridge prior to the addition of the electrification masts. Bill Fawcett.

Plate 1: the 1823 beam engine was the first used to power machinery at Robert Stephenson & Co.; it worked on the east side for 75 years. The engine minus its flywheel is now back on exhibition at South Street, Newcastle, on loan from Birmingham Museum and Art Gallery. Photo J. F. Addyman,

Plate 2: the Leicester and Swannington winding engine designed by Robert Stephenson in 1833. It remained in use until 1948 and is now preserved in the National Railway Museum. J.F. Addyman

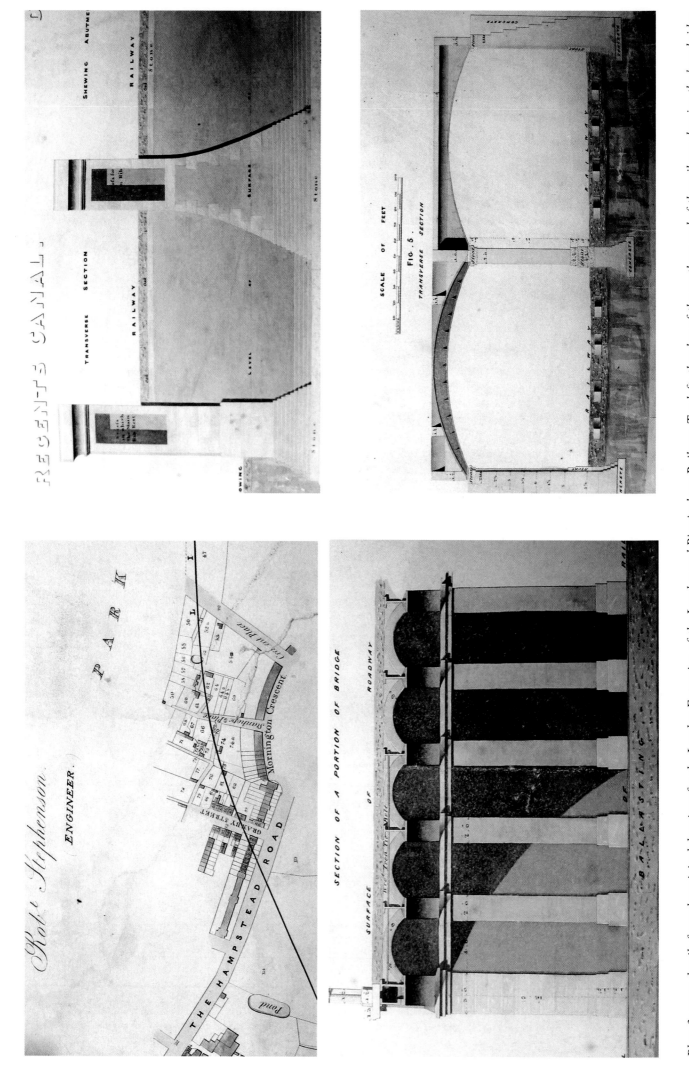

Plate 3: some details from the original drawings for the London Extension of the London and Birmingham Railway. Top left: the plan of the southern end of the railway showing the long bridge that would be needed to get under Hampstead Road and Granby Street. Top right: part elevation of the abutment of the Regent's Canal Bridge. Bottom: sections of Park Street Bridge showing the use of cast-iron beams and brick jack arches.

long adjacent embankment, with its five-arch viaduct, which was included in the same contract. One hundred and five years earlier, England and Scotland had been locked in deadly conflict, so when Queen Victoria formally opened the bridge, on 29 August 1850, it was described as 'the Last Act of Union'. Both the High Level and Royal Border Bridges have carried traffic for over 150 years, and are Listed Grade 1 structures. The High Level Bridge is described in its listing as, 'one of the finest pieces of architectural ironwork in the world.'

The curvature of the Newcastle and Berwick did not make it a very high-speed route. In steam days there were numerous speed restrictions of 60 m.p.h. or less; the Royal Border Bridge and its approach were restricted to 50 m.p.h., and the severe curve through Morpeth station to 40 m.p.h. (53) Morpeth curve is less than a quarter-of-a-mile radius, and was the scene of high-speed derailments in 1969 and 1984. The natural alignment, to the south of the Wansbeck viaduct, would have given a radius of one-and-a-quarter miles, but would have taken the line half-a-mile further from Morpeth. Criticism of the positioning of the intermediate stations between York and Gateshead, where they were all beyond the extremities of their towns, may have led to the sharp curve being used to get the railway nearer to Morpeth. The worst and longest gradients, of 1 in 150 and 1 in 170, were north of Alnmouth, where the railway had been forced to take a more difficult line because of Lord Howick's objections. (54)

The cost of the 'way and works', excluding the High Level Bridge and Central Station, averaged out at a very economical £12,000 per mile for the Newcastle and Berwick. (55)

Following the publication of *The Reshaping of British Railways,* or 'Beeching Report', in 1963, and the subsequent review of trunk routes with the electrification of the West Coast Main Line in progress, the Newcastle and Berwick was to be downgraded. Although the line had just been equipped with modern colour light signalling, singling of the track was considered, and, for a time, permanent way renewals were carried out with second-hand material recovered from lines that were closed by Beeching. The Serpell Committee Report (1982) even recommended complete closure of the line. Fortunately these short-sighted proposals came to nought, and the railway remains part of an increasingly buoyant East Coast Main Line.

The Atmospheric and Gauge Controversies of the mid 1840s

Robert became involved in two controversies during the construction of the lines to the North. The idea of atmospheric propulsion had been around for some time before its first practical demonstration in June 1840. It was welcomed immediately by some very intelligent people as a sort of 'philosopher's stone' that would transform railways. In 1843 a 1¾-mile extension of the Dublin and Kingstown Railway had been opened to Dalkey with atmospheric propulsion, and, after its trial on 19 August, it was described as a 'wonderful and extraordinary development.' The apparent success led a number of railways to consider its use, and in early 1844 the directors of the Chester and Holyhead Railway asked Robert to visit Ireland and report on the system. His report dated 9 April 1844 came to the following conclusions: -

'1st That the atmospheric system is not an economical mode of transmitting power, and inferior in this respect both to locomotive engines and stationary engines and ropes.

'2nd That it is not calculated practically to acquire and maintain higher velocities than are comprised in the present working of locomotives.

'3rd That it would not in the majority of instances produce economy in the original construction of railways, and in many would most materially augment their cost.

'4th That on some short railways where the traffic is large, admitting of trains of moderate weight, but requiring of high velocities and frequent departures, and where the face of the country is such as to preclude the use of gradients suitable for locomotive engines, the atmospheric system would prove the most eligible.

'5th That on short lines of railway, say four or five miles in length, in the vicinity of large towns, where frequent and rapid communication is required between the termini alone, the atmospheric system might be advantageously applied.

'6th That on short lines of railway, such as the Blackwall Railway, where the traffic is chiefly derived from the intermediate points, requiring frequent stoppages between the termini, the atmospheric system is inapplicable; being much inferior to the plan of disconnecting the carriages from a rope, for the accommodation of intermediate traffic.

'7th That on long lines of railway, the requisites of large traffic cannot be attained by so inflexible a system as the atmospheric, in which the operation of the whole depends so completely upon the perfection of each individual section of machinery.' (56)

The report included a number of pressure diagrams which indicated that a maximum partial vacuum of around 7lbs per square inch below atmospheric was the best to be hoped for. He did some experiments with the rope-worked Camden incline, on the L&B, just before it went out of service, and found that the loss of power due to friction and other causes, on an average working, was 45% compared with 74% on the Kingstown and Dalkey atmospheric system. (57)

The Stephensons, Locke, Rastrick, Bidder and Daniel Gooch (58) were strongly against atmospheric railways, but Brunel, Cubitt, Rendel, Macneill *and* Sir Robert Peel, as prime minister, were among those in favour. (59) Posterity has shown who was right, but unfortunately a lot of money and effort was put into this impractical idea before it was abandoned.

When it came to the question of gauge John Francis suggests that only the Stephensons, among the early engineers, were in favour of the standard, 4ft-8½in gauge, and that most others would have preferred something between 5 feet and 5ft-6in. (60) The standard gauge gave only four feet between the plate frames of the locomotives, and it was a very valid point that a slightly increased dimension would have allowed wider fireboxes, larger inside cylinders, and more space for their mechanism. In 1838 a Royal Commission had actually recommended 5ft-3in gauge for railways in Ireland, which was adopted.

In 1835 John Braithwaite had chosen a gauge of 5 feet for the Eastern Counties Railway and James Walker specified the same for the adjoining Northern and Eastern Railway. When Robert was brought in to extend these lines he continued them with the same gauge. However, when it became apparent that they would not remain isolated, but would have to connect with other railways, he made the decision that their gauge must be reduced to standard. The cost of altering the 90 miles of railway and its rolling stock was £52,000. (61) In the late 1830s, the Stephensons with G. P. Bidder also built the 3½-mile-long rope-worked London and Blackwall Railway to the 5 feet gauge of the nearby Eastern Counties. When the rope working was abandoned, in 1849, the gauge was converted to standard. (62)

Isambard Kingdom Brunel decided at a fairly late stage that the Great Western Railway should be built with its gauge almost 50% wider than standard. The dimension chosen for the 'broad gauge' was 7ft-0¼in. This gave, for a short period, advantages of stability and speed over standard gauge railways. However, it soon became apparent that where the Great Western came into contact with other railways the evils of 'the break of gauge' and the problems of transhipment of goods at numerous junctions were very salient. In 1845, only four years after the GWR main line had opened throughout from Paddington to Bristol, a Royal Commission had to be set up to settle the 'gauge question'. Although some engineers still had hankerings for a gauge slightly wider than standard it was obvious that Brunel and Daniel Gooch stood alone in favour of the broad gauge. The Commissioner's report was issued in January 1846, and the Gauge Regulation Act of 18 August 1846 sounded the death knell for the broad gauge. (63) The fact that trains, in countries with sensible railway investment, can run at average speeds of 200 mph on standard gauge track seems to prove its adequacy.

Although arguments still rumble on, as early as 1860 the Proceedings of the Royal Society contained this passage: -

'Mr. Robert Stephenson was considered as the leader in the celebrated discussion, called the "battle of the gauges," ...Events have since proved how correct were his views; and notwithstanding the brilliant talents of his friend, but then opponent, the late Mr. Brunel, the broad gauge did not spread beyond a certain district. It was, moreover, to his strenuous and persistent opposition that was due the rejection of the atmospheric system of traction, attempted to be introduced on the Dalkey, the Croydon, and the South Devon Railways.' (64)

NOTES AND REFERENCES

1.   Tomlinson, pp. 282-4.
2.   Bill Fawcett 1, *A Descriptive Catalogue of the Deposited Railway Plans held in York City Archives,* (1994) YCA DP 2/2.
3.   F. S. Williams, *The Midland Railway,* (1877) p. 39 and Tomlinson, p. 276.
4.   *Report of the Commissioners appointed to inquire into the Application of Iron to Railway Structures.* (1849), p. 332. When asked if he had acted as chief engineer, or as assistant engineer on these, and other railways, he replied, '*Always as engineer in chief.*' The NMR Leeds Committee minutes record that George Stephenson & Son were formally appointed Engineers on 18 July 1836 with joint remuneration of £2,000 per annum. The minutes of Birmingham and Derby Junction give George's resignation from its construction in favour of Robert and J. C. Birkinshaw because of his other commitments.
5.   Jeaff. Vol. 1, p. 239. The minutes and reports annoyingly usually refer to '*Mr.* Stephenson', when it could be George, Robert or even the contractor, John Stephenson.
6.   PRO RAIL530/2 NMR committee minutes, 23 September 1836.
7.   Whishaw, p. 379. A description of the line appears pp. 367-379.
8.   *C.E. &AJ.* Sept. 1839, p. 355 says the railway was only opened as a single line and that doubling was to be completed by early 1840.

9. Y&NMR half-yearly report, 29 Jan. 1841.

10. Fawcett 1, YCA DP 2/9 and 2/10.

11. Ibid. YCA DP 2/21.

12. Bill Fawcett 2, *A History of the York-Scarborough Railway,* (1995) p. 11.

13. Ibid. pp. 16-18. After the Dee Bridge disaster in May 1847, the bridge was propped as shown on p. 18. Due to the raising of the levels, for the 1877 York station, the superstructure was replaced, and the 11-arch viaduct on its approach was buried under an embankment.

14. *York Courant,* 12 Sept. 1844, p. 7.

15. Fawcett 2, p. 13.

16. Ibid. p. 37. The total cost for the double line railways exceeded £500,000.

17. W. Humber, *A Practical Treatise on Cast and Wrought Iron Bridges and Girders,* (1857) plates 11 and 12 give the construction details of this still extant span of the disused viaduct by J. C. Birkinshaw.

18. Tomlinson, p. 484.

19. Brian Lewis, *The Cabry Family,* (1994) pp.37-41. The reason for the BOT refusal of the second tube was that Great Northern trains had started to run through the bridge. Although their carriages were only 7'-3" over bodies, the GNR loading gauge width of 9'-5½" permitted them to mount large lamps on the sides of their stock. Due to the swaying of the trains the lamps were known to foul the ribs of the bridge. The earlier but larger Glenfield Tunnel on the Leicester and Swannington Railway which was 10'-0" wide at rail level and 12'-0" maximum width was restricted to vehicles 7'-7" wide.

20. *Encyclopaedia Britannica,* 8th Edition, 'Iron Bridges' p. 609.

21. Cook and Hoole, *North Eastern Railway Historical Maps,* (1991) p. 16.

22. R. W. Rennison, *Civil Engineering Heritage; Northern England,* p. 67. Also David Bremner, 'Account of the Victoria Bridge …' *Proc. I. C. E.* 1843, Vol. 2, pp. 97-9. When the line from Darlington to Gateshead was opened in 1844 a local newspaper gave the impression that, as R. S. had been responsible for completing the route, he had also designed the bridge. James Walker only claimed to have 'suggested the design', and, R. S. must have advised on its construction with the substitution of the three small arches for the solid abutments at each end of the bridge that so annoyed Walker.

23. Tomlinson, pp. 290, 298. The GNER half-yearly meeting on 6 September 1842 reported that the total expenditure had risen to £1,201,670.

24. Thomas Storey (1789-1859) was related to the Stephensons by marriage, and had practiced as a mining engineer in Lancashire, Shropshire and Wales. He became involved in railways in 1822 when he was asked to assist G. S. in the building of the S&DR; he subsequently became Engineer for the GNER and Bishop Auckland & Weardale Rly. The construction cost per mile of the GNER, excluding land, through such easy country was extremely high. His estimate was £7,921 per mile (Whishaw p. 138) but it cost £14,000 against the contemporary Newcastle & Carlisle's £12,000. The N&C encountered numerous river crossings, and much more rigorous terrain.

25. *York Courant,* 11 March 1841. There are numerous references in this paper over the previous two years to unprecedented wet weather and floods, although global warming was not blamed for them!

26. C. J. A. Robertson, *The Origins of the Scottish Railway System, 1722–1844* (1983) Chap. 5, 'The Battle for the Border' gives full details of all the rival schemes.

27. Tyne and Wear Archives. D/NCP/4/18. Deposited Plans for Northern Union Railway, 1 March 1838. (During this period it was possible to deposit plans in November and March.) Some concern about safety was raised by local M. P., Hedworth Lambton, arising from the lack of scrutiny that the Bill would receive because it was mainly joining together existing railways. R. S. defended the railway at the B.O.T., but Gen. Pasley had to report on 'its fitness as regards safety'. See H. Parris, *Government and the Railways in Nineteenth-Century Britain,* (1965) pp. 57-8.

28. Tomlinson, pp. 433-445. A letter dated 18 Oct. 1841 from R. S. to E. Pease is not against the principle of using the S&D but suggests an additional two tracks to carry the extra traffic.

29. Ibid. plate XXII, shows the extent of the deviations and the relationship of the proposed route to other lines.

30. GNER half-yearly meeting 7 September 1841. Also GNER minutes 21 March 1837 state that they were unable to reach an agreement with contractors for the viaduct proposed at Shincliffe, but no reference was made to an embankment at that time.

31. *York Courant,* 20 June 1844.

32. Ibid.

33. *Doncaster, Nottingham and Lincoln Gazette,* 23 January 1846.

34. *York Courant,* 20 June 1844.

35. GNER minutes 14 February 1837. Tomlinson quotes the excavation as 70,000 cu. yds. per mile. This compares with; 32,000 on the York to Darlington section of the GNER, 142,000 on the L&B, 70,000 on the Grand Junction, and 85,000 between London and Bristol.

36. Details from the original contract drawings in a private collection.

37. Tomlinson, p. 449.

38. Addyman and Fawcett, *The High Level Bridge and Newcastle Central Station,* (1999) pp. 25-29 describes Gateshead Greensfield station.

39. Tomlinson, p. 450.

40. R. W. Rennison, 'The High Level Bridge, Newcastle', *Transactions of the Newcomen Society* Vol. 52 (1980-1) pp. 180-207, expounds all the proposals from 1771 to 1850. A brief summary of this paper appears in Addyman and Fawcett, op. cit. with a map (p. 135).

41. N&DJ minutes, 8 September 1843, also PRO/RAIL 772/71.

42. *Proceedings of Newcastle Town Council 1844,* p.39, (7 Feb.)

43. Lord Howick (1802-1894) succeeded his father (of Reform Bill fame) to become 3rd Earl Grey in 1845. A letter from R. S. to I. K. B. dated 21 March 1845, states, 'I will do all I can, but I fear Lord Howick and he [Hudson] have so misunderstood each other that a reconciliation will be very difficult. Temper has in this instance like many others stepped in, and to all appearance is riding rough shod over reason.'

44. Addyman and Fawcett, pp. 34-70 gives extensive coverage of the design, construction and use of the High Level Bridge.

45. Minutes of Evidence, House of Lords Record Office.

46. Capt. R. M. Laffan R. E. 'Notes upon the High Level Bridge at Newcastle – to be appended to Captain Laffan's report dated August 11, 1849.' Handwritten document P.R.O. MT6 7/101.

47. *The Builder,* 16 September 1848.

48. Addyman and Fawcett, pp. 71-119, gives extensive coverage of the design construction and development of Newcastle Central Station.

49. A number of extravagant claims have been made about Dobson, over the years, particularly by his daughter, Margaret. A more recent, and highly regarded book, *Tyneside Classical,* (1964) by Wilkes and Dodd, although dismissing many of Margaret's claims, states (p. 144) that he designed the High Level Bridge!

50. This conclusion was reached after many hours of 'discussion'. Virtually all major stations had their train sheds designed by engineers, and in many contemporary medium sized stations, like Gateshead, the architect adopted the Euston truss, which had been developed by R. S. Euston trusses had always been used where the tracks were straight, and may never have been considered for a curved site like Newcastle. R. S. must been well aware of the first two arched train sheds in England; at Shoreditch, on the Eastern Counties by J. Braithwaite, and at Liverpool Lime Street by Richard Turner. The French had been using large-span arched roofs for train sheds and public buildings from the early 1840s. There is no indication at all that Dobson had any experience of any roof design in wrought iron. In *The Buildings of England; Northumberland.* (1957) p. 242, (Sir) Nikolaus Pevsner shrewdly points out, 'No attempt at integrating with this iron composition, the buildings or the platforms,'. Would a very capable architect with complete control allow this to happen?

51. The structure was originally named the Victoria Bridge. A later railway definition considered that a bridge became a viaduct when it had four or more spans. By force of habit, although qualifying as viaducts, many famous structures are always known as 'Bridge'. The men who built them were far too busy to worry what they were called!

52. G. B. Bruce, 'Description of the Royal Border Bridge over the River Tweed, on the York, Newcastle and Berwick Railway.' *Proc. I. C. E.,* 1851, Vol. 10. pp. 219-214.

53. As early as 13 Sept. 1838 R. S. had produced a report to a committee to promote a line from Newcastle to Edinburgh. A plan deposited on 1 March 1839 for the Great North British Railway from Edinburgh to Newcastle, via Berwick, was engineered by Grainger and Miller (Scottish end), and George and Robert Stephenson. The line was generally well to the east of the present main line, and was a lot better aligned; there was not a branch to Alnwick, but Morpeth was to be served by one almost five miles long. Tyne and Wear Archives, D/NCP/4/29.

54. Many of the curves, with the exception of Morpeth, were improved prior to the electrification of the route in 1991, so much so that a demonstration train, in Sept. 1991, averaged over 105 m.p.h., between Newcastle and Berwick, on its record-breaking 3½-hour journey from London to Edinburgh. The bypassing of Morpeth curve was considered under the 1955 British Railway's Modernisation Plan, but, by then, housing developments had blocked the only sensible route.

55. *Bradshaw's Guide* 1850, p. 153. The total capital expenditure quoted for the York, Newcastle and Berwick by 1850 was £10¾ million of which nearly £2 million was for the purchase of railways north of Darlington. The railways purchased were: Brandling Junction £K602.6, Durham Junction £K88.5, West Durham £K16, Pontop and South Shields £K325.6, Durham and Sunderland £K300, Wearmouth Docks £K98.8, Sunderland Docks £K93.5, Newcastle and North Shields £K315.7 and Tynemouth Extension £K46.6.

56. R. Stephenson, *Report to the directors of the Chester and Holyhead Railway on Atmospheric Railways,* (9 April 1844), p.40.

57. Ibid. p. 24.

58. R. B. Wilson (Editor), *Sir Daniel Gooch Memoirs and Diary* (1972) pp. 46-7. P. 47 quotes: 'Mr. Robert Stephenson made a careful report on the workings of the Dalkey line after we were there, and arrived at the same conclusion as I did.'

59. C. Hadfield, *Atmospheric Railways,* (1967), pp. 43-5.

60. J. Francis, *A History of the English Railway,* (1851 reprinted 1968) Vol. 2, pp. 64-5.

61. S. Sydney, *Gauge Evidence,* (1846) pp. 100-2.

62. Whishaw, pp. 255-269, gives a description of the line and explains the valid reasons for rope haulage because of the high fire risk.

63. Sydney, pp. xxvi-xxvii.

64. *London Royal Society's Proceedings* Vol. 10 (1859-60), p. xxxii.

CHAPTER SIX: THE CHESTER AND HOLYHEAD RAILWAY.

At the start of the nineteenth century the need for good communications between London and Dublin had become an issue of great political importance. The shortest sea crossing to Dublin was from Holyhead, on the western tip of Anglesey, but the road to the port through North Wales was, in parts, no better than a moderately good modern bridleway. In 1810 Thomas Telford (1757-1834) was asked to survey the route between Shrewsbury and Anglesey, and to suggest improvements. Funds were made available in 1815, and the great developments to the road, particularly through the Welsh Mountains, were completed as far as the ferry over the Menai Strait to Anglesey by 1819. Further improvements, including his outstanding 579 feet-span Menai suspension bridge, extended the route (the present A5) to Holyhead in 1828. Concurrent with the road works, harbour developments at Holyhead, firstly by John Rennie (1761-1821) and then Thomas Telford were completed, reducing the journey times from London to Dublin from 66 to 35 hours.

By 1838 the opening of the London and Birmingham and Grand Junction Railways had brought rail access from London to Liverpool, while the use of the sea crossing from Liverpool to Dublin, though twice as long as the one from Holyhead, had reduced overall journey times to less than a day. As Robert Stephenson had pointed out, further improvements '...could only be accomplished by extending the land journey and diminishing the sea voyage, or, in other words, by increasing the comparatively certain, and diminishing the uncertain part of the journey.' This could be achieved either via Holyhead or by avoiding the crossing to Anglesey and building a new harbour at Porth Dynllaen, almost 30 miles south-west of Bangor. C. B. Vignoles investigated the choice of routes to Porth Dynllaen by either following the north coast of Wales from Chester, or by taking more southerly routes involving crossing the mountains. Prior to 1840, George Stephenson and Francis Giles had each surveyed routes from Chester to Holyhead, but both intended to eschew the use of locomotives over the Menai and use Telford's suspension bridge for the carriages. An intermediate scheme, eliminating most of the difficult engineering works, but doing little for the journey times, was to build a harbour at Ormes Bay (Llandudno).

Figure 6.1: a 1940's postcard showing the Menai Straits and the Stephenson and Telford bridges from the air. The headland at Penmaenmawr that the railway had to skirt can be seen faintly in the top right hand corner. Author's collection.

During the early 1840s, various Government reports had indicated that a Chester and Holyhead Railway (C&HR) should be built, together with a railway bridge over the Menai, and further improvements to the harbour. Strangely, after what had happened on the Grand Junction, there was a suggestion in December 1843 that Joseph Locke and George Stephenson should work together on the railway. There must have been an important reason why the company wished to re-involve Locke with George Stephenson, but, whatever it was, the task inevitably fell to Robert under his commitment as

Engineer-in-Chief to 'George Stephenson & Son'.

The first Act for the railway received Royal Assent on 4 July 1844, but it omitted the significant five miles, which included the Menai crossing. Robert was appointed Engineer-in-Chief after the Act was passed, and he inherited the very daunting problem of finding a way to bridge the Menai Straits. (1) He was brave enough to accept the challenge despite having plenty of work in hand, in England and abroad (see Appendix 7). The Trent Valley and the Newcastle and Berwick were to go ahead in the next year, and instead of delegating virtually all the work on the latter to T. E. Harrison, he could have enjoyed himself by working in Northumberland again. The C&HR was to cause him more grief and worry than all his other works put together. I. K. Brunel was another of the very select number of engineers who could have built a Menai Bridge at that time. He had been involved in schemes, between 1839 and 1845, for a heavily graded railway from Worcester to Porth Dynllaen, which avoided the Menai crossing. If Stephenson, or Brunel had not accepted the task possibly a committee would have been set up, and it would be very interesting to know what they would have come up with.

The Menai Strait varies in width from 1,000 ft. to three-quarters of a mile, and to the south-west of Telford's bridge there are a number of rocky islets. One of these, called Britannia Rock, was conveniently placed right in the middle of one of the narrower parts of the Strait, and was large enough to found a bridge pier. The first option was for an arch bridge, and even though Telford had been refused permission to build one, it was worth having another try with the Admiralty. (2) As the Government wanted the railway, and steam vessels were starting to replace sailing ships, there was hope of a relaxation of the rules. Unfortunately, steam was not ousting sail with the same rapidity that railways were replacing stagecoaches and, because of the treacherous currents and baffling winds, the same draconian conditions had to apply. An arch bridge was designed, in outline, (Fig. 6.2), and methods of erecting it were investigated. However, Capt. Vidal R. N's report to the Admiralty, dated 7 April 1845, dispelled any hope of using arches. In order to protect the valid navigation interests he ruled that the clearance above high spring tides, over the whole width of the waterways, had to be 105 ft., and even the pier on Britannia Rock was restricted to a width of 50 ft. (3) The height was not a real problem but the other conditions forced the two main spans up to at least 450 feet; 100ft. longer than the proposed arch bridge, and more than twice the length of any rigid bridge built up to that time. Another restriction was that centring or scaffolding used during the construction of the bridge could not obstruct the channels. The task of designing a rigid railway bridge with these colossal spans, under these conditions, was not just difficult; it was becoming very nearly impossible! Robert wrote, 'I stood, therefore, on the verge of a responsibility from which I confess I had nearly shrunk'. There was the modest consolation that anything devised for the Menai Crossing could be adapted for the 400-foot-span bridge needed at Conwy (invariably spelt Conway in contemporary documents).

Figure 6.2: the unacceptable proposal for the arch bridge; an illustration from Edwin Clark's book.

Every conceivable option was considered for the bridge design, and most were ruled out immediately. A suspension bridge could give the required headroom and length of span but not, as yet, the strength and rigidity required for railway use; contemporary lattice trusses had the same defects, and it would be almost another decade before either was to be used with real success on very large railway bridges. (4) Anticipating that the arch bridge would be refused another idea was germinating in Robert's mind; this was to use a wrought-iron tube large enough for a train to pass through. In order to reduce wind resistance, in the event of a hurricane, early thoughts were that the cross section should be circular or elliptical, about 25 ft. diameter, and he instructed two of his assistants to start preparing drawings on this basis on 13 March 1845. (5) The railway was to be double track so a separate, totally independent, tube would be needed for each line. On 26 April the idea of tubular bridges was put to the

C&HR directors, one of whom was John Laird (1805-1874), a member of the well-known shipbuilding family. Based on his and others' experiences of the extraordinary strength of iron-hulled ships, he was able to reassure Robert that the tubular idea was sound. The Inspector-General of railways, General (Sir) Charles Pasley R. E. (1780-1861), accepted the tubes but insisted that the suspension chains, proposed as an aid during the construction, should be retained as permanent features. (6) Remembering the problems with Capt. Samuel Brown's 1829 suspension bridge for the Stockton and Darlington Railway, at Thornaby, Robert, '...considered there was considerable difficulty and several objections to rendering a flexible chain available for strengthening a rigid platform.' On 5 May 1845 during his evidence to the Select Committee set up to consider the new C&HR Bill he said 'My opinion is, that a tube of wrought iron would possess sufficient strength and rigidity to support a railway train.'(7) He wrote later that his evidence '...was received with much evident incredulity; so much so, that towards the end of that day's proceedings the Committee stated they would require further evidence, and especially that of the Inspector-General of railways, before they could pass the Bill authorising the erection of such a bridge' (8). The Bill received Royal Assent on 30 June 1845.

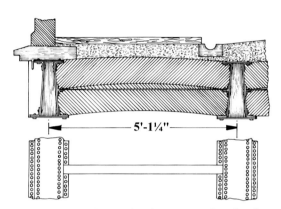

Figure 6.3: perhaps the first example of a box girder railway bridge over the Polloc & Govan Railway in 1841, The Girders were 18" deep and filled with concrete. G. D. Dempsey (1850)

Even the use of wrought iron was to be a novelty. Although it had been used in conjunction with cast iron in a number of early railway bridges, including the Stockton and Darlington's 1825 bridge over the River Gaunless, it did not find favour for a complete bridge until the early 1840s. Reputedly, it was first used, in 1841, for a box girder bridge to carry Carmunnock Road over the Polloc and Govan Railway, near Glasgow, with a span of just 31 ft. 6 in. (9)(Fig. 6.3) In the same year Robert had considered a similar bridge over the River Lea in Ware but had substituted wrought-iron plate girders instead. The reasons for engineers not using wrought iron for bridges were distrust of the material and of riveting, as well as the relatively small size of plates available, and the much higher cost. (10) Even Brunel, who had completed the large hull of the *S. S. Great Britain* in wrought iron in 1843 was currently using timber as an alternative to masonry, brick or cast iron for his bridges.

Having taken on such a task Robert was going to need all the help and advice that he could get. On 14 April 1845 (Sir) William Fairbairn (1789-1874), an old friend from his father's Willington Quay days, visited his office by chance, and as a result of their discussions Fairbairn agreed to conduct the experiments necessary to verify the design of the tubes. He was not the obvious choice; Robert Stephenson's Newcastle works, Vulcan Foundry, William Laird & Sons, or even Vernon & Kennedy could have done the work and come up with the same answers.

The practical problems ultimately to be resolved by the experiments were numerous and Robert explained them in the *Encyclopaedia Britannica* (1856): -

'In the design of the Britannia Bridge, it was [not] the mere arrangement of the material to resist the transverse strain [bending stress] which composed the difficult problem. It was rather the practical construction of any such structure at all; the difficulty of obtaining the materials required, or adopting such that were obtainable to such new purposes, and of devising a beam not merely of sufficient strength for its ultimate use as a bridge, but of sufficient independent rigidity for retaining its form not only when in place, but during its erection on its temporary scaffold, its flotation on unstable pontoons, and the ultimate raising of it into its place suspended isolated from four simple [temporary] chains.' (11)

The idea of reducing the maximum bending stresses by making the Britannia Bridge a continuous four-span structure appealed to Robert. However, it was essential to verify the contemporary very basic understanding of 'beam theory', and Fairbairn suggested that Professor Eaton Hodgkinson (1789-1861), who was the leading British authority on the strength of beams, should be invited to assist with theoretical work; he was available to work on the project from the end of August 1845. (12) The testing of model tubes to destruction started at Fairbairn's Millwall shipyard at the beginning of July 1845. In the initial tests on the tubes failure took place either by the tearing of the bottom plates along the line of the rivets, or by the buckling of the tops of the tubes. This buckling was not anticipated and, as there were no established formulae available to help, trial and error was to be the only way forward. (13) Other facts shown up by the early tests were that wrought iron was disappointingly weaker in compression than had been anticipated, and that the cheaper lap joints would have to be replaced by butt joints with cover plates; both these factors would increase the dead weight of the structures. Eaton Hodgkinson's experiments had suggested that although wrought iron was almost three times stronger in tension it had only 40% of the strength of cast iron in compression.

The experimental work took much longer than anticipated, and in February 1846, the only thing, of real value, which could be reported to the C&HR directors was that the concept of using rectangular tubes was definitely feasible. Contracts for the parts of the railway authorised by the 1844 Act were making good progress, and some work had to start on the bridges. Robert was under some pressure, and he confided to Eaton Hodgkinson, 'I am bound, even at the risk of not having arrived at the very best mode of distributing the material in the tube, to proceed: for the consequence of the delay, in a commercial point of view, after upwards of a million of money has been spent in finishing the works, is not simply the interest, but the loss of income;'(14) Francis Thompson (1808-1895), his architect, had been preparing drawings for the masonry work of both bridges, and provisional plans were ready for contractors to prepare their tenders in March. Frank Forster, one of the resident engineers, laid the foundation stone for the Britannia Bridge on 10 April 1846, and the contractors Messrs. Nowell, Hemingway and Pearson started their three-year task of building the towers and abutments. A month later Alexander Ross performed the same ceremony on the Conwy Bridge, where the contract had been awarded to William Evans. (15)

In March 1846, a personable young man called Edwin Clark (1814-1894) managed to get an interview with Robert Stephenson at his Great George Street office. Although he had negligible engineering experience he was highly intelligent, and had a good working knowledge of mathematics. He was appointed on a temporary basis to do some stress calculations but he was soon given an office of his own together with considerable responsibilities for the bridges. He wrote in jubilation to a close friend, 'I have got put into my hands by Mr. Robert Stephenson all his ideas and wishes about the intended bridge, by far the greatest work ever attempted by mortals … All is at present in embryo. I am sole manager of the plans and sole calculator of all the mathematical work, and have the liberty to perform any experiments.'**(16)** He was not to do all the mathematical work as Professor Airy (1801-1892), the Astronomer Royal, and Professor Pole (1814-1900), Stephenson's technical biographer, had to be consulted on the more complex problems, and Charles Wild, another of Stephenson's bright assistants, was involved. However, Clark was to be of great assistance in the design and erection of the bridges, and in 1850 he was to write an exhaustive two-volume work on them.

The design of the Britannia towers made provision for the use of chains to erect the bridge, but a lot of discussions and calculations failed to produce an elegant solution to the problem of getting the tubes into position. It was estimated that if chains were used for the erection, they could cost as much as £150,000, and the cost of removing them also would be high. However, if they were retained, it was considered that situations could arise, because of thermal expansion, where they would be sustaining either the whole weight of the tubes or none at all. **(17)** On 14 July 1846, while waiting for a train at Crewe station, Edwin Clark saw a small water tank being raised up on its base by 'jacking and packing' and realised that a similar method could be applied to the tubes of the bridges if they could be floated to the bases of the towers. Robert had held strong objections to floating the tubes, because of the rapid tides, but William Fairbairn was enthusiastic and immediately put the proposal in a letter to him. Robert's reply reiterated his caution but eventually, after a lot of argument and discussions, which resulted in defining the method to be used, instructions were given to the architect and resident engineers to alter the designs of the towers of the Menai and abutments of the Conwy to accommodate the floating and raising of the tubes. **(18)**

As early as 20 September 1845 Fairbairn had written a letter to Robert with a sketch closely resembling the final cross section of the tubes, but it was to be another ten months before they started experiments with rectangular cells at the top. (19) A Bavarian engineer, Karl Culmann (1821-1881) gave, in brutal terms, what he considered the reason for the delay. In his *Eiserne Brücken in England und America* (c.1855), he stated that Fairbairn 'had to teach himself by means of the tests, squandering in this manner time and effort to obtain in the end what can be found in any text book of mechanics.' Eaton Hodgkinson also came in for criticism by being initially too involved in theory and not giving enough input to the practical side! **(20)** Edwin Clark's view of the two gentlemen differs somewhat, '…nor can we fail to admire the zeal with which Mr. Fairbairn anticipates the results of the important investigation in which he was engaged, while his sanguine conclusions contrast forcibly with the abstract and minute deductions, the sceptical doubts and fears, of the exact Mathematician.'**(21)** Unfortunately, a lot of the earlier experiments were repeated with variations, which added little to the sum total of knowledge, and in view of the urgency to get the railway completed, one does feel that with more theoretical input the testing could have been streamlined considerably. In July 1846, when the first one-sixth-scale model was made, with a cellular top only, the proportions of the top and bottom of the tube did not even accord with the ratios implied by the earlier tests, and the base failed as it was much too weak. A breakthrough occurred when modifications were made which increased the weight of the model by only 20% but raised its resistance to failure by 2½ times. (22) Gradually the weaknesses were eliminated and the top, bottom and sides of the tubes were proportioned in the most economical way to accept the bending and shear stresses caused by the dead, live and wind loading. **(23)**

The *Encyclopaedia Britannica* (1856) describes the cells and their purpose: -

'These cells are rectangular, there being eight of them in the top and six of them in the bottom, and they run throughout the bridge. With respect to their importance, it must be observed that the whole section of the top of the Britannia tube at the centre is 648.25 square inches, and at the bottom 585.43 square inches, and the tube is 15 feet wide; the thickness of a single plate to ensure this section would therefore have been 2.7 inches* for the top and, and 2.3 inches* for the bottom; and had such a plate been procurable, nothing better could have been desired, and the cells would have been unnecessary ... the arrangement of the plates in cells is almost the only conceivable arrangement possible for obtaining the required section, allowing access, at the same time, to every part for construction and future maintenance. This alone led to their use in the bottom of the tube, where their form was totally unimportant. With respect to the top, however, it was of great importance, since thick plates could not be had, to ascertain the best form of cell for resistance to compression that could be devised with thin plates.' (24) [*The areas quoted are at the centres of the large spans, and include the vertical ribs, but the thickness is calculated without them.]

The tubes increased in depth towards their centres: the Conwy was 22ft. 5in at its ends and 3ft. deeper at its centre, and the Menai was 23ft. 0½in. at its extremities and 30ft. within the Britannia tower.

As late as the end of February 1847 the engineers were still over-correcting for the weaker compressive strength of the wrought iron, and were considering a double row of top cells for the tubes. Edwin Clark wrote to Robert on 25 February submitting that their *modus operandi* may be wrong in this respect. Robert agreed and increased the depth and thickness of a single row of cells to give the required cross-sectional area; this would also make fabrication much simpler. (25) The construction of the first Conwy tube started on 8 April 1847, even though the experiments were still to continue for another month. At this critical stage disaster was about to occur at another part of the railway.

Although the first C&HR Act was passed in July 1844, and Robert Stephenson was approached immediately, it was some time before the contract drawings could be prepared. This was because there were so many schemes for the next session of Parliament that, until after the 30 November deadline for depositing plans, there were just no engineers available for the work. The line was divided into fourteen contracts. The first work started in March 1845, and it was hoped that the whole of the line, including the bridges, could be opened in stages by the end of 1848. Despite all the difficulties, this deadline was met with the exception of the Britannia Bridge. Not all the delays were on the engineering side as lack of funds also slowed the work. The contractors were known and trusted and included: Edward Ladd Betts, Thomas Brassey, William Mackenzie, and John Stephenson; they employed a reliable workforce of up to 13,000 men.

The first mile of the Chester and Holyhead Railway was expensive to construct, requiring a tunnel, a viaduct and a bridge over the River Dee. The bridge was intended to be five brick arches, matching the 45 span approach viaduct, but foundation problems, in 1845, had led to the fatal decision to provide three-span, cast-iron girder bridges, for each of the two tracks. In accordance with a widely-used practice the girders were post-tensioned with wrought-iron trusses. (Fig. 6.4) The iron spans were 98 feet, and not only gave lighter construction than brick arches, but also eliminated two of the troublesome piers in the river.

The railway from Chester to Saltney Junction, where the Shrewsbury and Chester Railway (S&CR) diverged, had passed inspection by Gen. Pasley on 20 October 1846. Passenger trains on the, part-completed, S&CR had started running as far as Ruabon on 4 November, and the bridge was used frequently by heavy works trains for both railways. On the evening of 24 May 1847, a span of the Dee Bridge collapsed under an S&CR passenger train; the locomotive cleared the bridge but the five carriages plunged into the river, and the fireman, guard and three passengers lost their lives. (26) The disaster resulted in a coroner's inquest and a Board of Trade accident inquiry, and in Francis Conder's words '...almost the sole blot on the safe and brilliant course of Mr Stephenson's career'. A fuller account of the bridge failure and the subsequent investigations are given in Appendices 3 and 4. However, Francis Conder's report of a conversation with Timothy Tyrrell, the solicitor of the C&HR,

after the inquest, shows, in a nutshell, the marked disparity between an honest defence and the contentious defence philosophy employed: -

'Why, up to a certain point, your defence was perfect. You proved, by scientific evidence, first, that the bridge ought not to have broken; and, secondly, that, at least from any assignable cause, it could not have broken. You only wanted the witness to prove it did not break, and the case was your own. ...it was impossible not to admire the mode in which you carried your line of defence; but I should like to know why you selected that line?" "What other line was open to us?" was the reply. "It would have struck me in this way," said his interlocutor. "If you had come forward and said, 'Here has been a great calamity; the bridge which has broken was constructed according to the best scientific information of the day. You have in evidence that a hundred bridges are constructed, or in the course of construction, on the same principle; and you have heard some most eminent Engineers of the day state that they approved the principle. The Government Inspector-General of Railways has told you that he sanctioned the opening of the line, and considered the bridge to be safe, from his experience of similar bridges on a smaller scale. The failure of the girder of this great span has been the first intimation, to scientific men, that the formula required revision under altered circumstances. No human wisdom could have foreseen such a result. We are in the presence of a most unhappy, but a most instructive, experiment, which will be a safeguard for the future; and the Company will make every compensation in their power to the families of the sufferers. It must be regarded in the light of a casualty of war." Now if you had taken this line, I do not see how you could have been defeated; and I should like to know why you rather preferred to fight against the facts." "Because," said the Solicitor, "you should never admit any thing, especially with a jury. Between men like you and me, yours would have been, no doubt, the best course, but with a jury never admit anything. You do not know how it may be turned on you.'(27)

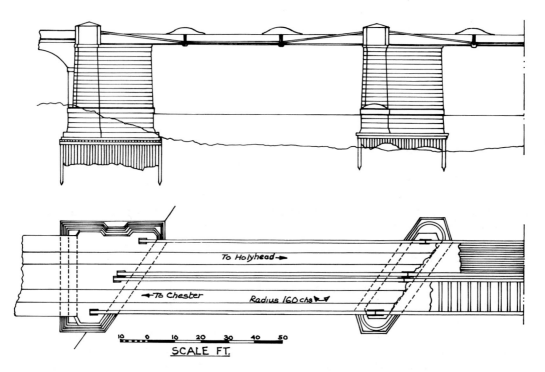

Figure 6.4: part elevation and plan of the trussed girder skew bridge over the River Dee. The 98 feet cast-iron girders were simply supported at their ends. J. F. A. based on the official report.

Despite Mr. Tyrrell's efforts the jury returned a verdict of accidental death, and that the bridge was not strong enough. Thomas Telford had written, in 1812, about the ingenuity and *hazard* involved in building bridges, and this is still very true of today's most spectacular structures, but in the middle of the nineteenth century, with inadequate knowledge of the theory of structures and the behaviour of materials, it was even more so. The Dee Bridge was by no means the first to collapse before 1850. Numerous bridges by prominent engineers had failed due to unforeseen design defects, poor materials, or exceptional weather. Engineers appeared to be quite blasé about them; I. K. Brunel is alleged to have remarked, when one of his bridges collapsed, 'Ah! I'm very glad, for I was just going to build a dozen of them.'! (28) During the 1840s, around six collapses a year were reported in the technical periodicals; most of these were during, or immediately after, construction; among the most spectacular were the viaducts at Barentin (1846), on the Paris and Rouen Railway, and over the Rivers Nidd and Rother, in Yorkshire (1848). Later, reputations rarely survived disastrous failures causing loss of life; Bouch was martyred for the Tay Bridge (1879). Gustave Eiffel designed no more structures, in the remaining 32 years of his life, following the 1891 collapse of his badly designed Warren truss bridge, at Moenchenstein in Switzerland; this resulted in the loss of 71 lives. (29) He had designed and built a number of spectacular bridges, and just two years earlier he had completed his famous tower. Robert Stephenson survived the Dee Bridge, not only because he was held in high esteem, but also because it was only a question of time, with the knowledge then available, before a similar accident could have happened to one or other engineer. His colleagues no doubt felt; 'There but for the grace of God.'

At their half-yearly general meeting, on 11 August 1847, the C&HR directors backed their engineer to the hilt, and did not permit any discussion of 'the lamentable accident'. They stated: -

> 'They have every confidence, however, that the sad event, in whatever way occasioned, will have the effect of leading the able Engineer of the Company to increase, if possible, that care and watchfulness for public safety, for which he has always been so highly distinguished, and in which his own eminent character is so much involved; and that no pains will be spared to insure both the soundness of the plan upon which the great works of this Company are founded, and the excellence of their practical execution.'

A description of the rest of the 85-mile line is appropriate at this juncture, and the brief one given by Edwin Clark is quoted from the point where it describes the railway crossing the Dee: -

> 'Following the embanked channel of this river, and the level shores of its estuary, it crosses the River Foryd by a pile and swing-bridge, and continues its course along the shore through the Rhyddlan Marshes, and through the limestone promontory of Penmaen Rhos, by a tunnel 530 yards long, until stopped by the bold headlands of the Great and Little Orme's Head. It now for the first time leaves the coast, and, passing through the narrow valley that separates these headlands from the mainland, crosses the River Conway beneath the Castle walls by means of the tubular bridge. Passing through the town of Conway and under the walls by a tunnel 90 yards long, it again reaches the coast at the Conway Marshes, and continues its course along the shore through the greenstone and basaltic promontories of Penmaen Bach and Penmaen Mawr, - the terminating spurs of the Snowdon range, by tunnels 630 and 220 yards long respectively, being carried for some distance after leaving Penmaen Mawr, on a cast-iron-girder viaduct over the beach. The sea walls and defences, on the one hand, along the exposed coast, are all on a magnificent scale; whilst, a timber gallery, similar to the avalanche galleries on the Alpine roads, protects the road line from the *débris* that rolls down from the lofty and almost overhanging precipices above it.
>
> 'The Ogwen River and valley are then crossed by a stone viaduct 246 yards in length; and between this and the Britannia Bridge the line passes through three ridges of hills perforated by tunnels, 440, 920, and 726 yards in length, through slate, greenstone, and primary sandstone; the River Cegyn, with its beautiful valley, being crossed by a viaduct 132 yards long and 57 feet high. The line thence continues rising to the level of the Britannia Bridge, and entering Anglesey, passes across the Maldraeth Marsh, and through a tunnel, in slate, rock, and clay, 550 yards in length. To enter the Island of Holyhead use is made, to a certain extent, of the embankment of the Holyhead Road Commissioners...' (30)

The most difficult problems, beside the bridges, involved the sea defences on either side of the headland at Penmaenmawr between Conwy and Bangor. By the time that the railway was finished Robert had 'arrived at the conclusion, that, in railway works, Engineers should endeavour, as far as possible, to avoid any necessity of contending with the sea.' However, when the contract documents were being prepared it was considered that it would be cheaper to follow the coastline using sea walls, retaining walls, and occasional short tunnels rather than to provide a long tunnel further inland. Nevertheless, such were the problems encountered that it was estimated that this decision cost £25,000 to £30,000 more than the tunnel, and unwittingly it provided a legacy of maintenance problems.

The sea walls at Penmaenmawr extend on both sides of the 220-yard tunnel through the headland,

and cover a total length of about a mile and a quarter. On the east side of the headland the walls are not continuous, as the railway goes into cuttings at three points. The first section of the east wall together with its avalanche shelter is shown in Fig. 6.5.

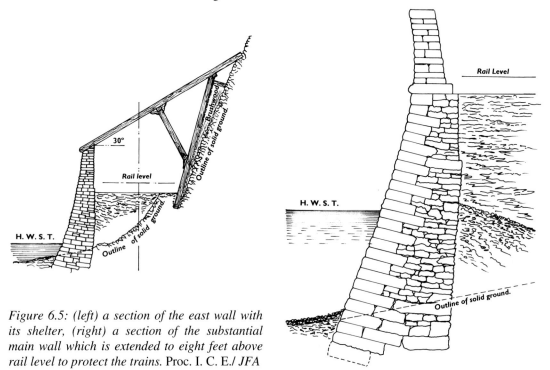

Figure 6.5: (left) a section of the east wall with its shelter, (right) a section of the substantial main wall which is extended to eight feet above rail level to protect the trains. Proc. I. C. E./ JFA

The longest continuous wall is to the west of the headland, and when its deepest central section was being built, and had reached a vulnerable, half-completed state, a severe northerly gale on 22 October 1846 caused so much damage that the work had to be condemned. Robert had witnessed the force of the storm and he decided not to attempt to rebuild the wall but to replace it with a viaduct. The viaduct had thirteen spans of 36 feet, formed of cast-iron trough girders on solid ashlar piers. This allowed the waves to expend their force on the sloping beach below the viaduct. The remainder of the wall was redesigned, with an improved profile and extra thickness, to provide even greater resistance to the seas. Its toe was protected by broken rock, with some pieces weighing as much as 17 tons. Single line working had to used, for a period in 1850, because of further damage to the retaining walls, and as an additional safeguard zigzag groynes formed with timber piles were provided at some locations. The force of the storms was so great that, even though more strengthening of the walls was carried out in 1855, severe damage was caused in November 1859, just one month after Robert's death. Joseph Locke was consulted, and repairs and further substantial works were carried out on his advice in 1860. Almost half the length of the railway is vulnerable to flooding, erosion, and storm damage, so repairs and remedial works have been needed throughout its life. With the exception of using the long tunnel at Penmaenmawr (which may have brought its own complications) it is difficult to see how the other problems could be avoided. Similar maintenance liabilities occur on other railways where it was necessary to follow the coast, for example; near Dawlish, Folkestone, Whitehaven, and Berwick. **(31)**

William Evans was awarded the contract for the Conwy tubes in October 1846, just five months after he had started the masonry work. William Fairbairn had suggested to the board that the ironwork, for the bridges could be built in sections, at established shipyards, and shipped to the Conwy and Menai for assembly. However, when William Evans suggested that he could build the complete tubes for the Conwy Bridge on site, it was decided to do the same at the Menai. Workshops and accommodation were provided adjacent to the bridges, machinery was installed, and large platforms, on which to fabricate the tubes, were built on the shores.

The platform for building the tubes on the tide-swept beach at Conwy was 420 feet long by 40 feet wide, and it was supported, at 12 feet centres, on frames carried on short piles (Fig. 6.6). Two overhead travelling cranes straddled the platform, and a further crane was placed at one end for unloading the plates from the vessels. The workshops, also partly supported on piles, were erected alongside the platform. These housed the steam engine for driving the punching, shearing, drilling machines, and the fan blower for the rivet furnaces. The riveting machine was in front of the sheds, and the rivets used were formed, on site, from iron bars.

Plate 4: a detail from one of a set of six drawings of the High Level Bridge prepared in 1858-9 by Robert Hodgson, who had been the senior resident engineer on the Newcastle and Berwick. The drawings may have been intended for use with a valedictory lecture on the bridge by Robert Stephenson. This one shows the raising of the central section of an arch. Bill Fawcett courtesy I. C. E.

Plate 5: J. W. Carmichael used the engineering drawings of the High Level Bridge to produce this accurate artist's impression before the construction had even started. Reproduced by kind permission of the University of Newcastle upon Tyne.

Plate 6: in January 1828 Robert wrote about convincing his father 'to reduce the size and ugliness of our travelling engines'. The mass of ironmongery on top of Locomotion's boiler makes the point!

Plate 7: Scores of original or replicas of locomotives built by Robert Stephenson & Co. can be found on display all over the world. This elegant long-boiler 2-4-0 was built soon after Robert's death for the Norwegian Railways and is now preserved in their museum. Photograph by Bill Fawcett.

Figure 6.6: one of the construction platforms for the Menai tubes showing an almost completed tube. The platforms were built to give positive camber of 8 inches in the centre of the tubes to counter the anticipated deflection of the tubes under their own weight. Edwin Clark Volume 3

Delivery of plates of the required size and quality was slow, and this was to delay the completion of the bridges. When they were delivered the plates were neither flat nor the exact size so they had to be sheared to the correct dimensions, and hammered on large cast-iron beds, or rolled until they were perfectly flat. Rivet holes had to be punched, and considerable accuracy was needed as usually at least three - but up to six - plates or sections had to be held together by numerous rivets. The punching machines needed a force of about 46 tons to pierce a one-inch hole in a three-quarter inch plate. On the first Conwy tube around 2,800 holes could be punched in a day by each of the machines. However, such were the advances in all branches of engineering that a greatly-improved machine was available for use on the later tubes, allowing over 3,000 holes to be punched each hour with ease and accuracy.

Before the fabrication of the Conwy and Britannia Bridges, riveting had been confined generally to boiler-work and shipbuilding, but for the next hundred years, until it was phased out by welding, it would be used extensively in all forms of heavy engineering. By 1850 both Locke and Brunel had built large riveted, bowstring bridges in wrought iron; Locke's were not long-lived, but Brunel's, over the Thames at Windsor, is still in railway use. A number of riveting machines had been patented, and it was intended to use them to reduce the amount of hand riveting as far as possible. This was achieved at Conwy but, because Luddite thinking prevailed at the Menai, nearly all the work on the Britannia was done by hand, though it may be added, to a very high standard. Large sections of the Conwy tubes were machine riveted before being lifted on to the platform for joining up.

A hand riveting team was made up of two riveters, a holder-up, and two boys. (Fig. 6.7) The boys were equipped with pincers, and one was stationed at the furnace to throw the red-hot rivet up to 60ft., with considerable precision, to the other boy who picked it up and inserted it in the hole in the plates. The holder-up maintained pressure, with a very large hammer, on the preformed head of the rivet while the two riveters, by alternating hammer blows, formed its other head. The average time for each rivet was about one minute. The worst job was for the holder-up and the boy who had to spend long periods cramped in the cells, at the top and bottom of the tubes, being subjected to the deafening blows of the riveters' hammers. A total of two and a half million rivets was used in the two bridges. (32)

Edwin Clark said of the men employed: -

> 'Only twenty years ago the Britannia Bridge would have been designed in vain. Not only was there then no machinery or tools for the manufacture and working of such heavy plates, but that intelligent and valuable class of men who carry out such operations

with an energy and skill in the practical detail, and a sound mechanical appreciation of what is required, which is delightful to witness, was not then called into existence, – they are a peculiar offspring of railway enterprise, and among the most valuable fruits of its harvest.'(33)

The fabrication of the Conwy tubes started in April 1847, and Robert Stephenson reported to the directors on 9 August that the work was progressing very satisfactorily: -

'The whole is now advancing rapidly; the plans for moving and raising the tubes are completed; the hydraulic presses and [lifting] chains are in progress, and will be ready in time; two of the pontoons are complete, and the others are in a forward state. One of the tubes on the platform at Conway is approaching completion; the whole of the bottom and a considerable part of the sides are finished; part of the top is in its place, a great portion of the remainder is finished and fitted, and in a few days a complete section of the middle portion of the tube will be entirely constructed.' (34)

Figure 6.7: riveting a tube showing a boy, a holder-up but only one riveter. Edwin Clark.

It was hoped to complete the first tube in September and to have trains running through it by November, but the slow supply of plates prolonged the fabrication into mid-December and, in any case, the abutments were not yet ready. The permanent cast-iron stiffeners and the temporary ones required to protect the tubes from damage during manoeuvring then had to be fitted. It was the middle of January 1848 before they were able to start removing the tube's supporting platform so that it could rest solely on the temporary masonry abutments, which had been built under each of its ends. The removal of the platform allowed the tube to be tested and proved, and the shore underneath it to be excavated to position the pontoons required for its floating. According to Edwin Clark 'a great number of high authorities' predicted complete disaster as soon as the tube became free of its intermediate supports, however, Robert Stephenson remained confident, and the critics were confounded. On 25 January, when the whole platform had been cleared away, the tube deflected almost exactly the 8 inches that had been calculated at its centre, and when it was subjected to an imposed load of 300 tons, it again performed faultlessly.

The floating and raising of the Conwy tubes were to be dress rehearsals for the much more difficult operations at the Menai where the 40% heavier tubes had to be floated in worse tidal conditions, and then raised to a far greater height. There were six pontoons for floating the Conwy tubes, and they cost £1,500 each. They were made of timber and were 98ft. long, 25ft. wide, and 8ft. deep; each was capable of supporting 460 tons. They were fitted with valves and pumps to allow them to be flooded and emptied as required. The scheme for raising the tubes differed greatly from the simple method that Edwin Clark had witnessed at Crewe. Large hydraulic presses were installed in the abutments, above the final position of the tops of the tubes, and by means of the chains these raised the tubes by six feet (one link) each day; the lift itself taking little more than half an hour. The tubes, when floated, were just 12in. shorter than the gap between the temporary recesses in the bases of the abutments. Considerable precision was needed to float 2,000 tons of tube and pontoons into the exact position even at the best time for the tides. Captain Claxton R. N., who had managed the re-floating of I. K. Brunel's *S. S. Great Britain* off the shores of Dundrum Bay in Ireland, took charge of the nautical details. This entailed supervising a force of Liverpool seamen whose job it was to control the floating and positioning of the tubes by time honoured naval methods using ropes and capstans. (Fig. 6.8) One cannot help feeling that the presence of one or more steam tugs would have been of great assistance. (Two were on standby at the Menai.)

Figure 6.8: the floating of the second Conway tube. In the bottom right hand corner the fully manned capstan playing out a cable that controls the progress of the tube can be seen. Clark Volume 3.

There was considerable public interest. The *Manchester Guardian* reported: 'So great was the crowd assembled, that every spot that commanded a view of the tube was crowded to excess.' On Monday 6 March, the pontoons lifted the first Conwy tube and it glided quietly and majestically across the water in a space of about twenty minutes. Unfortunately, just as it was approaching its final position one of the pontoons, which had moved out of line, fouled a rock at the Conwy end, and this prevented the other end of the tube from being brought home. Foresight had provided a temporary shelf for this eventuality, and, although not in its correct place, the tube was at least safe. It was not until the 11th, after a number of frustrating, unsuccessful attempts that the pontoons were re-positioned and the tube was moved its final few inches. On 8 April, with the hydraulic presses and lifting machinery installed in the abutments, and with the filling of those recesses in the masonry, that had allowed the tube to be positioned, the raising of the tube could start. It was lifted to three feet above its final level by the 11 April. An additional six feet of tube, which had been prefabricated, was added to each end to provide adequate bearing on the bedplates and the expansion rollers, which were also inserted in the abutments at this time. The tube was then lowered to its final level, about 17ft. above high water, and Robert drove the first locomotive through it on 18 April 1848. **(35)**

The bridge was approved for passenger traffic on 1 May and the directors of the railway and other friends gave Robert Stephenson a celebration dinner, in Conwy, on 17 May. Sadly it was to be significant as the last formal occasion that George and Robert attended together; but what an occasion! George must have been very proud of the praise lavished upon his son, but, inevitably, claimed some of the glory for himself. The contractor, William Evans, was not only competent, but also a bit of a character. Unlike Robert, he could never see any difficulties, and never became disheartened. In responding to his toast, he said his motto, like Nelson's, was, 'Brave a danger, and you will always win.' And, that was, of course, what all involved in the bridges had done. (36)

On the previous day, having completed all that was required of him, William Fairbairn had decided to resign. (37) Although Robert Stephenson's speech at the dinner gave him fulsome praise, it fuelled his, or his family's, feeling of resentment regarding the lack of universal acknowledgement of the extent of his contribution to the design. With the name Stephenson being a household word nearly all contemporary reports of the bridges naturally made little or no reference to anyone else. In 1849 Fairbairn produced a book giving his version of the events, which included a few extreme claims that were immediately rebutted by Sir Francis Head. Thomas Fairbairn then leapt to his father's defence, and finally Edwin Clark, with Stephenson's approval, wrote the two volume 'official history' of the bridges - in total over 1,500 pages in two years! See Appendix 5 for further details.

The feeling of elation at having completed and raised one tube must have been tempered by the thought that there were still five more to raise - four of them heavier and to be lifted much higher. Fairbairn, who was hardly involved in the floating or raising of the first tube said in his book 'I never thought of failure, I had no misgivings of the results.' To which Edwin Clark commented in the margin of his own copy 'Ignorance is bliss'! (38) Nothing was straightforward; the lifting of the second Conwy tube caused concern due to the cracking of the crosshead of one of the hydraulic presses. When this was discovered, towards the end of the operations, the tube was immediately under-built with masonry, and the crosshead managed to survive the remaining 2ft. 3in. of lift. This incident led to a complete redesign of the lifting apparatus of the Britannia Bridge. The second Conwy tube was lowered on to its permanent bed on 8 November 1848, and the Government Inspector passed it on 2 January 1849. (39)

The appearance of the bridge came in for some criticism. *The Builder* said 'Its unmitigated ugliness is much to be deplored.' (40) There were other adverse comments about the fake medieval entrances, which were required by the Act of Parliament to sympathise with Conwy castle. Even Professor Pole in Stephenson's biography states: -

'An attempt was made to give a style corresponding to that of the castle, but alterations subsequently introduced into the construction, and the omission of ornamental parts to save expense, crippled the design; and the circumstance of the tubular bridge not being parallel to, but considerably askew from the [Telford's] suspension bridge immediately alongside, is a sad eyesore. [The latter is not very apparent except when viewed from the castle.]

'The unfettered reign of private enterprise, which, under the dictatorship of the engineer, has of late so much prevailed in this country, has been no doubt a grand source of works of commercial utility, but it has doomed us to much bitter humiliation in matters of art and taste.' (41)

The ornamentation as completed is shown in figure 6.9. It was to become a fact of life, with the introduction of tubular and plate girders, that the simple elegance achieved by earlier traditional forms of construction was to disappear.

Figure 6.9: an engraving of the completed Conwy Bridge. Private collection.

The foundations for the Britannia Bridge were started on 10 April 1846, and Edwin Clark inserted the first rivet for the tubes on 10 August 1847. (42) The shorter end tubes, sited over land, were built in situ on substantial timber viaducts. By the middle of June 1849 the first large tube was ready to be floated. With the Menai being open to the sea, at both ends, the currents and tides were a far more complex problem than at Conwy and left little leeway for blunders. There was just ten minutes in the tide cycle when there was no current but this occurred some time before high tide. At high tide a reverse current could reach six miles per hour, and it was feared that if the floating were delayed it would be impossible to control 3,000 tons of tube and pontoons in these conditions. Wrought-iron pontoons were used here, four under each end. A model of the Menai Strait and the tube was created in a pool and methods of controlling the tube were rehearsed in order to evolve a detailed programme for the real thing.

Figure 6.10: building the towers and completing the land tubes of the Menai Bridge. Clark Vol. 3.

Captain Claxton again had charge of the floating and Robert Stephenson, in overall command, was supported both by Joseph Locke and I. K. Brunel; probably the only time that the 'Great Triumvirate' worked together on a project. The operation required no less than 650 men; nearly 400 of them were sailors, from Liverpool, who were employed on a temporary basis. The first attempt, on the evening of 19 June, had to be aborted as a capstan on one of the pontoons failed. It was repaired overnight and other complications that occurred during the next day were remedied by the evening, allowing the operation to be re-started. Despite all the rehearsals and instructions there were still problems with the ropes, and one jammed on a vital capstan which was pulled bodily from its mounting on the shore. The tube was then in imminent danger of being carried away and the pontoons being damaged on the rocks. Fortunately, Charles Rolfe, in charge of the failed capstan, had the presence of mind to enlist the help of the crowd of spectators, men, women and children, to haul on a spare rope to arrest the progress of the tube in a crucial, but successful, tug of war. The intention was for one end of the tube to strike the 'butt' below the Anglesey tower and the other end to swing round to its correct position at the Britannia rock. (Fig. 6.11) This was achieved and the crowd, 'whose sympathy and anxiety were but too clearly indicated by the unbroken silence with which the whole operation was accompanied' burst into prolonged cheering. (43) The crowd was several thousands who had come 'at considerable trouble and expense' to witness 'the Britannia Bridge', but many, according to Sir Francis Head, did not really know what they were about to see. Having waited for two days they seemed very happy to see the tube safely at the base of the towers, although some optimists had apparently expected to see it raised as well. Next morning a solitary figure was seen reclining in the centre of the directors' stand, 'who appeared to be in the exquisite enjoyment of a cigar, …as with unaverted eyes he sat indolently gazing at the aerial gallery before him. It was the father looking at his new-born child!' (44)

In order to raise the much heavier Britannia tubes (over 1800 tons had to be lifted) it had been decided to re-use the two smaller hydraulic presses from the Conwy at one end and to employ a single new press, with a 20-inch ram, at the other end. The twin presses were more difficult to install and operate but there were real problems in getting sound castings for the large single press. (Fig. 6.12)

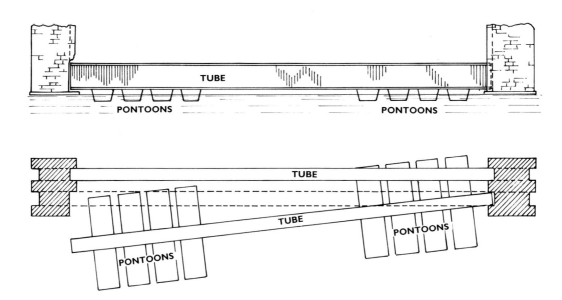

Figure 6.11: diagrams showing the method of floating a Britannia tube. G. D. Dempsey / J. F. A.

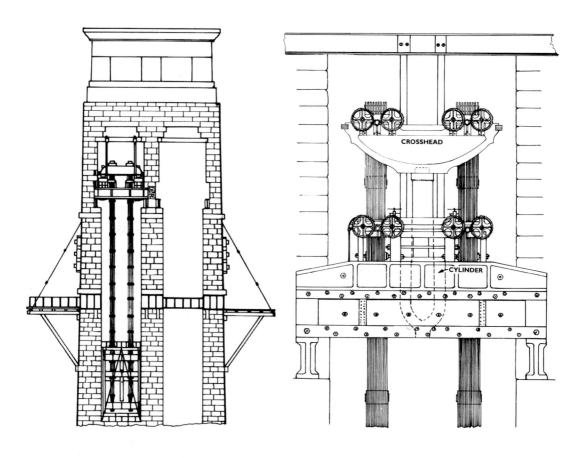

Figure 6.12: (left) the raising of a Britannia tube in progress using the two small presses from the Conway; the protruding cast-iron beams are slid into position when the tube is fully raised. (Edwin Clark Vol. 3) (right) the single press on the Britannia Bridge using the replacement cylinder. J. F. A.

The castings were made at Bank Quay Foundry, Warrington. Twenty-one tons of iron had to be run into the mould in order to get a finished press weighing about 13¾tons, and every technique possible was used to get a sound casting from such a large mass of metal. Again technology was being pushed to the limits, and the press, which was completed by Messrs. Easton and Amos, of Southwark, was probably the most powerful machine built up to that time. (45)

The treachery of iron when cast in large masses manifested itself when the bottom of the cylinder broke off, after the first tube had been lifted only 24 feet. Robert had insisted on temporary timber packing being inserted immediately below the tube as it was being raised, and this avoided the whole tube being damaged but, even though it had dropped less than 9 inches, there was moderate damage both to its end and to the lifting apparatus. The accident happened on 17 August 1849 and it was not until 1 October that the new press was in position and lifting could recommence; the cost of this setback was £5,000. **(46)** The tube had reached its final elevation on 13 October, and the bedplates and junction pieces of the tube were inserted in the towers during the next month.

The second tube should have been floated on 3 December, but for the parting of a main hauling line, which '…presented every appearance of having been cut mischievously by a sharp instrument'. The damage was repaired and the tube was successfully moved next day; it was raised to its final elevation on 7 January 1850. (47) Very considerable ingenuity was used in lifting the ends of the tubes, in succession by calculated amounts, during the operations for joining them together. (Fig. 6.13) 'In this manner the whole tube … became a continuous beam; the strains everywhere being nearly the same as though it had been constructed in one length and placed complete in its place.' (48) The tube was fixed in the Britannia tower and allowed to expand or contract by means of rollers in the other towers and abutments.

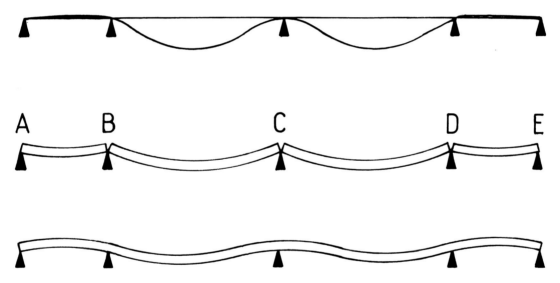

Figure 6.13: since around 1844 Robert Stephenson had been making some of his two-span bridges continuous over their centre support as he realised that this reduced both the stresses and deflections in the individual spans. The top diagram shows the deflections achieved from one of a series of experiments for the Britannia Bridge when different loadings were applied to a bar: in this case equally on the two centre spans. The problem with the Britannia Bridge was to convert four simply supported beams (centre), which did nothing to help each other, into a continuous beam (bottom). The method adopted was to raise end 'E' by nearly 16 inches, and rivet the two ends at 'D' before lowering 'E' to back its normal position. End 'B' of the long tube was then raised, not sufficiently to give perfect continuity but about half that amount in order to equalise the maximum stresses expected in each tube; then the joint at 'C' was riveted. End 'A' was then raised and 'B' riveted to complete the operation.

On 5 March 1850 Messrs. Stephenson, Bidder, Francis Trevithick (then LNWR loco. engineer), and others, had a canter over the bridge with three locomotives before the same engines hauled a train of 45 coal wagons and carriages through the tube and then carried the 700 passengers on to Holyhead. This train was long enough to extend over the two main spans and weighed over 500 tons. When Captain Simmons carried out the Board of Trade inspection on 15 March he got a maximum deflection of 0.676 inches, in one of the large tubes, with a load of 250 tons. Because of the continuity this load had the effect of raising the adjacent large and small tubes by 0.19 and 0.109 inches respectively. (49) His report regarding the continuous beam said: 'It is difficult to define the exact amount of this benefit, but it is undoubtedly considerable, and has been estimated by Mr. Stephenson as reducing the greatest strain on the metal from 5 tons 3 cwt to 3 tons per square inch, or increasing the strength in a like ratio. Judging, therefore, from prior experience of works constructed of this material, and having full reliance on the care and skill displayed in constructing this immense tube, I feel assured that every confidence may be placed in the security of the structure for the purpose of the transit of railway trains.' **(50)** This confidence was not misplaced as, before the end of its life, the bridge was to carry locomotives four times heavier than those in use at its opening without distress. Passenger services on the single line started in the early hours of 18 March.

The tubes for the other line were floated on 10 June and 25 July 1850. The whole bridge was opened to traffic on 19 October 1850, and the last section of the line, just under a mile long, was opened from Holyhead station to Admiralty Pier on 20 May 1851. Unlike the Newcastle and Berwick, which benefited by being on the royal journey from Scotland, there were no formal openings, but the large celebrations that took place at every significant stage were probably just as enjoyable to everyone.

The tops of the Conwy tubes had been roofed over with corrugated iron to protect them from salt spray, and this material had been ordered for the Britannia Bridge when economies were imposed forcing a timber covering to be substituted. **(51)** This curved covering, supported on a metal framework, spanned across both tubes and had a level walkway over its centre. It was on this walkway, on 14 October 1852, that the eleven-year-old Prince of Wales, accompanied by Prince Albert and Robert Stephenson, walked over the full length of the bridge. Prior to this feat, Queen Victoria and Prince Albert had had the design explained by Robert, and had inspected its interior a little way on foot. The Queen then continued through the tube in her carriage, 'drawn by a number of men,' apparently unconcerned about her consort and heir walking on the exposed platform overhead, 130 feet above the water. (52) It was the retention of this timber covering that led to the Britannia Bridge's irreparable damage by fire on 23-24 May 1970. See Appendix 6 for a description of the fire and replacement structure.

The appearance of the Britannia Bridge came in for more praise than the Conwy. Samuel Smiles justly acclaimed Francis Thompson's masonry work, with its lofty central tower, 230ft. high, and its lower side towers and abutments. 'The design of the masonry is such as to accord with the form of the tubes, being somewhat of an Egyptian character, massive and gigantic rather than beautiful, but bearing the unmistakable impress of power.' (53)

The engineering historian, L. T. C. Rolt, considered that the Britannia Bridge '...must undoubtedly rank as the greatest and boldest civil engineering feat of the early Victorian era.' (54) But immediately after the bridge was completed, there were still doubts, in some quarters, about the application of continuity. French engineers MM. Molinos and Pronnier made some erroneous calculations on the bridge, which led structural maestro, Clapeyron, '...in a Memoir presented to the French Academy in 1857, to make some strictures on that work, which would probably have been much modified, or altogether omitted, if the real state of the case had been known to him.' (55) Later civil engineers, with the advantages of hindsight and improved technology, also have been critical of its design. For example, in the early 1890s, Sir John Fowler was to compare the design of his new Forth Bridge with the Britannia. While acknowledging that it was a solid and safe structure built in accordance with the best knowledge of its day, he said its material is 'so placed that much of it contributes nothing to the strength of the bridge'. (56) Edwin Clark had admitted as much when he said that the small size of the iron plates then available had made the cover plates and rivets account for 31% of the weight of the bridge. The Forth Bridge had the advantage of using steel with a 50% higher ultimate tensile strength, and plates up to six times larger, but, in its turn, it was to be affectionately described as a 'brontosaurus of technology', by art historian, Lord Clark, in his T. V. lectures on 'Civilisation' in 1969!

When the first C&HR Act had been passed in 1844, it was forecast that the cost of strengthening Telford's bridge to take the railway carriages, and to form the approaches to it would be £100,000. When this was not allowed it was estimated that the arch bridge would cost an extra £150,000, which the directors thought 'will be amply covered by the capital of £2,100,000.' Because of the 'impossible' conditions imposed, the major bridges themselves were to take over one third of the original capital. The quoted the cost of the Conwy was £145,191, and the Britannia £601,865. **(57)** Extra engineering works together with additional commitments, like the purchase of the Mold Railway for £163,000, £200,000 towards further harbour improvements, and £333,000 for the company's fleet of steam mail packets, pushed the total cost of the undertaking up to nearly £4,000,000. An application to the Government for some assistance towards this extra expenditure, which it had forced the company to incur, was met with polite refusal. The mail contract was worth just £30,000 per annum, fixed for the next five years. (58)

There was the physical cost to Robert, who had aged at least ten years during the construction of the railway. He confided to Tom Gooch: -

'It was a most anxious and harassing time with me. Often at night I would lie tossing about, seeking sleep in vain. The tubes filled my head. I went to bed with them and got up with them. In the grey of the morning, when I looked across the [Gloucester] Square, it seemed an immense distance across to the houses on the other side. It was nearly the same length as the span of my tubular bridge!' (59)

After the floating of the final tube, he had confided to his friends 'that even the triumph of that day did not recompense him for the days and nights of anxious toil and thought, the cares and anxieties which had attended the work.' (60)

G. P. Bidder observed: -

'…that however bold he was in the conception of an idea, as for instance, the Britannia Tubular Bridge, yet no one, with whom I came in contact, watched with more anxiety the completion of these enterprises, than did Mr. Stephenson. His mind was ever occupied in anticipating how, and in what shape failures might arise, and no doubt, it might appear to many, that the precautions he took were often superfluous. But the experienced Engineer knows well, that if he relies on the chances turning up in his favour, without due precautions being taken, the enterprise is sure to be attended with some disasters; whilst the mere act of taking due precautions seems to have the effect of averting the consequences they are intended to guard against; in short, the Engineer is never justified in trusting to the favours of fortune, whilst he has the means of guarding against her caprices.' (61)

With the completion of the C&HR and the Newcastle and Berwick Robert had had enough, and he must have realised that he no longer had the stamina to take on major projects. He attempted to withdraw as far as possible from railway work, and to enjoy as much as he could the remaining years, albeit in failing health, left to him. Perhaps it was this semi-retirement that gave him a longer lifespan than either Locke or Brunel.

Figure 6.14: the Britannia Bridge 'bearing the unmistakable impress of power'.

NOTES AND REFERENCES

1. Peter E. Baughan, *The Chester & Holyhead Railway,* (1972) pp. 11-56 gives detailed accounts of the early proposals for the road and railway. Also *Civil Engineer and Architect's Journal* June 1840 p. 90 for details of the early proposals to use Telford's Bridge, where it was claimed that it would have a surplus load capacity of 621 tons with two trains of carriages standing on it, and Jan. 1844 pp. 454-7 for James Walker's 1843 Report, which recommended an arched bridge.

2. Edwin Clark, *Britannia and Conway Tubular Bridges,* (1850) pp. 15-21

3. Ibid. pp. 73-80. The passage around Anglesey, instead of using the Menai, could be very hazardous to sailing ships. The Earl of Lovelace reported: - 'In 1836, thirty-nine vessels went on shore at one time in Holyhead Bay' See 'Harbours of Refuge' *Proc. I. C. E. Vol. 7,* p. 367.

4. In March 1855 John Roebling (1806-69) was to complete his stupendous 821 ft. span double-deck suspension bridge over the Niagara; this carried a single-track railway on the top deck and a road below.

5. Clark, p. 26. Telford's bridge had been severely damaged in a storm in Jan. 1839 (*Proc. I. C. E. Vol. 1,* pp. 74,5)

6. Ibid. pp. 29, 65, 67.

7. Ibid. p. 48.

8. Ibid. p. 32.

9. G. Drysdale Dempsey, *Tubular and Other Iron Girder Bridges, 1850* (Reprinted 1970), pp.44, 45. A. Thompson was credited with the design, but the Engineer-in-Chief was J. B. Macneill.

10. Most railway engineers had experienced wrought iron rails de-laminating in service, which did not inspire confidence in the material for structural use. Also there were widely held views that wrought iron was in an 'artificial state' and, even when not under stress, would gradually return to its 'natural state', and in time possess no strength whatsoever. (See Herepath's 'Report on Locomotive Engines' *Railway Magazine* 17 Dec. 1842). Similar theories were still being expressed in *The Builder* five years later. In 1850 G. D. Dempsey said the largest plates he knew were 10ft. 7in. by 5ft. 1in. and most sources give the cost of wrought iron as three times that of cast.

11. Robert Stephenson, 'Iron Bridges'. *Encyclopaedia Britannica* 8th Edition (1856). p. 607. This text '…is somewhat damaged by typographical errors;' (Jeaffreson, Vol. 2 p. 31). This may have something to do with R. S's handwriting! Corrections are given in square brackets [].

12. According to his report to the C&HR board E. Hodgkinson was very well aware of the best available theory for the design of structures given by C. Navier's, *Resumé des leçons données a l' École des Ponts et Chaussées* (1826), and H. Moseley's, *The Mechanical Principles of Engineering and Architecture* (1843). But theory, no matter how good, is never enough. When box girders were enthusiastically resurrected, in the 1960s, modern theoretical knowledge did not prevent serious defects, which caused around 40 deaths during the construction of three bridges. This resulted in the Merrison Report (1972), and severe weight restrictions being imposed on bridges already in use until they were strengthened.

13. Jeaff. Vol. 2 p. 87. Also *Encyclopaedia Britannica* 8th Edition (1856) p. 606.

14. Clark. p. 511.

15. Ibid. p. 482-3

16. *Proc. I. C. E.* 1894 pp. 344-54. Edwin Clark was born in 1814, but failed to find a niche in life until he became involved in the C&HR bridges. He became Engineer-in-Chief to the Electric Telegraph Company in Aug. 1850, though he continued to design railways and structures in Britain and Europe. He also became a contractor for railways further afield, but his firm went into liquidation in 1879. (*The Engineer,* 11 April 1879) He lived in semi-retirement until his death in 1894. See also his obituary, *Proc. I. C. E.* 1895, pp. 344-54.

17. *Encyclopaedia Britannica,* p. 589. Also *Proc. I. C. E. Vol. 16* (1857), pp. 477-8 states under normal temperature variations, 'the vertical rise and fall at the centre [of the main spans] would be through a space of 6 or 7 inches, whilst the horizontal motion of the roadway itself would be only through a space of 2 or 3 inches.'

18. Clark, pp. 496-8. R. S's caution was justified as more near disasters occurred during the floating and raising than at any other time. 70 years later while attempting to raise the central span of the Quebec Bridge with hydraulic jacks it crashed into the water with the loss of 10 lives. This was the second major disaster on this site; the first, in 1907, caused 75 deaths.

19. W. Fairbairn, *An account of the construction of the Britannia and Conway tubular bridges.* p. 21.

20. Clark, p. 145. One of the basic 'discoveries', in Fairbairn's report to the directors, was that by increasing the depth of the tube you increased its strength!

21. Clark, p. 155. Unfortunately, because of the 'railway mania', Robert could not devote anything like as much time to the bridges as he would have wished (see chapter 8). He was called as a witness for or against some 60 railway Bills, so was very much tied up with parliamentary work in 1846, (it was the year when 64 committees sat for a total 867 days on Bills which resulted in the authorising of 4,540 miles of railway).

22. Jeaff. Vol. 2 pp. 90-1.

23. Wind loadings quoted for the bridges were as variable as the commodity itself. Edwin Clark's journal quotes 50 lbs. per square foot, his book, p. 470, gives 46 lbs. (a figure derived by Smeaton) and p. 787 only 20 lbs. *The Builder*, 28 Feb. 1850, p. 94, quotes 17.5 lbs. measured in a gale on the Britannia Bridge, and Capt. Simmons used 30 lbs. in his calculations for his report on the Conwy Bridge. No wonder poor old Bouch did not know what to use for his Tay Bridge! After the Tay Bridge disaster a Board of Trade report, in 1881, specified a maximum of 56 lbs. per square foot.

24. *Encyclopaedia Britannica,* (1856) p. 608.

25. Clark, pp. 522-4. The original correspondence on this matter is in the I. C. E. Archives.

26. Inquest evidence as reported in the *Chester Chronicle* on 28 May 1847.
27. F. R. Conder, *Personal Recollections of English Engineers,* first published 1868, reprinted as *The Men Who Built Railways* with notes by Professor Simmons 1983, pp. 137-142.
28. *Proc. I. C. E. Vol. 94,* 1888, p.120.
29. Ibid. *Vol. 107,* pp. 456-7 states: 'The bridge was from the beginning too weak in parts and defective in design.'
30. Clark, pp. 2, 3.
31. Henry Swinburne, 'Account of the Sea-Walls at Penmaen Mawr, on the line of the Chester and Holyhead Railway', *Proc. I. C. E.* 1851, pp. 257-277. Leslie & Paxton, *Bright Lights,* p. 88 report R. Stevenson measuring wave pressures of nearly 3 tons per sq. ft. at Skerryvore in 1845. For later works on the railway, see P. Baughan, pp. 272-276, and W. Sivewright, *Civil Engineering Heritage; Wales and Western England,* pp. 14-19.
32. Clark, pp. 623-632. A rough estimate in Clark's journal (p. 26) quotes over £15,000 for the temporary workshops, accommodation, machinery, etc. at the Menai. This cost included a single platform, on which to build the tubes, at £3,000; three platforms were used.
33. Ibid, p. 530. Sir F. Head, *High-ways & Dry-ways,* (1850) p. 63, expresses similar favourable views.
34. Ibid. pp. 633-4.
35. Ibid. pp. 639-647. Surprisingly, and totally out-of-character, Gen. Sir Charles Pasley, who had been eased out of the Railway Inspectorate in 1846, wrote a strong and somewhat 'uncourteous' letter to *The Times* about the methods to be used for the erection of the bridges. His conclusions '... are so clearly based in ignorance of the proposed plans, that I abstain from making any comments thereon;' wrote R. S. to the directors, of the C&HR, on 9 Aug. 1847.
36. *Manchester Guardian,* 20 May 1848.
37. Thomas Fairbairn, *Truths and Tubes* (1849), pp.41-2, quotes his father's letter of resignation.
38. W. Fairbairn, p. 21. Edwin Clark's annotated copy is in the Institution of Civil Engineers' Archives.
39. Clark, pp. 651-658.
40. *The Builder,* 25 Mar. 1848, p. 154.
41. Jeaff. Vol. 2, p. 111-2.
42. Clark, p. 663.
43. Ibid. pp. 675-684.
44. Sir F. Head, pp. 37-55.
45. Clark, pp. 617-9.
46. Ibid. pp. 690-1. See also Samuel Smiles, *Lives of the Stephensons,* 1874, pp. 272-3, for R. S's own account of the incident. R. S. states that the tube dropped only one inch, but, due to the compression of the timber packing, the 8-9 inches quoted by Clark is more likely. One workman was killed, and the fractured head of the press was placed on a memorial plinth near the bridge. Amongst the assistant engineers then working on the Britannia Bridge was (Sir) George Grove, later to become famous for his musical dictionaries, and he was delegated to take the bad news to R. S. The messenger was not shot, and he reported, 'He was very kind, and kept me to dinner.' The new press and part of the lifting equipment was shown at the 1851 Exhibition by Bank Quay Foundry; it won a medal.
47. Ibid. pp. 697-703.
48. Ibid. p. 705.
49. Ibid. pp. 706-710.
50. *Appendix to Report of the Commissioners of Railways 1850,* p. 8. The Conwy Bridge caused far less concern about its strength, at the design stage, but by 1899 two additional piers had to be added, reducing its span by 90ft. and making it continuous over the new supports.
51. *The Builder,* 5 Oct. 1850, quotes 66,000 sq. ft. of galvanized iron being required by the directors of the C & H R to roof over the Britannia Bridge.
52. *Illustrated London News,* 16 and 23 Oct. 1852, pp.319, 331.
53. S. Smiles, *The Lives of George and Robert Stephenson,* (1874), p. 268.
54. L. T. C. Rolt, *Victorian Engineering,* 1980 reprint, pp. 27-8.
55. *Proc. I. C. E. Vol. 29* p. 43, John M. Heppel in discussion on 'Resistance of Materials'.
56. T. Mackay, *The Life of Sir John Fowler,* 1900, p. 308.
57. Clark, pp. 814-5. It has been stated that the Britannia Bridge was the most expensive bridge that had been built up to that time. The cast-iron Southwark Bridge (1819), over the Thames, which was half the length of the Britannia, cost £660,000, and the rebuilding of London Bridge (1824-31), together with its approaches, cost £1,458,000.
58. C&HR Half-Yearly Reports, Aug. 1844 et seq.
59. Smiles, (1862) p. 435.
60. Jeaff. Vol. 2 p. 167.
61. *Proc. I. C. E. Vol. 19,* p. 217.

CHAPTER SEVEN: WORK OVERSEAS IN THE 1850s

Report for the Development of the Swiss Railway System

As soon as the construction of the Stockton and Darlington Railway got underway, a stream of curious overseas visitors were observing it and reporting home on its developments. Within a short time George and Robert Stephenson were being consulted by many foreign powers that wished to introduce their own railway systems. They had both visited Belgium in 1835, and George, although officially retired, went to Spain in 1845 to survey the route of a proposed railway. It was the arduous mountainous terrain, which he had to investigate, late in the year, that led to the severe attack of pleurisy which left his constitution fatally weakened. Robert was consulted by virtually every country in Europe, together with Russia and India.

Robert's involvement in India came about after Lord Dalhousie (1812-60) was sent there to become 'the greatest of Indian proconsuls'. His energetic rule, from 1847 to 1856, embraced the provision of new communications by road, canal, railway and the electric telegraph. British engineers were brought in to do the work, and Robert became consulting engineer for the first 200 miles of the Great Indian Peninsular Railway, which ran from Bombay. He did not visit India and the site work was supervised by James and George Berk(e)ley. Little documentation has survived regarding Robert's input to this and the other foreign railways that he was consulted on, but the report that reluctantly he had to give on Swiss railways remains in its entirety. The Swiss report, written 20 years after the establishment of the steam locomotive, gives an indication of how Robert would plan a mountainous country's system from scratch, while observing fairly severe financial constraints.

It came about after a new Federal Constitution had been adopted in Switzerland on 12 September 1848 in an attempt to bring some control over the disparate aims of the twenty-two cantons. One of the results in December 1849 was that the Federal Council decided that impartial experts should be consulted to give them advice on the future development of their railways. This was because individual cantons had started to promote their own lines without any reference to a strategic national plan. An independent report by a world-renowned expert may provide a good political weapon to bring them to heel. Obviously the cantons should have an input, but the overall control must rest with the state. In their remit of 7 June 1850 it was apparent that the Federal Council had a very good idea of what was really wanted but not necessarily how to achieve it. (1)

When Robert was consulted on the task he was rather committed. His retirement dinner in Newcastle was scheduled for the end of July, the Parliamentary term did not end until 12 August, also, not least, there was still the last tube of the Britannia Bridge to raise. After five years of problems on the Chester & Holyhead Railway he also deserved a holiday, and he suggested that G. P. Bidder should go in his stead, but this was not acceptable to the Swiss authorities. Then Robert had hoped to leave on 15 August, spend about a month on the report, and incorporate a brief cruise in the Mediterranean on his way back. **(2)** However, when it was found that the formal opening of the Newcastle & Berwick had to take place at the end of August, he and Bidder, could only start their visit to Switzerland in September before Robert went on to make his first trip to Egypt. (3)

Henry Swinburne went out in June to do all the legwork, and consult with the Swiss engineers. When he wrote to Robert, on 8 July, already he had found fault with their choice of routes. Robert replied in a chauvinistic vein: -

'It must really be delightful if you have discovered a better line than any of the local engineers, I think it is not at all improbable, for I have often been astonished at the ignorance of some of the Continental Engineers in appreciating the features of a country. They seem to have no feeling for the subject, what sometimes appeared to me so simple and obvious to be axiomatic appeared to them difficult and requiring a lengthened demonstration' He concluded; '**I quite concur in your notion that a modest beginning is absolutely necessary.**' (2)

In 1815 Sydney Smith had described Switzerland 'as an inferior sort of Scotland'. Whether this view still persisted in England, or whether the Swiss authorities had impressed upon the engineers a need for restraint, the result was a report that was lacking in enthusiasm for a railway system. This is shown from their opening remarks: -

'In fact, if the railways in the neighbouring countries were less advanced it would not be necessary to replace the roads in Switzerland by railways, as the roads are so good. However, having weighed up the situation we have decided to recommend a network of railways that will help the Swiss industries to develop and to further communications.

'The questions that are linked to the establishment of a railway network involve all the cantons and require the most serious and deep attention. At first sight, the variety of interests seems to be in opposition to each other – this comes from the insular spirit of each canton – which does not look to the general good.'

Robert's private opinion was: 'The designs for the Swiss Railways almost bring to my mind the mania of '45. The Cantons represent the rival Companies of that year and each contests its position with as much tenacity and temper.' (4)

The report was completed in Geneva on 12 October 1850. The printed document comes to seventy A5 pages, and is somewhat repetitive and disjointed as if the problems of writing in French made the editing of their flow of ideas difficult.

Inevitably, their report condemned mistakes made in England and highlighted two serious errors; firstly that unlimited competition is a good thing, and, secondly that the shortest lines, without taking into account the population or the type of terrain, are the best. With its limited resources and mountainous landscape they stressed that it would be deplorable if Switzerland made the same mistakes as England. There was intended to be no competition within Switzerland, but there was a prospect of rival lines in the Rhine valley, where the river was the frontier with Germany and Austria.

Fortunately there were numerous valleys, which would allow the construction of railways, and the majority of the population was situated in these. Sometimes the direction of a valley was not ideal; obviously, any deviation would need very steep inclines or long and costly tunnels. In these cases the choice between what could be achieved and what could be achieved *economically* must be made. This resulted in few lines being considered in the sparsely populated and mountainous southern half of the country, where the inhabitants were going to have to make do with their 'good roads' over their spectacular passes.

Since the 1830s considerable improvements had been made in locomotive performance, and much steeper gradients than the 1 in 330 used on the London and Birmingham were acceptable. On the Swiss lines gradients as steep as 1 in 60 were proposed for locomotive haulage. Tender locomotives of the 2-4-0 wheel arrangement were recommended, but, in order to avoid damage to the track, the engine without its tender should weigh about 17 tons. Its coupled wheels should be 4ft-9in to 5ft diameter, and its two cylinders 15in bore by 22in stroke. It was expected to travel at about 25 mph on nearly level track, and haul a train of 30-35 tons up a 1 in 60 gradient at 12 mph.

The greater part of the proposed rail network coincided with the principal valleys, but where slopes steeper than 1 in 60 were encountered, auxiliary power would be needed. This could be an additional locomotive, a stationary engine or water power. On very steep gradients fixed engines were more reliable than locomotives, and were firmly recommended for heavy goods traffic. There were problems and costs in acquiring stationary engines in Switzerland. However there was an abundance of water in the upper valleys that could be used as auxiliary power. There are no exploitable coal reserves in the country so all this fuel must be imported. Unfortunately, hydroelectric power was not available until the late-nineteenth century, but after it did become accessible the Swiss railway network was largely electrified between 1904 and 1930.

The system of water power proposed for Switzerland, in 1850, had been used on an incline, between Beck Hole and Goathland on the Whitby and Pickering Railway in 1836, (5) and had since found favour in some Alpine regions. The procedure was to use a number of reservoir wagons, each filled with about 8 tonnes of water, at the top of the incline, and these descended to haul a train and the other set of empty reservoir wagons up the gradient. Some water could be left in the lower reservoir wagons to regulate the speed of light trains. It was stressed that there was no higher accident rate on inclines than elsewhere, but that the reservoir wagons must have very good brakes in case the cable failed! Water worked inclines were cheaper to work and cheaper to construct, and could be used independently or as an auxiliary to the locomotive.

The first railway in Switzerland had been opened in 1844 from Basel across the frontier to St.-Louis in France, (6) and clearly it was necessary to link Basel to the other major cities in Switzerland. The worst problem in the new Swiss system would be getting from Basel directly to the Aare valley, at Olten, which was the key to the access to Lucerne, Bern, Lausanne and Geneva. Basel to Olten was only 36.5 km, but it involved a long climb of 1 in 66 to Hauenstein and then a precipitous drop into the Aare valley. A number of inclines or a tunnel up to 3.5 km long were considered, but the line would be very expensive and difficult to build and, with the use of inclines, tedious to travel on. The alternative, following the valleys via Brugg, was about 55 km longer, and the problem was partly resolved by completing the first, relatively short, Hauenstein Tunnel in the late 1850s. It took five years for Peto, Brassey and Betts to bore this 2 km tunnel that was started in 1853. (7) It was not until 1916 when the 8km lower Hauenstein Tunnel was opened, as part of the improved route to the St. Gotthard, that a really satisfactory solution was achieved.

The report stated that Lucerne should be served from Olten, and Bern and Thun from Lyss; both junctions are on the Aare valley line. As far as the Federal Council was concerned, the line southwards to Lausanne could pass on either side of Lake Neuchâtel; the report chose the east side but the main line was eventually built on the west. From Yverdon, at the south end of the lake, the 'easiest and least expensive' line followed the valley of the River Venoge to Lausanne. Here was the greatest surprise of all - there was not to be a railway to Geneva! Already there were 'magnificent roads along the lake and good steamboat services', so they considered that the railway was not, as yet, justified. 'The expenditure would not even be justified in England where we have made great sacrifices to satisfy the impatience of the English people who do not want any delays; this has become so great as to become proverbial.' Some things never change! They conceded that when the growing needs of the population did require a line to Geneva, it should then be linked to France. The problems of transhipping goods and passengers did not even merit a mention.

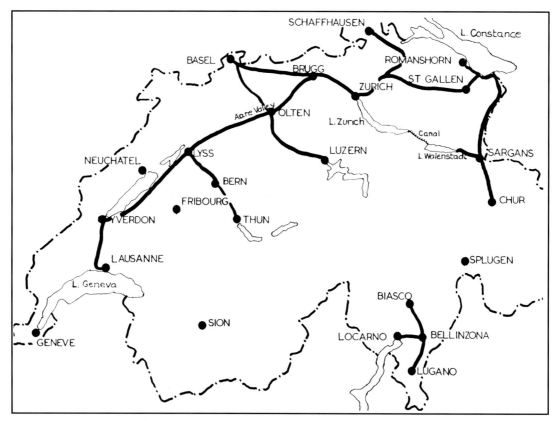

Figure 7.1: map of the railways of Switzerland as discussed in the report. J. F. Addyman.

The report recommended that the line eastwards from Basel to Zurich and Lake Constance should cross the River Aare at Brugg where it would form a junction with the Aare valley line. The east line would continue to Baden where it would join the recently completed railway to Zurich. From Zurich they proposed to go on via St. Gallen to Lake Constance at Rorschach, and continue as an 'international route' southwards down the Rhine valley to Sargans and Chur. From Sargans a branch to Walenstadt would connect with the steamboats on the lakes Walensee and Zurichsee, and their linking canal, to complete a circuit back to Zurich. They even gave, as an example, that the boat journey from Edinburgh to Perth (a scheduled service) was preferable to the railway and ferry! With Lake Constance forming the frontier they suggested a line only as far north, along its shores, as Romanshorn.

Schaffhausen and Zurich should be linked but they thought this was possible only by a 17 km detour to the east of the direct line; the line actually built detoured to the west. With the resources available they did not consider it would be viable to link Fribourg with Bern. In the extreme south lines radiating from Bellinzona to Biasca, Lugano and Locarno would be very difficult to build, and 'would be a considerable drain on the state.'

The table shows some of the lines that they considered could be built, together with their construction costs, and expected annual receipts. Amongst the worst immediate returns, were those forecast on the 'international route' from Lake Constance to Sargans. The English yardstick for viability on easy rural branch lines, costing around £7,000 per mile to build, was that the annual receipts should exceed £520 per mile. (8) With the exchange rate, in 1850, being 15.7 French francs to the pound, these figures are equivalent to 68,300 and 5,075 French francs per kilometre respectively. If the traffic estimates were correct this indicates that there was going to be a considerable shortfall on the more expensive Swiss lines. For example, Olten to Solothurn was to cost three times as much as a cheap British line, but was only expected to make twice the return. This explains their reluctance, in the report, to recommend railways if there was a reasonable alternative.

The table and figure 7.1 indicate the extent of the initial proposals for the railways.

Projected Railways	Length (Km)	Construction Cost French Franc/Km	Construction Cost £/Mile	Total Annual Receipts/Km (French Francs)
Basel-Olten	36.5	370,000	38,000	20,200
Basel-Brugg	70.0	200,000	20,500	-
Olten-Solothurn	37.0	199,000	20,400	10,620
Olten-Lucerne	54.0	167,000	17,200	6,110
Soluthurn-Lyss	25.0	136,000	14,000	10,620
Lyss-Bern	22.5	192,000	19,700	11,550
Bern-Thun	27.5	100,000	10,250	5,780
Lyss-Yverdon	65.5	158,200	16,200	9,550
Yverdon-Lausanne	46.5	160,000	16,400	9,550
Olten-Zurich	64.5	197,400	20,200	14,610
Zurich-Rorschach	98.5	150,000	15,375	12,750
Winterthur- Scaffhausen	28.5	224,000	23,000	6,380
Rorschach-Sargans	65.0	127,500	13,000	5,320
Sargans-Chur	22.0	155,000	16,000	8,510
Sargans-Wallenstadt	16.0	127,500	13,000	5,320
Biasco-Locarno	41.5	143,000	14,700	5,310

During Robert's speech in Montreal in August 1853, he mentioned the Swiss railways as an example to the Canadians, 'capital was now flowing in, the country being satisfied because there were no rival lines; and **there was no doubt of their completion**.' **(9)** Many of the lines were completed by 1860, and Geneva had been connected to the French railway system. The line from Yverdon to Lausanne was started in 1852, with G. H. Phipps as the Engineer-in-Chief, and J. M. Heppel as the resident engineer; it was completed in 1856. G. W. Hemans (1814-85), assisted by H. E. Fortescue, was engineering some of the lines in the east of the country at the same time. (10) Traffic growth far exceeded the pessimistic estimates, and Bradshaw quotes that the average receipts per kilometre, for the whole Swiss System, had exceeded 20,000 francs by the 1870s. **(11)**

Works in Egypt

After completing the report on the Swiss railways Robert became involved in supervising the first railway construction in the African continent – the line from Alexandria to Cairo. (12) In the 1840s the improvement of the Transit across Egypt, in preference to the journey round the Cape, was of growing importance, and this had led to Robert's first visit, which was concerned with the feasibility of railways and a canal. (13) Unlike other transport projects the aim was to carry goods across the country rather than to provide for the commercial well-being of Egypt. A canal linking the Mediterranean and the Red Sea was first proposed in the 1830s, but the Suez Canal was not to be completed until 1869.

Robert had first been involved in 1847 as one of twelve directors of the international Société d' Études pour le Canal de Suez. He investigated, together with his old friend Paulin Talabot (French) and Alois von Negrelli (Austrian), possible routes for a canal. When a new survey, which the directors had commissioned, showed that there was no difference in level between the Mediterranean and the Red Sea, they came to the conclusion that the project was impractical. (14) Robert visited Egypt in the late autumn of 1850 and spent two or three weeks exploring 'the country with a view to railways, and to the practicability of executing the proposed canal.' **(15)**

There were strong British political objections to a Suez Canal. When it was debated on 17 July 1857 Lord Palmerston (1784-1865), the prime minister, condemned the scheme as 'one which no Englishman with his eyes open would think it desirable to encourage.' Robert spoke after him, and explained to the House that when the 1847 investigations had shown the difference of level between the Mediterranean and the Red Sea 'was found to be nil ['providing no scouring power to maintain a clear channel'], the engineers with whom he was associated abandoned the project altogether, and he believed justly; and one of them - M. Paulin Talabot - made an adverse report, which was published in the *Revue des deux Mondes* of May 1855.' A small number of M. P.s supported the canal, and when the question was raised again on 1 June 1858 Robert spoke vehemently against it, and reiterated that it was physically impossible to construct. **(16)** As president of the Institution of Civil Engineers his opinion carried considerable weight, but the persistence of a former French diplomat, Ferdinand, vicomte de Lesseps (1805-1894), was ultimately to prove him to be wrong. On 25 April 1859, six months before Robert's death, de Lesseps was to formally turn the first spade of sand to start work on the Suez Canal. British doubts remained even after the canal was completed. Sir John Rennie visited it and while expressing admiration for its construction he had doubts about its viability. He thought problems of alluvial deposits, sand blown into the canal and evaporation 'would render the canal practically useless, that is to say, that it will not be worth the while of the Company to maintain it.' **(17)**

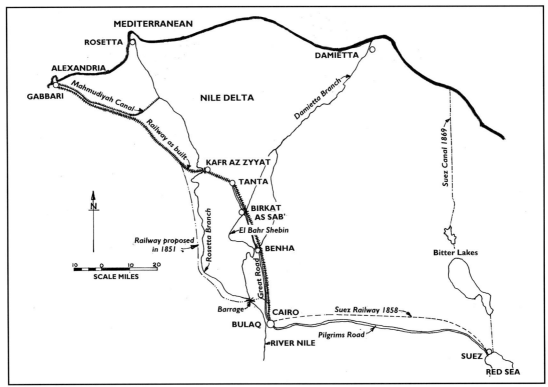

Figure 7.2: a map of Egypt showing the railway and other features. When the railways were completed from Alexandria to Suez the 220 miles were covered in 13 hours. Alan Clothier /J. F. A.

In 1850 the Overland Route through Egypt entailed the use of small horse-drawn boats on the Mahmudiyah Canal for the first 44 miles from Alexandria to the Rosetta Branch of the Nile. **(18)** Larger steam boats were used for the 120-mile journey to Bulaq wharf at Cairo, and the remaining 90 miles on the road across the desert to Suez was achieved by animal power. With the benefit of improvements already carried out, by people like Lt. Thomas Fletcher Waghorn R.N. (1800-50), the volume of traffic on the Overland Route had exceeded that round the Cape in the 1840s. **(19)**

Egypt's ruler, Pasha Mohamet Ali, had approved an 1834 proposal by R. H. Galloway, and contracts for rails and locomotives were let with the intention of making a railway from Cairo to Suez. Galloway's death and politics intervened, so the project was neglected until it was 'dusted off' in 1843 with J. A. Galloway as engineer. After Pasha Abbas succeeded Mohamet Ali, in 1849, he decided to proceed with another railway and, at the end of 1850, he sought out the man recommended by the British Consul, namely Robert Stephenson. (20) Oddly, unlike his predecessor, the new Pasha decided his railway should follow the canal and river from Alexandria to Cairo, leaving the desert section to Suez as a road. Robert 'surveyed' the route on his return to Alexandria, and expressed himself 'disheartened about the future of any railway scheme along the canals' owing to their winding nature.

In March 1851, Charles Murray, the British Consul, approached Robert on behalf of the Pasha to ascertain whether he would be prepared to act as Engineer-in-Chief for a railway from Alexandria to Cairo. Robert replied in the affirmative on 24 March, (21) and perhaps, as he had had enough of building colossal bridges for the moment, he was glad his remit avoided bridging the Nile or other major rivers. The line was proposed to leave Alexandria, at the docks in Gabbari, and follow to the south of the Mahmudiyah Canal for over 30 miles, before taking a direct route to the Rosetta Branch of the Nile. Both branches of the Nile were to be crossed north of Cairo by the Barrage, a regulating dam being constructed by a French engineer, E. Mougel. The Consul's assessment was that the Pasha wished to take the whole responsibility of the cost of materials and labour, leaving to Robert only the 'scientific department in all its branches.' (21) The plans and estimates were matured at Great George Street. Michael Andrews Borthwick (1810-56), as Robert's chief assistant, made his way to Egypt in late June to get the contract, worth £56,000, signed for the design, planning, supervision of the construction and commissioning of the line. (22) On 12 July 1851, Stephan Bey signed for the Pasha and Borthwick for Stephenson. The estimated cost of constructing the railway was £840,000, and the time for completion two to three years. (21)

The Pasha had already made alterations, and reneged on some of the agreements so it is not surprising that politics intervened on something as basic as the choice of route. The Pasha had been swayed by a French counter-proposal, which made good sense, but was really aimed at delaying the railway as they favoured the canal. The southern half of their route was to lie further east, across the fertile Delta, and serve Tantā and Benha, but it would involve major river crossings. Borthwick was not made aware of this change until his visit in July to sign the contract, but he examined it before his return to England and found that the southern end mainly followed the 'Great Road'. He wrote to Consul Murray, on 6 August, saying that the 42 feet wide Great Road, '...as finished between the Mansuriyah Canal [just north of Cairo] and Benha and between Birkat as Sab' and Tantā (presuming it is elevated enough to be above the inundations, which I am informed it is) is adequate for the purposes of a railway, which would not necessarily occupy much more than a third of its width, leaving the rest for ordinary traffic.' He expressed his concerns about the nature of the river at Kafr az Zayyāt, and his personal opinion was that, allowing for the savings from using the formation of the Great Road, the alternative would cost an extra £120,000. (21)

When he returned to England on 23 August he reported to Robert who accepted his views, and wrote to the British Consul on 25 August. Robert made it clear in his letter that he preferred the original route, and had serious doubts about the bridges, which he could not resolve until he visited the country again. The Consul rebuked Robert for his temerity! In the next letter, of 19 September, Robert stated quite frankly that he still had a predilection for the original route, but that during his forthcoming visit he was quite prepared 'to go dispassionately into the whole subject.' He pointed out that 'crossing of the Nile twice invokes grand questions not merely on the original construction, but in the future working of the line - His Highness may rest assured that the whole subject shall have my serious attention immediately on my arrival, which shall not be delayed beyond I hope the first week in November.' (21)

The Pasha wanted to know whether it was the difficulties of the river crossings or the increased cost that lay behind Stephenson's reluctance. As the revised route was of more benefit to Egypt the Pasha was prepared to make an additional sacrifice of money and time in order to obtain this. Three days before Christmas 1851 Robert was ready to report his and his team's findings on the revised route. He made it clear at the outset that '...when my attention was first drawn to the question, on my visit to Egypt a year ago, it was presented simply as a means of communication between Cairo and Alexandria'. He had not even been aware of the existence of the Great Road, or the full extent of the rich and productive district of the Nile Delta. In addition the Government was not pursuing with any urgency the Barrage by which it had been hoped the original route would cross the Nile. Taking these factors into consideration led him to the honest conclusion that the new route, even with its difficult river crossings, was the best for Egypt. (21)

He proposed to use swing-bridges at Benha and Birkat as Sab' with their piers and superstructure constructed of iron. His reason for using iron cylinders, or caissons, for the piers was to enable work to be carried out without interruption during the period of the annual flood. The bridging of the Rosetta Branch of the Nile at Kafr az Zayyāt would not only be very difficult and expensive but, also because of its width, take several years to complete. Here, based on J. M. Rendel's chain ferry at Plymouth, and probably influenced by Thomas Bouch's recent success over the Firth of Forth, he proposed to introduce a steam ferry for the trains. The ferry, which would carry an entire train, would add about half an hour to the journey time compared with a bridge. (23)

In order to save money, and possibly with some lack of foresight, Robert suggested that the railway should be built with a double track formation, but that only a single line should be laid. However, doubling was necessary within seven years of its opening, and the large single-track bridges remained bottlenecks until they were renewed from the 1890s. More successfully, he specified that Greaves' all-iron track should be used. This 1846 development carried the rails in chairs cast on semi-spheroidal domes, or pot-bowls, which were laid directly on to the trackbed of soil or sand; the 4ft. 8½in. gauge being maintained by tie-bars. (Fig. 7.3) **(24)** Its suitability to Egypt was proven by the fact that it was used for around 50 years in the main lines, and at least 130 in sidings. **(25)**

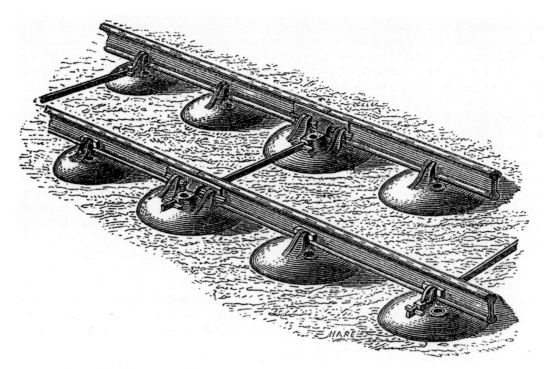

Figure 7.3: Greave's surface-packed sleepers as used on the railway. Proc. I. C. E.

The detailed survey work started in January 1852 with Henry Swinburne in charge of the southern half and Henry James Rouse the northern. The earthworks and culverts were started in April but progress was erratic due to the lack of experience of the Egyptian supervisors and their reluctant forced-labour. Under the contract, the Pasha was responsible for, amongst other things, the cost of the materials and labour, and his 'economical' use of ill-equipped forced-labour caused considerable problems for the English supervisors. Fortunately, Robert had insisted that a contract be let to an English firm '...of great experience and responsibility for laying [with native labour] of what is technically called the "permanent way"'. (21) Edward Baines designed the stations, and, later, following the death of Henry Swinburne from cholera in June 1855, he became the resident engineer.

The contract for assembling the bridges, ferry and laying the permanent way was let to Edward Price of London, and work commenced in May 1853. Grissels of London supplied the ironwork for the bridges. (26) Robert's own description of these was given in the eighth edition of the *Encyclopaedia Britannica*: -

'In the larger viaduct [Benha] there are ten spans or openings, the two centre ones comprising one of the largest swing-bridges that has been attempted.

'The total length of the swing-beam is 157 feet; it is balanced at the middle of its length on a large central pier. When open to the navigation a clear water-way is left on either side of the central pier of 60 feet. Each half of the beam sustains its own weight as a cantilever, 66 feet long.

'The eight remaining spans are 80 feet in the clear, arranged four on each side of the centre portion; and the total length of the viaduct between the abutments is 865 feet.

'The piers consist of wrought-iron cylinders, 7 feet in diameter below the level of the low Nile, and 5 feet in diameter above that level. They were sunk by a pneumatic process to a depth of 33 feet below the bed of the river, through soil of a peculiarly shifting character, and are filled with concrete.

'There are six of these cylinders in the centre pier which support the swing-bridge; and the adjacent piers on either side of the centre have each four cylinders; each of the remaining piers has two cylinders only. The tops of the cylinders are covered by cast-iron circular plates which rest entirely on the concrete, special care being taken to avoid any contact with the cylinders. On these circular plates rest the upper cast-iron plates which connect the piers, and form a seating for the bearing-plates of the beams.

'The beams or tubes are 6 feet 6 inches deep, and 6 feet 6 inches wide at the bottom, tapering to 6 feet wide at the top, and they rest at their ends on rollers working between planed surfaces to admit the motion caused by expansion and contraction.

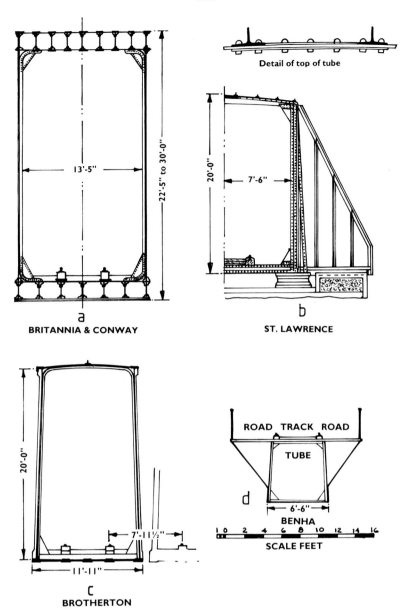

Figure 7.4: the variations in the cross-sections of Robert Stephenson's tubular bridges. (a) The design used for the Conwy and Menai bridges with cellular tops and bottoms. (b) A half-section of a typical span of the Montreal Bridge, the triangular sections are only over the piers. (c) The much lighter Brotherton Bridge over the River Aire with the tube too narrow for larger trains. (See chapter 5) (d) Benha Bridge, the forerunner of modern tubular bridges.

'The tubes carry a single line of way on their tops, the rails being laid on longitudinal sleepers, and there is also a roadway 4 feet wide [cantilevered] on either side, supported by wrought-iron brackets bolted to the sides of the tube.

'These roadways are of corrugated iron, resting on the brackets, and stiffened by strips of bar-iron placed transversely on the top.

'The six cylinders for the central pier are also provided with cast-iron circular plates, as before described, and surmounted by a framework of cast-iron, uniting the tops of the cylinders, and serving as the lower tramway for the rolling machinery.

'The revolving machinery of a turn-table containing eighteen accurately turned conical rollers, their angle being determined to the greatest nicety, and corresponding with the angular surfaces of the tram-plates between which they revolve.

'The diameter of this turn-table is 19 feet from centre to centre of the rollers.

'The whole of the rollers, together with the wrought-iron circular frame to which they are attached, form an independent system, usually termed the "live-ring," held in its position by the central pivot. The frame of the "live-ring" is connected with the rollers by radial spindles with gun-metal gudgeons at the periphery and the centre. And, to prevent any difference in angular speed between the rollers and the centre portion, a very excellent arrangement is adopted, which consists of a diagonal strap passing over the central wheel, and extending to the outer periphery. This strap is keyed up to any adjustment in which it firmly keeps the radial spindles.

'The swing-tube is firmly attached to the upper tram-plate by a system of cast-iron bracket-work and strong bolts and nuts; forming, in fact, as is most essential at this point, an exceedingly rigid attachment. The centre pivot is of forged iron, 9 inches in diameter, and turned accurately to fit its bearings. To ensure a firm fixing for this pivot, it is made to pass through the entire depth of the lower tram-plate into a socket provided for that purpose, in which position it is firmly keyed. The bridge is turned with facility by a capstan worked by two men, with gearing communicating with the large rack surrounding the lower tram-plate. [The original idea had been to use a steam engine to turn it. For drawings of the Benha Viaduct see rear endpapers.]

'To prevent accidents to the swing-bridge when open, "fenders" are placed up and down stream, similar in construction to the piers of the bridge. At the bearing ends of the swing-bridge arrangements are made for locking it in its position. These consist of fixed inclined planes attached to the under surface of the bearing ends of the tube, and corresponding wedges which slide on the piers, which are made to recede and advance by means of a screw turned by gear-work.

'In the Birket-el-Saba Viaduct the swing portion forms spans on each side of 43 feet, and the fixed portion consists of two spans of 70 feet each. In other respects the viaducts are precisely similar.' (27)

There was a problem during the construction of the piers on the Benha Bridge due to scouring of the river bed in the abnormally high annual flooding of 1853/4. It was found, after the waters had subsided, that the foundations had been exposed to a dangerous extent. Robert's solution required the removal of the concrete from the cylinders forming the piers, and extending them so that they could be driven deeper by amounts varying from 10 to 25 feet. This was achieved by Hughes Patent Pneumatic Apparatus, which had been developed for driving the cylinders at Rochester Bridge in 1851. The bridge at Birkat as Sab' and the jetties for the ferry at Kafr az Zayyāt were also similarly modified. In December 1856 the contractor claimed £26,766 for the extra work, but Robert recommended to the Railway Divan that he should only be paid £12,000 over and above the contract price of £330,000. (21)

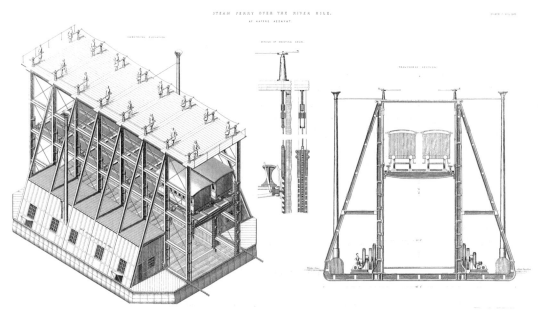

Figure 7.5: the cumbersome design of ferry for use at Kafr az Zayyat. The figures on the top deck are ready to work the screws to adjust the level of the train deck to the mooring jetties Proc. I. C. E.

Robert Stephenson, C. H. Wild and G. D. Dempsey designed the chain ferry which crossed the 1800 feet Rosetta Branch of the Nile at Kafr az Zayyāt. It was manufactured in Newcastle from ironwork supplied by Haywood's Foundry, of Derby; its cost including the jetties was £18,000. It was very large, being 60 feet wide, 80 feet long and about 60 feet high; it was made of cast-iron sections and had a timber upper deck that carried two tracks. The height of the deck could be raised or lowered to suit the river level by ingenious adjusting screws designed by his cousin, George Robert Stephenson (1819-1905) (28) This was necessary since there could be a seasonal variation in water level of as much as 27 feet. Two horizontally mounted 15-horse power engines each drove 9 feet diameter chain wheels; the chains were at 28 feet centres. The specially shaped mooring jetties extended into the river to reduce the passage to 1,100 feet. The time taken for the crossing was six minutes, but the total time allowing for loading and unloading took around half-an-hour. (29)

The ferry was brought into use around June 1856. However, within a year of its commissioning, the Pasha, when in a hurry, was delayed by the breaking of one of the chains, and he ordered it to be replaced by a bridge. (29) G. R. Stephenson designed the single-track tubular swing-bridge, which superseded the ferry. Pasha Said formally opened it on 25 May 1859; it cost £135,000 and weighed 2,634 tons. **(30)** This was one of 38 wrought-iron bridges that had been constructed at Robert Stephenson & Co.'s Newcastle works by 1863. (31) In 1877, Alfred Garwood, the first British Locomotive Superintendent, discovered the ferry in a neglected state at Cairo, and he arranged for it to be put into use for ferrying rolling stock across the river at Cairo (Būlāq), as there was no bridge there until the closing years of that century. (32)

In 1855, in order to save the costs of an English consultancy, the Pasha decided to use one of his own government's engineers, M. Mouchelet, a Frenchman, to continue the line to Suez. (33) Presumably it was felt that enough experience and knowledge had been acquired, from watching the British engineers, to 'go it alone'. Robert had intentionally reduced the number of Britons employed on his railway in order to allow the indigenous labour to become responsible for many of the tasks, so he may not have been at all concerned by this turn of events. However, he was highly critical of the route chosen to Suez. It was completed on 5 December 1858, (34) and Robert took a journey over it a few days later. He described it in a letter to G. P. Bidder as being 'a great engineering blunder' as it climbed to a height of 700 feet, whereas if it had been built a few miles further north it could have been level! (35)

Robert met the Brunels in Cairo as planned on 20 December 1858, and they dined together with a few mutual friends on Christmas Day at the Hôtel d'Orient. Although Isambard was in very poor health, he was in very high spirits - 'as free of care as a schoolboy'. (36) It is gratifying to find that two of the greatest engineers that have ever lived should spend their last Christmas together in such happy circumstances - but wouldn't we like to know what they talked about?

The following letter sent later by Pasha Said gives an indication of the regard in which Robert was held in Egypt in spite of his opposition to the canal. (37)

'My Dear Mr. Stephenson,

I have just learnt from Mr. Hugh Thurburn that your health has been deteriorating for some time, and I don't want the post to go without telling you how this bad news has affected me.

I would like you to believe that this letter is not just a simple act of politeness, but to see it instead of proof of the attachment that I have for you and the great esteem that I have always had for your honourable character and for your great ability. I also hope that you will be well enough to honour me by sending a word to me in reply, as soon as your state of health permits this.

Believe me, my dear Mr. Stephenson, that the sincere wishes that I send you for many more years of life, are not less precious to our country as to your own. Be assured of my affectionate good wishes.

Mohamed Said.

Cairo, 17 October 1859.'

Unfortunately Robert was already dead, and to paraphrase Gray's Elegy, 'Honour's voice could not provoke the silent dust, or flattery soothe the dull cold ear of Death.'

The Victoria Bridge over the St. Lawrence River

On Robert's first visit to Canada in October 1827 he was not impressed: -

'...we passed over into Canada, which is far behind the [United] States in everything. The people want industry and enterprise. Every Englishman, however partial he may be, is obliged to confess the disadvantageous contrast. Whether the cause exists in the people or the system of government I cannot say – perhaps it rests with both.' (38)

The earliest railway in Canada had been authorised in 1832, but railway construction did not take off until the late 1840s. It was obvious that the development of the large, but very sparsely populated country, whose waterways were frozen for more than four months of the year, would be stultified without an efficient railway system. Finance was desperately needed to promote the railways, and Britain was looked upon to provide much of the investment and engineering expertise. The first real impulse given to railway promotion was derived from the Railroad Guarantee Act of 1849, by which the Canadian Government was obliged to assist private companies to build railways. **(39)**

A consortium, including two of the contractors that had been involved in the Chester & Holyhead Railway, namely Peto, Brassey, Betts & Co., had become interested in the possibility of building lines in Canada. In 1852, they offered to raise the finance and construct a trunk line from Toronto to Montreal, and possibly a bridge over the St. Lawrence. **(40)** From April 1852, another C&HR personality, former resident engineer Alexander M'Kenzie Ross (1805-1862), **(41)** collected information, and estimated the costs of railway construction in the province. He was accompanied by the contractor, (Sir) William Jackson M.P., who was later to join the consortium that built the railway. They thought a complete system of railways could be built, but emphasised that in order to be viable the scheme would have to include a bridge over the St. Lawrence in the vicinity of Montreal. **(42)**

A number of projected railways agreed to become part of the system, which was to be known as 'The Grand Trunk Railway of Canada' (GTR); its first Act was passed in 1852, with capital of £3,000,000. The next year the company was authorised to increase its capital or borrow another £1,500,000 to construct a railway bridge over the St. Lawrence; this was to become known as the Victoria Bridge. (43)

Before the Victoria Bridge was built the only connection to the south shore of the St. Lawrence, and with the United States, was by paddle-wheel ferry boats and barges, of very shallow draught; these could operate only in the summer. When the river was frozen over, sleighs had to be used, but at least twice a year, for two or three weeks, the river was impassable even for these. (44)

At the site of the bridge, determined by the location of Montreal, a small shallow lake, known as La Prairie Basin, forms the St. Lawrence. (Fig. 1.5) The bed of the lake is solid rock, and strewn with boulders, which vary in weight from one to twenty tons. Some granular and boulder clay deposits in the centre of the river, which cover the bedrock to a maximum thickness of only twelve feet. The greatest depth of water in summer was found to be 15 feet, and in winter 40 feet. The river was nearly a mile and three-quarters wide, at the point chosen to bridge it, but the main problem was caused, not by the length but by the weather, particularly the behaviour of the ice. Had it not been for the ice it was an ideal situation to build a bridge. (45)

Ice starts to form around the beginning of December, and by January there is an enormous mass of broken ice, which comes down into the river from the lakes above; also immense quantities of spongy ice, known as 'anchor ice', form at the rapids within a very short time. The ice continues to accumulate, and eventually the river becomes so full, and its current so sluggish, that the channels choke and a 'jam' takes place causing the river level to rise. As the water continues to rise, the jam against which the ice field rests eventually gives way, and a whole section of the river, which is frozen into one large sheet, moves down stream with destructive inevitability. It is this phenomenon, known as the 'shovings', which occurs around the beginning of January and the end of March, that was so dreaded by the communities around Montreal. The edges of the huge ice field plough into the banks to a depth of several feet, carrying away everything in reach. In places the ice packs to a depth of thirty feet and it goes crushing and grinding until another jam takes place. (46)

In January 1855, James Hodges (1814-79), the contractors' agent for the bridge, witnessed a typical shoving: -

> 'The whole of the river and the La Prairie Basin was one mass of packed ice, which, being held up by the jam below, had been accumulating and rising for four days. At last some slight symptoms of motion were visible. The universal stillness, which prevailed, was interrupted by an occasional creaking, and every one breathlessly awaited the result, straining every nerve to ascertain if the movement was general. The uncertainty lasted but a short period, for in a few minutes the uproar arising from the rushing waters, the cracking, grinding, and shoving of the fields of ice, burst on our ears. The sight of twenty square miles (over 124,000,000 tons) of packed ice (which but a few minutes before seemed as a lake of solid rock) all in motion, presented a scene grand beyond description.' (47)

Obviously no temporary works could withstand this battering, and the permanent piers of the bridge would need to be immensely strong.

In 1846 the Hon. John Young, of Montreal, was impressed by the need to bridge the St. Lawrence, and on his instigation several surveys were carried out to select a site for, probably, what would be a timber structure. Thomas C. Keefer made the latest and most detailed survey in 1851 at a cost of $8,000 (£2,000). (48) Unsurprisingly, in the autumn of 1852, A. M. Ross recommended that a tubular bridge would answer the purpose, and, inevitably, Robert Stephenson's opinion was requested on the construction of it. (49) At the end of the year, A. M. Ross, by now designated Engineer-in-Chief of the whole of the GTR, **(50)** returned to England to consult Robert with the information that he and Mr. Keefer had obtained about crossing the St. Lawrence. By 18 March 1853 their joint plans and estimates for the bridge were ready, and sent to the Canadian House of Assembly. The bridge was to carry a single track of the 5ft. 6in. gauge which had been, unwisely, adopted for the railway. **(51)**

Figure 7.6: The after effects of a shoving at Montreal. Illustrated London News *March 1859*

The two engineers sent a letter to the Board of Railway Commissioners, on 6 June 1853, with a description of their intentions: -

'...the site selected for the bridge embraces as wide a range of deep water as can be obtained by any line crossing the river ... the width from bank to bank is 8,600 feet, the deep water channel occupying about one-seventh of this width.

'The abutments of the proposed structure are placed 6,588 feet apart, and the piers (twenty-four in number) occupy 450 feet of this space, leaving 6,138 feet clear waterway, which is equal to 93 per cent. of the whole, having an average summer depth of 9 feet water, the navigable channel being 15½ feet deep.

'It is proposed to fill up the intervening space between the abutments and the shores on either side (700 feet in length on the St. Lambert, and 1,300 feet on the Point St. Charles side) with solid embankment composed of stone.

'The piers are proposed to be built of solid masonry, of such form and proportions as will be in every way calculated to withstand any pressure to which they may be liable from the moving ice.

'The superstructure is proposed to be of wrought iron, constructed in every respect on the same principle as the Britannia Bridge over the Menai Straits, on the Chester and Holyhead Railway, and in uniform spans of 242 feet, excepting that over the navigable channel, which is intended to be 330 feet.

'The strength is calculated to resist four times the actual load to be sustained, and equal to ten times the moving load, reckoned at one ton to the lineal foot.

'The clear headway above summer water level is placed at 60 feet for the whole width of the centre opening, a height which, from the best information we can obtain, is ample for the passage of any craft which can come down rapids. [The Lachine rapids where the St. Lawrence fell 42 feet in two miles were eight miles upstream]

'From the pier on either side of the centre opening, the height gradually diminishes at the rate of 1 in 130 to the extreme ends of the tubes, and at this point falls towards the shores at a rate of 1 in 100, to suit the local requirements connected with the railways on either side of the river.' (52)

Because of the cost and size of the bridge, it was appropriate that Robert should visit Canada to see the site, discuss the problems and explain the design in detail, as well as to give his personal commitment to the project. He left England in July 1853, and remained in Canada until September. On 19 August 1853, the citizens of Montreal gave him a magnificent banquet, and in return he gave them, in the opinion of his contemporaries, the best speech that he had ever made. As usual his eloquence was driven by his frustration about the lack of overall control of railway development in England, and the chaotic, and uneconomic situation of the numerous, unnecessary, competitive lines that had emerged. He pleaded with the Canadians, at the start of their railway building, not to make the same mistakes. He reassured his audience about their proposed bridge's ability to resist the ice shoves, and justified the choice of the site. (53)

William Jackson, who had carried out most of the negotiations between the GTR and the Canadian Government, joined the contractors, and the contract for the bridge was signed on 29 September 1853, between Messrs. Jackson, Peto, Brassey and Betts and the railway company. A clause required, 'The Bridge when completed to be in perfect repair, and of the best and most substantial character, and to be approved by the said Robert Stephenson'. Also stipulated was that Robert could only be replaced by a nominee of the president of the Institution of Civil Engineers, but A. M. Ross could be replaced by an engineer nominated by Robert, in the event of either's inability to complete their duties. (54) Robert died just before its completion, and G. B. Bruce, A. M. Ross and B. P. Stockman jointly carried out the final inspection.

Preparatory work started, in October 1853, to build or acquire the barges, steam tugs and other plant and equipment needed to complete the temporary and permanent works. Quarries of very hard limestone were opened up to supply the quarter-of-a-million tons of masonry required in the construction of the bridge and its approaches. In an attempt to speed up the work the contractor decided to build two large cofferdams on the shore during the winter. This would allow them to be floated, into the positions where the bridge piers were to be constructed, as soon as the ice melted. When the December ice became safe to work on, the positions of the bridge piers were accurately set out, and marked with pins driven into the bedrock. Soundings were taken through the ice to find the profile of the rock floor within the areas where the cofferdams were to be placed. (55)

Despite all their preparations the spring of 1854 burst upon the country before the barges, steamboats and dams were ready. The caissons, to form the dam for the north abutment, and the floating dams for Nos. 1 and 2 piers were eventually towed into position, and scuttled with some difficulty against the five miles per hour current. It took three months to complete and seal the abutment dam, to permit the masonry work to commence. The current, the boulders, a fissure in the bedrock, and a collision with a raft, meant that the floating dams for the first two piers were much delayed; they were not ready to enable their masonry to be started until mid-July, and mid-November respectively. The awkwardness of positioning the floating dams, and the impossibility of getting skilled labour to do the work, led the contractor to try to construct cribwork cofferdams for Nos. 5 and 6 piers. Although rarely used in Britain, at that time, cribwork was widely used in North America for foundations and retaining walls. Again problems caused by the current meant that the crib dams were not ready for use in 1854, though the experience gained made it easier for the future. (56)

When winter set in the contractors did not have time to remove the temporary dams, and the January 1855 shoving, already described, took them all in its path. The only permanent work to suffer from the enormous onslaught of ice was some 9,000 cubic yards of fill in the uncompleted embankment approach to the north abutment. (57) There was not a lot to show for the very hard work carried out in the first year, but it was not just the physical complications of the site that slowed the project. North America was going through a construction boom, and skilled labour was at a premium; strikes were also numerous. To make matters even worse, a cholera epidemic struck the site in July, causing deaths and leading to the dispersal of some of the gangs. (58)

Inflation occasioned by the Crimean War caused financial embarrassment for the GTR, and the contractors carried out little preparatory work during the winter of 1854–5. The programme adopted for the second year was modest; it entailed finishing the masonry of No. 2 pier, but only attempting to build Nos. 3 to 6 piers and the south abutment to above summer water level. (59) During 1855, the cost and other factors led to substantial criticism of the bridge and its design. Some religious fanatics even thought the very act of building it was an affront to God!

Although Robert was isolated from the day-to-day problems, he had to defend the design against cost-cutting suggestions, by a Mr. Liddell, that were presented by the directors of the GTR. On the rest of the railway the contractors were completing their work faster than the GTR could pay, and, to try to alleviate the situation, the directors suggested that the engineers redesign the bridge to reduce its cost by a quarter. (60) (Jeaffreson actually states that the cost had to be reduced *to one-quarter*,) (61). This could only be achieved if the bridge was built entirely of timber, but current experience, in the United States, indicated that timber railway viaducts could have a life expectancy of as little as ten years. **(62)**

With the winter conditions prevailing on the St. Lawrence, for a timber bridge to survive even ten years would have been amazing.

I. K. Brunel, Edwin Clark and A. M. Ross were asked for their opinions in support of the original design. Isambard inevitably suggested that bigger was better; 'After much consideration of the "Victoria Bridge" my impression is that a considerable saving could be effected by increasing to a moderate extent the spans and the weight of the iron and diminishing the number of piers.' **(63)** Without the full details of the costs this was a tempting thought. However, the large navigation span used over twice as much iron per foot run as the smaller ones, and even if all the spans had been made 330 feet the savings from eliminating just six piers would have exactly balanced the increased cost of the iron. The estimates (64) for the original design were: -

Approaches and abutments	£200,000
Piers	£800,000
Superstructure	£400,000
Total	£1,400,000

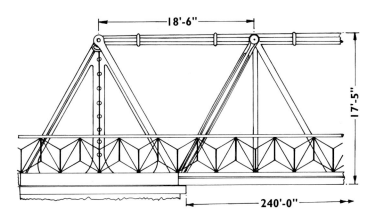

Figure 7.7: a comparison between Wild/Cubitt's design at Newark Dyke and Macneill's Boyne Bridge.

Over 100 years later, when the economic possibilities of the box girder were eventually appreciated, and the technology fully developed, it was to become a viable and quick way of building substantial bridges. However, in November 1855, Robert had to justify his design against the latest suspension, lattice, and Warren truss bridges, which his critics thought could save a significant amount of money if they were used.

> 'The tubular system is openly declared by some to be a wasteful expenditure of material for the attainment of a given strength; in short, that in the scale of comparative merit, it stands at the lowest point. This, if it were a fact, would not be extraordinary, since it was first proposed for carrying railways over spans never before deemed practicable; but in the following remarks I hope to convince you, in the simplest manner, that (except in particular cases) whilst it is not a more costly method of construction, it is the most efficacious one that has hitherto been devised.' **(65)**

He then compared examples of the other bridge types. The capability of John Roebling's brand new 821ft. span suspension bridge over the Niagara Gorge to carry rail traffic was due, in part, to the possibility of tying the underside of its deck to the rocks below. **(66)** If a multi-span suspension bridge had been used over the St. Lawrence, the ice shovings would have precluded the use of similar ties. Robert's report suggested that, even if 700 feet suspension spans could have been satisfactorily designed, the cost of their large masonry towers would have been greater than that of the more numerous piers for the tubular bridge. It was calculated that there was a theoretical overall saving of 10%, over the suspension bridge, in favour of the more practical tubular design. It was made clear in his report that it implied absolutely no criticism of the use of the suspension principle at the Niagara. He quoted what A. M. Ross had written to him, '...no other system of bridge-building yet devised could cope with the large span of 800 feet'. (67)

Robert then demonstrated 'that no saving *of importance* [it. sic] can be made in the construction of the roadway of the Victoria Bridge, as it is now designed, by the substitution of any other description of girder.' Joseph Cubitt (1811-72) had used a Warren truss to carry each of the separate tracks over the Newark Dyke on the Great Northern Railway. **(68)** Although it looked a lot lighter, each span actually weighed 292 tons for a length of 259 feet, against an estimated 275 tons for a length of 257 feet on the Victoria Bridge (the dimensions are overall). (Fig. 7.7) The weight of the smaller spans of the Victoria Bridge, when built, averaged 303 tons, but their deflection, when loaded with one ton per foot run, was less than one quarter of that of the similarly loaded Newark Bridge. A comparison was also made with Sir John Macneill's (c.1793-1880) imposing contemporary lattice girder bridge over the River Boyne, in Ireland. **(69)** As this bridge was for double track some assumptions had to be made, but it was calculated that a tubular design would have provided a lighter two-track structure, with lower compressive stresses. (70)

Criticism of the expense of the masonry piers, with the ice-breakers incorporated in their design, (Fig. 2) has been shown to be unjustified by the fact that they have survived to this day with only normal maintenance in their brutal winter environment. **(71)** The alternatives proposed would certainly have disappeared very early in their lives.

His conclusions were unequivocal: -

'I have to state to you (my deliberate opinion) that the present design now being carried out for the Victoria Bridge is the most suitable that can be adopted, taking all the circumstances into consideration, to which the question relates. In making this statement, I must ask you to bear in mind that I am not addressing you as an advocate for a tubular bridge. I am very desirous of calling your especial attention to this fact; for really much error prevails upon this point, through the impression that in every case I must appear as an advocate: no one is more aware than I am that such inflexible advocacy would amount to absurdity.'

'Over the St. Lawrence we are, fortunately, not compelled to adopt very large spans; never so large, in fact, as have been already accomplished by the simple "girder" system. It is under these circumstances that the suspension system fails, in my opinion, to possess any decided advantage in point of expense; whilst it is certainly much inferior as regards stability for railway purposes.' (72)

When the report was presented to the directors, one of them felt sufficiently embarrassed to resign. The GTR's situation was fairly desperate, and having failed with the hard-nosed engineers, the directors had to look elsewhere for economies. The contractors were then targeted, and forced to agree to arbitration, which reduced their prices, and required them to waive their contingency claim of £100,000. (73) The final cost of the bridge came to £1,356,021, i.e. 90% of its authorised capital. (74)

The late start, caused by the financial uncertainty, meant that the progress on the piers and cofferdams was slow, and in 1855 did not even reach the modest target set. As agent for the contractors, James Hodges suggested that the contract be abandoned at the end of the year, but, to paraphrase his words, 'Different views on these matters prevailed, and it remained to the contractors to complete the works they had commenced.'(75) Work on the piers went on steadily, but sometimes very eventfully, over the next four years. Occasionally, when they thought that they had the measure of the tricks and manners of the river, and tried to steal a march on it, it did not behave predictably and they ended up worse off. Once the dams were sealed and pumped out the masonry work could be completed very quickly because of the large, accurately shaped stones that were used; these weighed between five and fifteen tons. As an example, the foundation stone for the last pier of the bridge was laid on 12 August 1859, and by 26 September the whole 108,000 cubic feet of its masonry had been laid. (76)

The final cross section of the tubes is shown in Fig. 7.4. According to Jeaffreson it was originally intended (as at Benha) that the trains would run on top of all but the three centre tubes. **(77)** Hodges says that the design was modified after Robert visited Canada, and it is very probable that this alteration was made to give increased clearance above the river to avoid damage by the shovings. Enough confidence had now been gained with tubular bridges to enable the cellular construction, used on the C&HR tubes, to be dispensed with, even on the 330 feet navigation span. The smaller tubes were originally intended to be continuous over four spans, but because of large temperature variations and other factors, it was decided to join the spans only in pairs and fix them on their centre pier.

The wrought iron for the Victoria and the other iron bridges, together with locomotives and rolling stock for the GTR, were manufactured in England, at the contractors' Canada Works, which had been specially set up in Birkenhead. George Robert Stephenson and Benjamin Prior Stockman prepared the drawings, and George Harrison supervised the manufacture. (78) Early problems with the exact alignment of the rivet holes during assembly in Canada, led to them being drilled slightly undersize at the works, and then reamered on site. James Hodges was very impressed by the accuracy attained in the preparation of the ironwork. 'In the centre tube, consisting of 10,309 pieces, in which were punched nearly half a million of holes, not one piece required alteration, neither was there a hole punched wrong!' (79) The total weight of iron used was 9,044 tons.

Like the small tubes of the Britannia Bridge all the tubes of the Victoria Bridge were to be assembled in situ. Robert emphasized to the contractor that the tubes needed to be supported on very substantial timber staging, as any settlement during assembly, which caused delays, could result in the complete loss of a tube and its staging by the onset of the shovings. (80) Assembly of the first tube started on 15 August 1857, and the last was completed on 12 December 1859. The shortest time taken to complete a span was 39 days, and the longest was 84 days. (81)

In June 1858, the contractors made the very positive decision to attempt to complete the bridge by the end of the next year; 'From that day the greatest activity prevailed, and every one seemed animated with the desire to accomplish the work.' (82) In order to fulfil this, it was necessary to construct the navigation tube and three of the others between the early January shovings and the final break up of the ice at the end of March. The prospect of working against the clock, in temperatures as low as minus 30°C, was daunting. However, considerable precautions, ingenuity, determination, and an element of good luck, meant that their objective was achieved. On 12 October 1859, the day of Robert's death, only four of the 25 tubes remained uncompleted. (81) The bridge was ready for the first trains to cross it on 19 December 1859, and on 25 August 1860, the 19-year-old Prince of Wales drove the last rivet and formally opened the bridge. Contemporary opinion considered it 'a wonder of the world.'

A decade after its opening coal-fired locomotives started to replace the older wood-burners, and their more corrosive exhaust gases started to damage the bridge. An almost continuous aperture, 20 inches wide, was cut in the centre of the top of the tube, apparently without significantly weakening the structure. This not only provided ventilation but also lighted the bridge.

Within 40 years much of the GTR's main lines had been doubled to accommodate the burgeoning traffic, and the single line bridge over the St. Lawrence had become a severe bottleneck. **(83)** Work on the replacement, the Victoria Jubilee Bridge, started in October 1897. It was built to carry a double track railway, two carriageways and footways. It used the old piers but was cantilevered out to give a total deck width of 66ft. 8in. In these days when it is necessary to close down sections of our railways for several weeks in order to carry out relatively simple alterations, it seems incredible that the longest time that this river crossing was closed to rail traffic during the replacement was *two hours*! The double track railway was opened on 13 December 1898. (84)

Figure 7.8: a contemporary engraving of the completed bridge viewed from the upstream side. It was then the longest in the world. Jeaffreson Volume 2.

NOTES AND REFERENCES

1. *Rapport sur l'établissement de Chemins de fer en Suisse par MM. R. STEPHENSON, M. P. et H. SWINBURNE, experts appelés par le Conseil fédéral.* (1850). I am most grateful to the late Sister Marie Madeleine for locating a copy of the original report in a Swiss library, and to my own sister for her expert translation of the document.

2. The letter from R. S. to Swinburne, dated 14 July 1850, gives his intended movements. He had expected to send his yacht ahead to Genoa, and sail as far as Greece before returning in it to England. Another letter, dated 3 July, includes the well-known remark about the anticipated dinner at Newcastle being his crucifixion. Northumberland County Record Office ZSW 539/32.

3. E. F. Clark, *George Parker Bidder,* (1983) p. 73.

4. Letter dated 15 September 1850, from R. S. in Zurich to Mr Starbuck

5. W. W. Tomlinson, *The North Eastern Railway Its Rise and Development,* (1914) p. 302. J. I. C. Boyd, *The Festiniog Railway* (1975) states that R. S. was consulted about the inclines on this railway in 1835 and that a water wheel was used to assist the haulage of wagons up them.

6. Werner Stutz, *Bahnhöfe Der Schweiz,* (1983) gives many of the opening dates of the Swiss lines.

7. A. Helps, *Life and Labours of Mr. Brassey,* (1872) p. 163.

8. The figure of £10 per mile per week was quoted frequently in reports and evidence for rural branch lines. The average receipt for all the lines in the U. K. in 1850 was £36.5 per mile – the lowest figure in 30 years.

9. There was, in fact, competition and in 1918 1,510 out of 2,980 total mileage was owned by the Swiss Government (*Railway Magazine* 1918, p. 183.)

10. *Proc. I. C. E. Vol. 96,* 1889, p. 332. *Vol. 15,* 1856, p. 79 says C. B. Vignoles completed this line! Also *Vol. 20,* p. 173.

11. *Bradshaw's Railway Manual, Shareholders' Guide and Directory 1890,* p. 380. The average for all lines in the U. K. in 1870 was £2,909 per mile per annum, or £56 per week.

12. Alan Clothier has kindly made available his extensive research, from primary sources in Britain and Egypt, for this section.

13. *Proc. I. C. E. Vol. 10,* pp. 369- 380, Joseph Glynn, 'On the Isthmus of Suez and the Canals of Egypt'.

14. *Encyclopaedia Britannica,* (1973) Vol. 21 pp.366-7 gives comprehensive details of the early proposals.

15. Glynn, op. cit. p. 379. Some years after the first investigation Negrelli wrote a false and vitriolic attack on R. S. regarding his lack of involvement in the canal issue. Although Negrelli had only sent deputies to Egypt, in the first case, but Robert had been in the country, he accused him of not investigating the canal route. It appeared in the *Austrian Gazette* on 18 June 1858, and suggested that Robert had lied both to the Institution and to Parliament about his investigations. It was strenuously refuted in a subsequent issue. (See J. F. Layson, *Famous Engineers* (1888), pp. 227-230, for details of the correspondence)

16. Jeaff. Vol. 2, pp. 148-152. Also John Pudney, *Suez,* (1968) pp. 5, 50-71. C. Beatty, *Ferdinand de Lesseps,* (1956), pp. 159-60 states that because of a misunderstanding of the newspaper report of the debate, de Lesseps actually demanded satisfaction from R.S. The misconception was cleared up and they again resumed their cordial relationship.

17. *Autobiography of Sir John Rennie,* (1875), p. 141. When R.S. had visited the Bitter Lakes in the autumn of 1850 he had found them completely dried up due to evaporation.

18. Ibid, p. 132, states that the Mahmudiyah Canal '…was frequently filled up by the sand blown in from the desert and the adjacent shores.' It had been completed in 1815.

19. Egyptian National Railways (E. N. R.), Railway Museum Archives, Cairo: un-referenced. After the opening of the Suez Canal de Lesseps erected a bust to the memory of T. F. Waghorn as the originator and pioneer of the commercial route through Egypt.

20. Henry Swinburne, 'Nile Cruise' (1851) I. C. E. Archives.

21. P.R.O. FO 141/19.

22. Lionel Wiener, *L' Egypte et ses Chemins de Fer,* (1932) Appendix 'A' gives the contract details.

23. T. Sopwith, 'Account of the Steam Ferry over the River Nile at Kaffre Azzayat.' [This is one of the variations of spelling used for Kafr az Zayyāt.] *Proc. I. C. E.* Vol. 17.

24. *Proc. I. C. E. Vol. 11,* pp. 252 gives the date of introduction of this type of chair as 1846. Hugh Greaves took out around a dozen patents for permanent way, including one in 1846, but none resembles this type.

25. P.R.O. FO 881/5503 gives report by Marindin and Farrer (1887) on Egyptian Railways, which speaks highly of this track when properly maintained. Alan Clothier located some in a siding in Upper Egypt as late as 1987, and it can be seen also supporting two Robert Stephenson & Co. locos in the E.N.R. museum in Cairo.

26. *Illustrated London News,* 1 March 1856.

27. *Encyclopaedia Britannica,* (1856) pp. 609, 610. Jeaff. Vol. 2, p. 176 refers to this description as 'terse'!

28. *Proc. I. C. E. Vol. 163,* pp.386-8, for G. R. Stephenson's obituary.

29. T. Sopwith op. cit.

30. *The Engineer,* 24 June 1859, p. 439, where it is wrongly attributed to Robert Stephenson. H. J. Rouse was the resident engineer.

31. J. G. H. Warren, *A Century of Locomotive Building,* (1923) p. 409.

32. A. E. Garwood, *'Forty Years of an Engineer's Life at Home and Abroad'* (c. 1903) p. 109.

33. *Railway Times,* 6 September 1856.

34. P.R.O. FO 141/36.

35. Jeaff. Vol. 2, pp. 248-9.

36. Letter from R. S. to G. P. Bidder, Cairo, 22 December 1858.

37. Ibid. pp. 261-2. The original is in French.

38. Jeaff. Vol. 1, p. 110.

39. J. M. & E. Trout, *The Railways of Canada,* (1871), pp. 50, 57. Although the first railway had been opened in July 1836, only 66 out the ultimate maximum Canadian railway mileage of 44,000 miles had been completed by 1850. During the 1850s another 1800 miles were added of which 870 were built for the GTR. (*Proc. I. C. E. Vol. 20* p. 115.)

40. Ibid. pp. 68-9. (Sir) Samuel Morton Peto (1809-89) was now chairman, and (Sir) William Jackson a director of the C&HR.

41. Professor Sir Alec Skempton, (Editor), *Biographical Dictionary of Civil Engineers, Volume 1,* (2002) p. 586, gives some details of A. M. Ross's career, as does *The Illustrated London News,* 19 February 1859, pp. 176-8, 180. His death on 8 Aug. 1862 is reported in *The Engineer* 15 Aug 1862, p. 93.

42. J. Hodges, *Construction of the Great Victoria Bridge in Canada,* (1860), pp. 3, 4. *I. L. N.,* 1859 p. 178. Few copies of Hodges' book have survived but a photocopy of the complete work is in the I. C. E. Library. (An original was sold in North America for $20,000 in 2003!) Some biographical information about Hodges is given in R. S. Joby, *The Railway Builders,* (1983) p. 75.

43. Trout, p. 70.

44. *Canadian National Magazine,* August 1950, pp. 2, 22.

45. Hodges p. 5.

46. Ibid. pp. 5, 6.

47. Ibid. pp. 29, 30.

48. Trout, p. 68-71.

49. Jeaff. Vol. 2, p. 199-200. Hodges, op. cit. p. 4.

50. *I. L. N.* 1859 p. 178 states, 'In December, 1852, Mr. Ross was proposed as engineer-in-chief for carrying out the works of the Grand Trunk Railway to completion. This was accomplished; but not without a good share of such abuse as the disappointed in every country usually level against men in any prominent position, or who are more successful than themselves.' It has been suggested that, sadly, this 'abuse' and a controversy arising from it, which was stirred up by G. R. Stephenson, may have hastened his demise 'after a long and severe illness', within two years of the bridge's completion. The inscription at the entrance to the bridge made it clear, on the same line, in same size lettering, that Robert Stephenson and Alex. M. Ross were the engineers.

51. Trout, p.62, suggests that the wider gauge was adopted contrary to the weight of evidence. T. C. Keefer expressed '...the opinion that time would vindicate the sufficiency of the narrow gauge, and that most authorities to which he referred, including that of Mr. Robert Stephenson, were in favour of narrow [4'-8½"] gauge.' He was right; the gauge was altered to standard in the 1870s!

52. Jeaff. Vol. 2, pp. 199-202.

53. Ibid. pp. 181-6.

54. Ibid. pp. 187-8.

55. Hodges, op. cit. pp. 11-19.

56. Ibid. pp. 19-25.

57. Ibid. pp. 30-1.

58. Ibid. pp. 26-7.

59. Ibid. p. 31.

60. A. W. Currie, *The Grand Trunk Railway of Canada,* (1957) p. 45.

61. Jeaff. Vol. 2 p. 210.

62. *Proc. I. C. E. Vol. 107,* 1891, 'Presidential Address' p. 13 states that from around 1865 timber bridges in America were being superseded by iron ones, but in 1885 over 85% were still timber. See M. Chrimes, *Civil Engineering 1839-1889,* p. 133.

63. R. A. Buchanan, *Brunel,* (2002) p. 96. R. S's letter of 1 Nov. 1855, requesting I. K. B's opinion did not give any details of the costs.

64. Hodges, p. 96.

65. Ibid. pp. 85-99, gives R. S's letter to the directors in full. Jeaffreson gives its date as 5 Nov. 1855.

66. Roebling's suspension bridge was cable-stayed from above, and, during construction, because there was no navigation involved, he had been able also to tie the deck to the rocks below by means of 56 stays; even so trains were restricted to 3 mph. See *Papers and Practical Illustrations of Public Works of Recent Construction both British and American,* Weale (1856) These ties were an afterthought and they do not appear either on the copy of Roebling's drawing published in Weale, or on some early illustrations. They were added after the even larger Wheeling suspension bridge (road), in West Virginia, was destroyed in a gale on 17 May 1854. Roebling's bridge was largely rebuilt by 1886, and a steel arch replaced it in 1897. The initial success of Roebling's suspension bridge compared with contemporary British bridges was because of his use of air-spun cables, which he had patented in 1841, rather than chains. In an early example of unjustified 'Stephenson bashing' the *Illustrated London News,* 9 April 1859, when reporting on a routine inspection of Roebling's bridge said, 'Mr. Stephenson, however, has not such a favourable opinion of the structure, and considers that a tubular, and not a suspension bridge, ought to have been erected. To this high opinion it may be added, however, that a tubular bridge would have cost three-quarters of a million or more, and that the suspension bridge has been constructed for less than £80,000' What R. S. actually said, when writing about the Niagara Bridge, was that he considered, '...this work as one of the most remarkable that

claims our attention.' (*Enc. Brit.*), and '…neither can any one who has seen the locality fail to appreciate the fitness of the structure for the singular combinations of difficulties which are presented.' (Report to G.T.R. directors, 1855)

67. Hodges, pp.95-97.
68. *Proc. I. C. E. Vol. 12*, p. 601, states that former C&HR engineer, C. H. Wild, suggested the design of the bridge.
69. James Barton, 'On the Economic Distribution of Material in the Sides, or Vertical Portion of Wrought-Iron Beams.' *Proc. I. C. E.* 1855, pp. 452-8, gives a description of the Boyne Viaduct. J. B. Macneill had built the first iron lattice girder railway bridge in Britain, on the Dublin & Drogheda Railway, in the early 1840s, but unfortunately it needed an additional pier and other modifications so that it '…could no longer be considered as a true lattice bridge.'(W. Humber, *A Practical Treatise on Cast and Wrought Iron Bridges and Girders,* [1857], p. 93) Within 7 years of its construction the Boyne Viaduct also required an intermediate pier to support its main span. The lack of success of this prototype, and other early lattice bridges, led a number of engineers, including Stephenson and Brunel, to avoid lattice construction. A development in 1851, on a six span bridge over the Vistula at Dirschau, was to combine the tubular idea with the dense lattice sides on the American Town principal. Each span was 130.88 m. The bridge was completed in 1857 and partly destroyed by the Polish army on 1 September 1939. A similar two span bridge at Malbork over the Nogat was completed in 1857. (W. Ramm, *Die Alte Weichselbrücke in Dirschau. (2004)*)
70. Hodges, pp. 91-4, 102.
71. A letter from A. M. Ross to R. S. 'as to ice breakers confirming the propriety of the design of the Victoria piers' was sent with a letter of 11 Jan. 1856 to I. K. B.
72. Hodges, p. 98.
73. Currie, p. 45.
74. Trout, p. 81.
75. Hodges, pp. 34, 5.
76. Ibid. p. 67.
77. Jeaff. Vol. 2, p. 209. The Egyptian tubular bridges had all been built with the tubes under the track. Hodges, p.8, illustrates the contemporary St. Anne's Bridge over the River Ottawa, by A. M Ross, which had only three of its numerous tubular spans with trains passing through them.
78. Hodges, pp. 62, 81.
79. Ibid. p. 62.
80. Ibid. p. 45.
81. Ibid. p. 83.
82. Ibid. p. 53.
83. A 1911 Encyclopaedia states: 'For a few winters, while the bridge accommodation at Montreal was restricted to the old single track Victoria Bridge, railway freight trains were run across the ice in winter on temporary tracks.'
84. *Canadian National Magazine,* August 1950, p. 22.

Figure 7.9: Hodges' impression of the only way a tubular bridge could be built over the Niagara.

CHAPTER EIGHT: OTHER DETAILS OF HIS LIFE AFTER 1833.

With Robert's appointment as Engineer-in-Chief of the London and Birmingham Railway in September 1833 it was no longer tenable for him to retain his house at 5, Greenfield Place, Newcastle. He had frequent long absences from it while working on other lines and completing the Parliamentary work for the L&B. Instead, early in 1834 he took a comfortable house on Haverstock Hill, in Hampstead, close to the railway. (1) London remained his home for the rest of his life, but many years later he said with regret, 'The Robert Stephenson of Greenfield Place is the Robert Stephenson I am most proud to think of!' (2) At that stage he had youth, vigour, ambition and a young wife to spur him on, with the prospect of the colossal engineering of the L&B occupying much of his energy for the remainder of the decade. An indication of his workload in the 1830s is that, by June 1840, he had already engineered over 300 miles of railway at a cost exceeding £11 million. (3)

The 1840s were marred by tragedy and difficulties, and burdened by overwork. In his personal life he suffered the loss of his wife who died on 4 October 1842 after a long and painful fight against cancer. This left him vulnerable to depression and loneliness. His wife's health had always been delicate, and the 13-year marriage was childless. On her deathbed Fanny pleaded that Robert should remarry, but he never did. (4) Six years later, in 1848, his beloved, but often exasperating, father died unexpectedly. George married his housekeeper, some years his junior, a few months before his death, and everyone had anticipated him having years of life ahead of him. (5)

In professional life the decade had started with near bankruptcy for Robert due to his innocent involvement in the Stanhope and Tyne, and had been marred later by the Dee Bridge disaster. The additional workload caused by the railway mania, the battle of the gauges, and the atmospheric disputes was something he could well have done without. These made it necessary for him to brief himself on numerous schemes prior to tedious, but searching, questioning by Select Committees. The peak of the mania occurred in 1845-7, at a critical time when the design and development of the tubular bridges for the Chester and Holyhead deserved his total attention. Samuel Smiles described this imposition with justifiable feeling, and went on to blame it for the early deaths not only of Stephenson, but also Brunel, Locke and his partner, Errington: -

> 'But much of his labour was heavy hackwork of a very uninteresting character. During the sittings of the committees of Parliament, almost every moment of his time was occupied in consultations, and in preparing evidence or giving it. The crowded, low-roofed committee rooms of the old Houses of Parliament were altogether inadequate to accommodate the rush of perspiring projectors of Bills, and even the lobbies were sometimes choked with them. To have borne that noisome atmosphere and heat would have tested the constitutions of salamanders, and engineers were only human. With brains kept in a state of excitement during the entire day, no wonder their nervous system became unstrung. Their only chance of refreshment was during an occasional rush to the bun and sandwich stand in the lobby, though sometimes even that resource failed them. Then, with mind and body jaded – probably after undergoing a series of consultations upon many bills after the rising of the committees – the exhausted engineers would seek to stimulate nature by a late, perhaps a heavy, dinner. What chance had any ordinary constitution of surviving such an ordeal?' (6)

The astonishing list of railways that he had some engineering involvement with in 1847 is given in Appendix 7. His auspicious reputation made his opinion valued on any engineering subject. He was a Commissioner for Health in Towns, and in the 1840s London and Liverpool even consulted him on their water supply problems. In addition he was called in to advise on river improvement schemes in East Anglia, with G. P. Bidder and Sir John Rennie. (7) Jeaffreson rightly observes: -

> 'From 1840 to 1850, he had never known a day free from grave care. No sooner was one stupendous under taking brought to a close, than others rose to take its place. For the greater portion of that time he had under his care many distinct affairs, any one of which would have over tasked the powers of a man of ordinary capacity.' (8)

Fanny's death caused Robert to leave Haverstock Hill; though it had been convenient during the building of the L&B it was too far from town and from the society of the clubs which he now frequented to lighten his loneliness. He went to live in Cambridge Square in 1843, but scarcely had he moved in when the place caught fire. George was staying on the night of the fire, and when Robert and the servants dashed out of the house in panic in their nightclothes, George, 'with his presence of mind and readiness for action', managed to appear fully dressed with his overnight bag in his hand! (9) Robert returned to the house after it was repaired, but around November 1847 he left it for 34, Gloucester Square, a little nearer to Hyde Park. This move, of a mere 200 yards, needed an outlay of almost £10,000 for the purchase of the property, but set against an income of £30,000 a year (about £3 million at present day values) this was negligible. (10)

He shared the house with brother-in-law, John Sanderson, and his wife; they had four servants and a groom. Robert enjoyed riding so having his own stables at the rear was most convenient. The house was filled with books, clocks and scientific instruments, and 'had almost the appearance of a museum.' His interest in geology was shown in the cabinet that held his South American mineral specimens and various types of coal. He had paintings by Sir Edwin Landseer and Francis Danby together with a number by John Lucas. The well-known paintings of the group of engineers at the Britannia Bridge, the ones of his father and the family group at Killingworth were all by Lucas. One entitled 'The Stepping Stones', which represents a girl carrying a small child over a stream with the Britannia Bridge in the background, is reputed to commemorate a little girl who was killed during the bridge's construction. After the Great Exhibition he made a shrewd purchase of Hiram Powers' 'Fisher Boy', the companion to his internationally famous sculpture of the 'Greek Slave' of 1843. (11)

Robert was a member of several clubs, (see Appendix 8) but he became a member of the most exclusive club of all when he was invited by the electors of Whitby to stand as their member of parliament. He was elected on 30 July 1847, and he held Whitby for the Tories until his death. (12) George Hudson had hoped to stand for Whitby in 1841, but the seat did not fall vacant, and he was elected instead as M.P. for Sunderland in 1845. Hudson maintained interests in the development of the town by his Whitby Building Company, and was instrumental in Robert's nomination as 'a fit and proper candidate'. (13) Jeaffreson gives a somewhat sentimental explanation: -

'The invitation was unanimous. All shades of political opinion were merged in a common desire to pay a well-merited compliment to the man who had been tested by years of arduous service. At any time this expression of confidence would have been agreeable to him; but coming to him when his reputation was under the cloud temporarily cast over it by the failure of the Dee Bridge, it made a deep and permanent impression on his heart.' (14)

Robert was no doubt flattered by his election, but he made little impact until 1850 when he defended the Great Exhibition in his maiden speech. It was most unusual for him to take on a commitment that he did not put a lot of effort into, but this was because of his railway workload. However, neglect of his constituency did not go down too well in Whitby, and he nearly lost the seat in the 1852 general election.

Parliament had avoided making sensible legislation when it was most needed at the start of railway development, but recently, W. E. Gladstone (1809-98), as President of the Board of Trade, had included some sensible and some disagreeable requirements in his 1844 Act. Joseph Locke entered parliament for Honiton in the same general election as Robert, and the pair might have hoped to lead the opposition to any future 'nonsense'. Later, when the Post Office wanted to put the railways at a disadvantage, Robert put his views on Government legislation very clearly in his presidential address to the Institution of Civil Engineers on 8 January 1856. 'The extraordinary feature of the Parliamentary legislation and practice consists in anomalies, incongruities, irreconcilabilities, and absurdities which pervade this mass of legislation.' Again nothing changes!

There were other causes that Robert would have liked to champion during his terms, if the opportunity had arisen, for example railway construction in Ireland. He had been touched by the plight of the poor in Ireland when he first visited the country in 1823. In 1846 Lord George Bentinck (1802-48) was trying to get Parliament to do something practical to mitigate the appalling effects of the famine there. He argued that Ireland had enough food for her poor, but that the poor had no means of buying it, and he supported a programme of subsidised railway construction to provide employment and wages. George Hudson, Robert and a number of other railway engineers were in favour of the idea, for purely altruistic motives. Robert prepared some figures for the amount of labour that could be employed in gainfully extending the Irish railway system, and Lord Bentinck used them in his speech in support of his Bill on 4 February 1847. He concluded that 1,500 miles of railway construction would employ 110,000 men and, by providing support for their families, at least 550,000 people would benefit. Although their fellow-countrymen were starving to death, the House killed the idea, and several thousand men, women and children, by deferring the Bill. **(15)**

During his time in Parliament Robert usually voted in support of his party but generally did not take part in debates unless the subject touched on his professional life. He was vehemently anti-free trade, 'protectionist to the marrow, ...To his dying day he argued warmly in favour of this great commercial fallacy'. His stubbornness, but inner uncertainty, was demonstrated when, towards the end of his life, he would lose his temper if friends discussed the subject. When the abolition of the Corn Laws was finally voted, in 1859, he was 'in the memorable minority of 53 against the equally memorable majority of 468.' (16)

He spoke on professional subjects: water supply (25 March 1852), sewage (17 June 1853), Ordnance Survey maps (19 June 1856), and against the Suez Canal (17 July 1857 and 1 June 1858). On maps he preferred them to be only to a scale of one-inch to the mile, and considered the larger scales, even the superb 25-inch, to be useless for railway construction. **(17)** Although his political judgements were often wrong, he was a respected and well-liked member of a House where convictions were usually similarly awry.

It was inevitable that Select Committees considering railway subjects should call on his expertise. Robert gave evidence to the Railway and Canal Bills Committee, in February and March 1853, which had taken under its remit the investigation of railway amalgamations. In the answers to his first questions he felt that it was Government policy 'to encourage amalgamation decidedly', and he confirmed his well-known dictum, 'where combination is possible competition is impossible.' He thought that within a few years all the railways would be amalgamated, but, in fact, it took 80 years longer than he predicted. Together with other witnesses he felt that some sort of board of *experts* should be set up to review proposals for new railways, in preference to the normal system of 'volunteering' M. P.s to Select Committees, regardless of any knowledge that they may have had of railways or the district to be served. He provoked the committee by suggesting that the French and Belgians handled the authorisation of railways better than the British did! Edward Cardwell, the chairman of the Select Committee, and then President of the Board of Trade, agreed when he formally reported to the Speaker of the House at the end of the inquiry; -

> 'It has appeared in evidence, that one of the most important objects which could result from our labours would be the adoption by Parliament of some mode of dealing with railway legislation, more consistent, more uniform, and more comprehensive than the present plan.'

He suggested how this could be done but, as usual, the sound recommendations were shelved, making everyone's efforts a total waste of time! (18)

In 1854 Robert was able to use his position as an M. P. to overturn an Admiralty condition in the Act relating to the construction of the North Eastern Railway's new coal-shipping dock at Jarrow, on the River Tyne. Tyne Dock, a long-held ambition of his friend T. E. Harrison, was to be built on a tidal waste, known as Jarrow Slake. Because the dock was to occupy 50 acres of the Slake, the Admiralty, with their usual bizarre reasoning, required a compensating excavation either opposite the Slake or further upstream. Robert's action saved the company from wasting between £30,000 and £40,000. **(19)**

Robert became involved in the Prince Consort's 'Grand Industrial Exhibition', in the summer of 1845, and served for a few weeks as chairman of the executive committee before becoming a member of the Royal Commission on 12 February 1850. (20) Most significantly he was instrumental in getting the acceptance of (Sir) Joseph Paxton's (1803-65) outstanding, but uninvited, 'crystal palace'. The design for the exhibition building, originally approved by the committee in June 1850, less than a year before the exhibition was due to open, was an enormous and ludicrous brick structure crowned with a cast-iron dome by I. K. Brunel. (22) On 21 June 1850, by accident or design, Paxton joined the same London train as his friend Robert Stephenson at Derby, with his completed drawings. What happened when Paxton pushed these unsolicited plans into Robert's hands is recorded in a letter he sent to his wife, Sarah, on that evening: -

> 'He pointed out it was too late, the whole thing had been settled and decided ... Stephenson then lit a large cigar and began to examine the plans slowly and carefully. Nothing was said for a long time, Stephenson being unaware that his cigar had extinguished itself. Then he rolled up the plans with one word "admirable". He was quite delighted with my plan and has promised to aid and assist me in every possible way.' **(23)**

Robert fulfilled his promise, and arranged an interview between Paxton and Prince Albert on 24 June. The Prince did not like the brick monstrosity, and was most impressed by Paxton's light and airy design. The preliminary plans and specifications were submitted to the committee on 10 July, and the Crystal Palace was officially accepted on 15th. (24) Paxton wrote to his wife that during this period 'Stephenson sticks closer to me than a brother.' (25)

Criticism of the Great Exhibition by Colonel Sibthorp, M. P. for Lincoln, led to Robert's maiden speech to the House of Commons on 4 July 1850. Sibthorp had been against anything progressive including parliamentary reform, Catholic emancipation, free trade and, most particularly, railways. Robert's speech 'made a most favourable impression on the House.' (26) Due to the outstanding efforts of (Sir) Charles Fox, and his firm Fox & Henderson, the Crystal Palace was ready for opening on 1 May 1851.

Robert's health had been irreparably damaged by years of overwork and strain when he decided to retire from railway work in this country. His retirement dinner was held on the platforms of the still uncompleted Central Station in Newcastle on 30 July 1850, 'as a mark of respect for his talents, science, and unblemished character.' However, Robert referred to it, in a private letter, as his crucifixion! The Hon. Henry Thomas Liddell, son of George's patron, Lord Ravensworth, presided for the occasion, which had 400 invited guests. The last tube of the Britannia Bridge had been floated just five days before, and the near-disasters with the earlier tubes had made Robert very tense. The concerned chairman was moved to say: -

> 'I am afraid his own health may have in some degree suffered by the anxiety he underwent on that occasion; and if he should feel unable duly to answer the compliment paid him on this occasion, I firmly believe that to the anxiety of mind he has undergone during the last few days may alone be attributed to that inadequacy.' (27)

Earlier in his speech H. T. Liddell had referred to the amount of railway construction that Robert had been involved in. The exaggerated figures give some idea, at least, of his participation in the lines: Eastern Counties and branches, 296 miles; London and North Western and branches, 377 miles; Midland, Birmingham and Derby, and branches, 302 miles; North Staffordshire, 148 miles; South Eastern, 25 miles; Whitehaven and Furness, 69 miles; York and North Midland, 220 miles; other lines in the North East, 215; independent railways, 136 miles; Florence and Leghorn, 60 miles. This made a total of 1,850 miles, but a more accurate assessment of his *major* involvement would give about half this figure. (28)

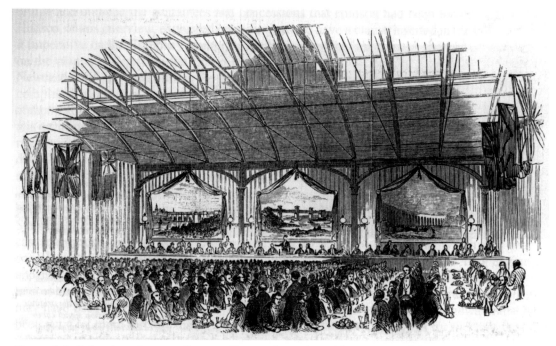

Figure 8.1: Robert's retirement dinner at Newcastle station with portraits of the High Level, Britannia and Royal Border Bridges behind the top table. Illustrated London News, *10 August 1850.*

Robert did reply, and gave an indication of the changing roles of principal engineers, particularly on the almost complete York Newcastle and Berwick Railway whose toast he proposed: -

> 'He observed that an "engineer-in-chief", as the phrase now went, had little to do in these days, but to indicate the original arrangements of the great works which the people of this country were accustomed to see springing into existence around them. No one felt more intensely than himself the value of the assistance that was rendered to a principal engineer by his associates. The engineers of former times, as you would learn from their histories, were drawn into excessive detail. When they flourished society was not in the same condition as now; intelligence was not so widely diffused. Smeaton had not only to plan but to execute; he had to devise even the machinery and the apparatus by which the work was to be done. But society has changed its aspect. The modern engineer has only to say, "Let this or that be done," and it was done. There were contractors with immense capital, and possessed of ample intelligence and skill for its direction, who would undertake the execution of any works, however difficult or stupendous. Over the works in this district with which his name had been associated, he had exercised only a general superintendence – he had done little more than lend them his name – it was to others the

merit of their construction was chiefly due; and he felt it to be most fortunate for him to have conjoined with Mr. Thomas Harrison. On that gentleman the whole responsibility had devolved; and it was owing to his exertions and skill that those works had been executed without a single flaw.' **(29)**

On 24 April 1846, some time before the tubular bridge controversy (Appendix 5), T. E. Harrison had been equally self-effacing when he wrote about the High Level Bridge. 'The plans have been prepared under my direction: the designs are not mine but my friend Mr. Robert Stephenson's.'(30)

Regardless of his health problems, 1850 was a propitious time to retire from railway engineering in Britain. A recession and the exposure of George Hudson's malpractices, in the first half of 1849, had meant that investment in railway construction had virtually dried up. Many companies were unable to promote extensive new works until well into the next decade. **(31)** A letter that Robert wrote to the computer pioneer, Charles Babbage (1791-1871), on 13 September 1849, sums it up, '...I dare say you are fully aware of the state of our profession just now - many leaving it and many half starving in it.' Dividends in Hudson's companies had sunk to less than 2% in 1850 and took several years to recover anything approaching their earlier value; the shares that Robert had inherited from his father must have depreciated considerably in the short term.

T. E. Harrison shone in the inquiry held into the affairs of the York Newcastle and Berwick following George Hudson's departure, and in the subsequent reorganisations he became not only the engineer but also the general manager of the company. In 1851, Robert, being acceptable to both parties, was brought in to arbitrate in a dispute between Hudson and the YN&B. This concerned the financial effect of Hudson's lease of the Newcastle and Carlisle and Maryport and Carlisle Railways had on the YN&B, and Robert awarded £793 in favour of the YN&B. (32) This just one of scores of questions in which he acted as arbitrator throughout his career. One in 1847 regarding the purchase of Liverpool's Water Companies by the Corporation involved the sum of £622,000. (33)

Robert's plans for a carefree retirement were thwarted, in some ways, by commitments that he had accepted earlier. The construction of a railway in Norway arose from a holiday in 1846, and his involvement in the Egyptian one from his canal consultations of 1847. In the autumn of 1846 he was worn out by the continual hassle of the committee room contests provoked by the railway mania, and sailed to Norway with G. P. Bidder to enjoy some relaxation. However, hardly had they begun to enjoy having nothing to do when the Norwegian government consulted them about the question of a railway from Christiania (Oslo) to Lake Mjösa. Robert supported the idea, and when the line was proceeded with, in 1850, he became Engineer-in-Chief. He visited Norway in connection with their railways, in the autumns of 1851, 1852, 1854 and 1859, and even made loans available to help extend the line to Trondheim. (34) He received the commission for the Victoria Bridge in Canada as a result of the respect that his former resident engineer, Alexander Ross, had for his judgement and the report on Swiss railways as a result of his international stature.

On 15 June 1850 Robert wrote to his friend, partner and mentor Edward Pease: 'I find it a very difficult matter to bring to a close so complicated connection in business matters as that which has been established by 25 years of active and arduous professional duty.' (35) It is doubtful if Robert would have been happy to retire completely from all but his Parliamentary work, and his learned societies, but he would certainly have wished to have fewer demands made upon him. He was called on by genuine organisations and by former colleagues who considered it most important to have his suggestions and seal of approval for their current projects. Unfortunately, because he was so friendly and approachable, cranks who wanted his opinion of their harebrained schemes also besieged him both at the office and at home. When he gave reports they were lucid, concise and reasoned, as exemplified by this one of September 1851, on the viaducts on the Huddersfield to Penistone line, for the Lancashire and Yorkshire Railway directors: -

'It affords me satisfaction to be able to report to you my entire conviction of their perfect safety. Their strength is abundant and I consider their mode of construction simple and efficient.

'Wooden viaducts for railway purposes are frequently comprised of complicated trussing for the purpose of obtaining the greatest amount of strength from the least consumption of material. This, as a purely scientific question, is no doubt interesting, but practice had led me to look upon it as worse than useless, for the timber is cut up into small parts and the number of joints so increased as to lead to rapid decay both in the quality of the structure and in the firmness of the structure.

'In the viaducts I examined this defect has been avoided, the timber is employed in larger masses, the parts are fewer in number and properly applied. I do not feel it is necessary for me to report to you in detail on technical matters. I will only therefore add that you may rest assured that both structures are perfectly safe and only require careful and periodical examinations by your resident engineer who should from time to time make reports on them to the Board.'(36)

The last work that Robert undertook in Britain was to rebuild the famous iron bridge, of 1796, over the River Wear at Sunderland. In the early 1850s the bridge had been endangered, and the *Illustrated London News* takes up the story: -

> 'In the early part of 1853 the Bottle Works on the south-west side of the bridge required considerable enlargement, occasioning a large portion of the limestone rock to be blasted: one of the blasts proved too powerful, and a mass of rock under the abutment fell into the river, causing alarm for the safety of the bridge. This side of the bridge was at once shored up, and a large mass of masonry added to the abutment. The engineers who reported on the stability of the structure recommended the corporation to erect a new bridge. Robert Stephenson, Esq., C. E., furnished the design for the proposed bridge, which preserved many of the leading features of the old bridge, the roadway being at the same time considerably widened [to 41ft. 6in.] and levelled. Mr. Stephenson entrusted the new erection to the eminent contractor, Benjamin Lawton Esq., in conjunction with Messrs. Hawks, Crawshay, and Co., of Gateshead, at a cost of about £35,000.'

The work was completed 'with marvellous rapidity' by March 1859, but, due to Robert's poor health, was supervised by George Henry Phipps. (37) The bridge was finally replaced in 1929 by a utilitarian steel three-pin arch, which has none of the appeal of the Tyne Bridge of the same vintage.

Unlike many prominent Victorians, Robert never occupied a country estate, but found a more congenial outlet in his successive sailing yachts *Titania*, on board which he enjoyed playing host to his friends. The first *Titania*, one hundred tons, was launched in 1850 and provided a very enjoyable form of relaxation until its destruction by fire at Cowes in 1852. It has sometimes been alleged that Robert could have outbursts of bad temper, but his reaction to the news of its demise was amazingly calm. His cousin, George Robert, had been allowed to borrow the vessel at any time when Robert did not need it, as on this occasion when, unfortunately, an overheated flue from one of the cabin fireplaces set light to the yacht. When his cousin arrived at Gloucester Square in obvious distress, Robert was dining with a party of friends. Robert invited him to dine with them, and, after hearing the explanation, he said 'Never mind, old boy, we'll have a finer vessel than the old *Titania* before we are many months older.'

John Scott Russell (1808-82), Brunel's collaborator for the *Great Eastern*, who had built the first *Titania,* was instructed to build the new one of 184 tons; it was launched on 21 June 1853. While Robert was waiting for the replacement, he wrote to his old friend Constantine Moorsom, on 25 May: -

> 'I find I can get no peace on land. I am therefore preparing another sea lodging-house. I find it no easy matter to get rid of the multitude of questions which follow on a tolerably long professional life. Indeed I feel that nothing gives me actual freedom from attack, but getting out of the way of the postman. The sea, therefore, is my only alternative. Ships have no knockers, happily.' (38)

The new yacht was ninety feet long, and twenty-one feet over beam, and 'was a yacht for a sailor to criticise with approval'. The saloon and sleeping cabins were large, the former being sixteen feet by fifteen feet and eight feet high. It had a crew of sixteen and 'a good cook', an extensive library and 'a first-rate cellar'. Despite his unfortunate experience, Robert was still generous in his loan of the vessel to his friends. One notable example was in 1856 when Professor Charles Piazzi Smyth, Astronomer Royal for Scotland and brother of Henrietta (Baden) Powell, **(47)** was sent to Tenerife to make scientific observations. Smyth's funds were very limited, so Robert placed *Titania* and her crew at his disposal. (38)

In the autumn of 1857 Robert visited the haunts of his youth in the company of Charles Manby (1804-84), the long-serving secretary of the Institution of Civil Engineers. At Killingworth they walked the well-trodden highways and he showed where he worked, fished and played pranks. He then sought permission to enter the cottage where he had spent his formative years, and had been engaged in memorable discussions with his father and like-minded prophets of the age of steam. The friendly Northumbrian woman who opened the door welcomed him inside, and he found many of the contents as he remembered. He was even able to demonstrate a secret drawer, which his father had made in the desk that was unknown to the occupants; sadly it turned out to be empty. After gossiping for a few minutes he rose to leave, and, with tears in his eyes, he crossed the familiar threshold for the last time. He later visited Wylam to see the house in which the Stephenson family had occupied a single room at the time that his father was born. As a memento he ordered an excellent clock from Isaac Jackson, an ingenious self-taught mechanic in the village, for which he paid £39 – about as much as his grandfather would have earned in a year. (39)

He also visited the Forth Street factory, which in his later years was generally for pleasure as the business was doing well. It was now fabricating bridges, caissons, dock gates, and ships as well as locomotives and engines. Edward Pease makes several references to the works in his diaries. In August 1848, when his other investments were depressed, he wrote: 'I see everything except the Forth Street concern sinking'. At the end of the year he recorded, 'Pecuniarily I have cause to admire how an effort to serve a worthy youth, Robert, the son of George Stephenson, by a loan of £500, at first without expectation of much remuneration, has turned to my great advantage. During the course of the year I have received £7,000 from the concern at Forth Street.' (40)

Figure 8.2: Robert Stephenson based on a photograph taken in 1853. Jeaffreson Volume 2.

After Robert's final visit to Killingworth, he took G. P. Bidder and other friends on a cruise in *Titania* up the east coast of Scotland, and through Telford's Caledonian Canal before turning south to spend a day on his last inspection of the Britannia Bridge. One of his guests, an old school friend, then town clerk of Gateshead, wrote: -

'I can never forget the interest which the designer and executor of that magnificent monument of skill and enterprise excited in us, as he described in his quiet way the general design, the objects to be effected by the different parts, the difficulties encountered and overcome in the erection, and the fact that if each of the enormous tubes were sawn through the middle, the bridge would carry the trains. The principal part of the description was given on top of the tube, on a beautiful morning, in full view of the Naples-like scenery of the Menai Straits, and the distant Welsh mountains, Snowdon and its associates. We smoked a cigar in quiet contemplation before we left the spot, none of the party being disposed to speak'. (39)

During his lifetime, Robert's contributions to society were recognised by a variety of honours. Foreign decorations included the Order of Leopold, presented by the King of the Belgians in 1841, and the Grand Cross of St. Olaf, by the Norwegians in 1848. In 1855 his work on the tubular bridges was recognised at the Paris Exhibition, when he was awarded the Great Gold Medal of Honour. Simultaneously, his collaborators: William Fairbairn, Eaton Hodgkinson and Edwin Clark, received first-class silver medals. The same works also earned Robert the Legion of Honour from the French Emperor, Napoleon III. (41) He was made a Fellow of the Royal Society in 1849, and Durham University awarded him a Master of Arts degree in the following year. In 1857 Oxford University conferred on him the Doctor of Civil Law; at the same ceremony his fellow civil engineers, I. K. Brunel and Sir John Macneill, explorer David Livingstone and General Sir Colin Campbell (later Lord Clyde) were similarly honoured. (42)

Queen Victoria offered him a knighthood in 1850, but when he declined *Punch* took up cudgels on his behalf and on behalf of the engineering profession: -

'A Knighthood has been offered to Mr. Stephenson, and the honour courteously declined. We have a singular scale of awards in England. Lord Mayors are made baronets by the dozen. Generals, who carry off victories in India, [e.g. Lord Clyde] are made lords and marquises. A peerage is given to a banker, from the overpowering merit which a million pounds sterling was supposed to confer upon him. And yet to an engineer, who occupies the first rank in his noble profession in England, perhaps in the world; to a man who has fought with Earth, Air, and Water, and left a beautiful work upon each as a monument of his victory; to one who has enriched his country with gifts of genius, such as the Tubular Bridge, the High Level Bridge, and the Border Bridge, the offer of a knighthood is made! If Mr. Stephenson had been a tallow-chandler, and had the honour of opening the Temple Bar to her Majesty during one of her visits to the city; if he had been a lord mayor, and had eaten a public dinner with Prince Albert; if he had been the *Attaché* for years to come to some Hanway-Yard of a German Principality, or the Complete Letter-Writer of some grateful minister, a smaller compliment could not be paid to him! We are glad that he sent back the insulting offer; for we should have called it a national disgrace, and have grieved for it as a national sorrow, if a man, like Mr. Stephenson, whose works, from their magnitude and noble grandeur, are looked up to all over the world, should have done anything petty and mean to have caused their author, and the science he honours, to be looked down upon!' (43)

Robert was on the council of the Institution of Civil Engineers from 1837 to 1839, and continuously from 1845. He was a vice-president from the end of 1847 until he served his two-year term as president for 1856-7. His father was the president of the Institution of Mechanical Engineers from its formation on 27 January 1847 until his death 18 months later; Robert succeeded him, and held the position until 1853, when William Fairbairn took over. (44)

Jeaffreson's description, at this later phase in Robert's life, elaborates on Conder's earlier one when the London and Birmingham was being built. 'His social disposition rousing sympathy by means of a fine presence, a countenance singularly frank, an unaffected bonhomie, and that pleasant richness of voice that impresses the hearer with an idea of intellectual and moral excellence.' (45)

Even after removing the High-Victorian gloss from Jeaffreson's account of Robert's character, one is left with an extremely competent, civilised, well-respected, generous, but not faultless, individual. Other contemporary sources confirm this picture. If you can judge a man by the company he keeps, Robert's circle of friends indicates a diverse range of interests across the whole spectrum of society. His Sunday luncheon parties included not only the other members of the 'Great Triumvirate' but also politicians and experts in many academic fields, such as writers, Egyptologists, geologists, and artists.

(46) Another guest, Rev. Professor Baden Powell, gave his surname to the founder of the scout movement, whose Christian names were Robert Stephenson and Smyth. **(47)**

Engineers like the Rennies, C. B. Vignoles, J. U. Rastrick, and Joseph Locke who had had great differences of opinion with 'George Stephenson and Son' all became friends and, often, important supporters of Robert. The fact that his ability and self-effacing charm were able to dispel the bitter relationships that had been provoked by his father weighs greatly in his credit. George would never have maintained a friendly relationship with Isambard Brunel, had he been his contemporary. Robert frequently found himself in direct opposition to Brunel, in a professional capacity, but remained as close a personal friend as with any in his own team. There are many touching examples of their support for each other in times of stress; the most obvious being during the construction of the Britannia Bridge and the *Great Eastern.*

Shortly after Robert's return from Canada in 1853, he suffered an irreparable loss by the death of his brother-in-law, John Sanderson, who had not only been one of his closest friends for many years, but also the indispensable manager of Robert's personal and professional finances. After this Robert could not bear the solitude of the house at Gloucester Square, and took apartments in a hotel, about a mile away in Berkeley Square, which he occupied for about a year. (48)

Blows like this coupled with declining health to make his private life melancholy, but he managed to present a cheerful face in the company that he sought to assuage his grief. In the circumstances he could so easily have become a hypochondriac or a wet blanket, but: -

> 'No description of his demeanour in the society of men would be complete if it did not contain the word "jolly". He was the embodiment of joviality, without the faintest touch of boisterous awkwardness. "I never in all my life knew a more clubbable man than Robert Stephenson: it is impossible for a more clubbable man than Robert Stephenson to exist," is the emphatic testimony of Dr. John Percy.' (49)

When he attended dinners as at the Royal Society Club: -

> '…Robert Stephenson was one of the principal attractions and causes of enjoyment. He thoroughly enjoyed them, always stopping late for "just another cigar and a little more talk" – and retiring at midnight to a friend's house, or another convenient club, for "a little more talk and just another cigar."' (42)

His health in his youth can never have been as delicate as his contemporary biographers suggest. The workload of the 1830s and 1840s, even without the grief and setbacks, would have sent most ordinary healthy mortals to an early grave. If the group portraits of around 1850, at the Britannia Bridge and, perhaps more reliably, with the Great Exhibition Committee, give any idea of his appearance then he looked robust and healthy. Immediately after his retirement his health was still reasonably good, but when he had made his penultimate visit to Killingworth, in 1856, he looked so grey and worn that an old friend did not recognise him. 'What don't you know me, old friend?' asked the crestfallen Robert. After a pause, the friend said, 'Why, it must be Robert Stephenson.' 'Ay, my lad,' he answered: 'it's all that's left of him.' (50) His photograph taken with Brunel, next to the *Great Eastern,* at the end of 1858, shows him in sad decline – a man with 'all the stuffing knocked out of him'.

His last Christmas was spent with Isambard and Mary Brunel in Cairo. Brunel returned to England to fight his dual battles against fatal disease and 'the Leviathan', but Robert spent a few weeks in Paris before returning to London in early February 1859. On his return; 'The deep-seated mischief in liver, stomach, and nerves, of course remained untouched, but the distressing symptoms were less apparent.' He continued to live a fairly normal life until June. He attended Parliament, clubs, societies, and the various committees that he had been pressed to join. When Dr. John Percy called to see him on 17 June he found his health in a more precarious and wretched condition than he had ever seen it. Robert was depressed but also suffering from lassitude and loss of appetite. However, he hoped he would be able to get away once more to enjoy the benefits of sea air. (51)

In August, Robert sailed in the *Titania* from Harwich to Norway, to see the completed railway, with Tom Gooch and G. H. Phipps among his guests. The Bidders and their party accompanied them in their yacht *Mayfly*, and together they entered Christiania fjord on 21 August. Robert was well enough to make the 80 mile return trip over their railway, and to attend a celebration dinner in Christiania, on 3 September, to mark the completion of the line. Robert, as guest of honour, was given a copy of the chairman's speech in English, and a copy of his appeared in translation in the local papers to overcome the problem of language. Just before Robert rose to respond he was overcome by nausea and faintness, but managed to give a curtailed version of, what turned out to be, his last public speech. As usual he was careful to give credit to others, in this case the British Consul and G. P. Bidder: -

> 'He [Bidder] has the honour of having built the railway for an extremely low cost; he has built it for the sum of £450,000, which is less than, under the circumstances, could have

been hoped or expected. … It is quite true, as I read the translation before me, that I have been occupied in great works in other places. I have been employed in Canada, in Egypt, in Belgium, in Russia, and I may say in nearly every country in Europe. But if I could ascribe to myself the whole merit here among you, I should act unjustly towards the two gentlemen I have already named, Mr. Bidder and Mr. Crowe [the Consul], to whom so much is owing – to whom more is due than to me. But let me express my sincere gratitude for the present festival by which I am so much honoured. It is probably the last time I shall meet the citizens of Christiania. I shall leave your country on Monday.'(52)

By Monday, 5 September, his condition was so bad 'from jaundice in a most aggravated form' that it was thought possible he might die before reaching England. The nightmare journey was made worse by extreme weather conditions, and it was dawn on the 14th before they entered Lowestoft harbour. His return home to Gloucester Square seemed to provide some respite and gave, initially, some little improvement in his condition. The announcement of the death of Isambard Kingdom Brunel on the 15th was news Robert could have done without. While his spirit hovered in that twilight state between life and death there was universal concern for him. 'A continual stream of callers enquired at the door, and intelligence of his state was daily sent by rail or telegraph, to the chief centres of British industry.' (53)

Just before mid-day on 12 October 1859, Robert Stephenson breathed his last.

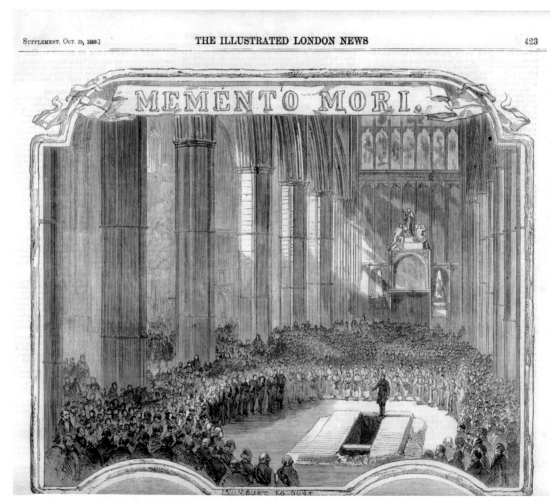

Figure 8.3: the funeral of Robert Stephenson. Illustrated London News, *29 October 1859.*

The colossal extent of Robert's life's work made him known to thousands of people, from Queen Victoria herself to the humblest of her subjects who had laboured, at some time or other, on one of his projects. Even people who had never set eyes on him were saddened by his death, and public opinion demanded that he be buried in Westminster Abbey. The obvious route for the cortège was through

Hyde Park but the Queen's permission was needed for this concession 'for which no precedent exists.' When the Institution of Civil Engineers made the request the answer came back: -

'Her Majesty considers as the late Mr. Stephenson is to be buried in Westminster Abbey, in acknowledgment of the high position he occupied, and the world-wide reputation he has won himself as an Engineer, his funeral, though strictly speaking private, as being conducted by his friends, partakes of the character of a public ceremony; and being anxious, moreover, to show that she fully shares with the public in lamenting the loss which the country has sustained by his death – she cannot hesitate for a moment in giving her entire sanction …' (54)

The funeral took place at midday on Friday 21 October, with a dense silent crowd lining the route taken by the cortège between Gloucester Square and the Abbey. Three thousand people crowded into the Abbey including 'the best and wisest in the land.' Rarely in our history has a mere commoner had such last respects paid to him or been so genuinely and widely mourned. He was laid to rest, in the centre of the nave, beside Thomas Telford, the only other engineer ever to be buried in Westminster Abbey; 'thus the two engineers who have spanned the Menai Straits, the one by road and the other by rail, sleep side by side.' **(55)**

On the day of the funeral, ships on the Thames, Tyne and Wear flew their flags at half-mast, and banks, offices and shops closed at noon in many towns in the North East. His own schooner *Titania* fired, at minute intervals, a 56-gun salute, one for each year of his life. Fifteen hundred people, including all the workmen from Robert Stephenson & Co., attended a noon service in St. Nicholas' Church in Newcastle. Later, George Robert Stephenson, as a trustee of Robert's estate, rewarded this spontaneous mark of respect from the men by arranging for £500 to go to their Sick Fund. (54) **(56)**

An emotional Joseph Locke, as president, had to address the Institution of Civil Engineers about the deaths of Brunel and Stephenson, on 8 November 1859. Of the latter he said: -

'Of that friend, I feel it to be a difficult task to speak, without giving way to feelings better fitted for the closet than a public assembly. Robert Stephenson was the friend of my youth, the companion of my ripening years, a competitor in the race of life; and he was as generous a competitor, as he was a firm and faithful friend. This will, I know, find an echo in the hearts of all around me; and your feelings will supply that laudation, in which it would seem inappropriate for me to indulge.

'Like Brunel, Robert Stephenson commenced his professional career under his father, George Stephenson. His early years were devoted to the improvement and construction of the Locomotive Engine, and to him we owe the type of those machines, many of which are now actually in use on railways. From the time of the Liverpool and Manchester Railway, when our joint Report contributed, in a great degree, to the adoption of the Locomotive Engine as the means of transport, and of the subsequent London and Birmingham Line, with its long Parliamentary contests, its Kilsby Tunnel, and other difficulties inherent in so new an undertaking, a multitude of other lines followed, in which there had to be foreseen and provided for, numerous difficulties, all of which were met and surmounted with coolness and consummate skill. Among these great works may be mentioned the Royal Border and High Level Bridges, and more especially, the Conway and Britannia Bridges, which were the first examples, on so vast a scale, of the Tubular principle, invented by him; as also the Bridges across the St. Lawrence and the Nile, remarkable alike for their grandeur of conception and successful execution.

'To my present hearers, the enumeration of the works in which Robert Stephenson was engaged would be as a "twice-told tale." Still we cannot look back without interest upon the days of the "Battle of the Gauges," - the discussions upon the Atmospheric System, - and the numerous topics which have been argued within and beyond these walls.

'In the enjoyment of a distinguished name and reputation, Robert Stephenson, like Brunel, has been cut off while still in the middle period of life; and although he pursued his profession with a persevering energy, although he accomplished in it those triumphs of the successful application of a mind well trained and stored with practical and theoretical Knowledge of various kinds, and achieved some of the greatest works of art which have been witnessed in our day, he obtained, at the same time, an eminence in the scientific world rarely reached by any practical professional man.' (57)

Travellers on the many lines that Robert Stephenson built may consider appropriate the words that Sir Christopher Wren's son wrote about his father, 'If you seek his monument look around.'

NOTES AND REFERENCES

1. Jeaff. Vol. 1, p. 181. The address given on one of his patent applications suggests that he had a temporary house in Hampstead for a few months before moving to Haverstock Hill.
2. Jeaff. Vol. 2 p. 232.
3. J. Weale, *Ensamples of Railway Making* (1843), p. xli
4. Jeaff. Vol. 1 p. 255.
5. S. Smiles, *The Lives of the George and Robert Stephenson,* (1879), p. 354.
6. Jeaff. Vol. 2 p. 135.
7. Ibid. pp. 137-8. In 1854 R. S. reported on water supplies of Manchester and Glasgow, and in 1858-9 he was involved with London's sewage problems and the choice of suitable pumping engines for Bazalgette's scheme.
8. Jeaff. Vol. 1, p. 260.
9. Ibid. pp. 259, 60.
10. Jeaff. Vol. 2, pp. 159, 60.
11. Ibid. pp. 160-1.
12. Ibid. p. 145.
13. Ibid. pp. 264-5.
14. Ibid. p. 144.
15. Jeaff. Vol. 2, pp. 131-4, also *Proc. I. C. E.* Vol. 18, pp. 28-9. The 1,500 miles of railway had already been authorised but only 123 miles had been built. The railways were estimated to cost £23 million, but the Government preferred spending £8 million on ruining the roads in Ireland instead!
16. Ibid. p. 145.
17. Ibid. pp. 145-55. In contrast, Sir Daniel Gooch never spoke once during 25 years as a member.
18. Evidence to Select Committee 1853, and letter dated 6 June 1853.
19. Discussion on T. E. Harrison's paper on Tyne Dock, *Proc. I. C. E.* Vol. 18, pp. 490, 523. This was almost certainly the last time that R. S. took part in a discussion at the Institution. The date was 3 May 1859.
20. J. A. Auerbach, *The Great Exhibition of 1851* (1999) p. 39.
21. Jeaff. Vol. 2, p. 166.
22. A. Buchanan, *Brunel* (2002), p. 138.
23. Letter Chatsworth House Archives. The meeting with R. S., on the train, may not have been accidental. Paxton had met R. S. at the floating of the third Britannia tube, ten days earlier, and he may have been well aware of R. S's intended movements.
24. Auerbach, p.51.
25. Letter Chatsworth House Archives.
26. Jeaff. Vol. 2. pp. 145-6.
27. *Gateshead Observer,* 3 August 1850.
28. Ibid.
29. Ibid. This version has more immediacy than the carefully edited version in Jeaff. Vol. 2, pp. 138-9.
30. Ibid.
31. *Builder,* 20 April 1850 states that out of 56,000 then employed in the railway industry only 107 were engineers. This explains why many sought employment abroad or in the expanding electric telegraph industry.
32. PRO RAIL 772/82.
33. *Proc. I. C. E.* Vol. 12, p. 481.
34. Jeaff. Vol. 2, pp. 130-1.
35. J. G. H. Warren, *A Century of Locomotive Building* (1923), p. 140.
36. J. Marshall, *The Lancashire & Yorkshire Railway,* Vol. 1, (1969), p. 233.
37. *I. L. N.* 19 February 1859, p. 186.
38. Jeaff. Vol. 2, pp. 169-72.
39. Ibid. pp. 237-42.
40. Sir A. E Pease (Editor), *The Diaries of Edward Pease* (1907), pp. 261, 4.
41. *Proc. I. C. E.* Vol. 19, p. 178.
42. Jeaff. Vol. 2 p. 231.
43. *Punch,* Vol. 19, p.113.
44. Skempton, p. 658.
45. Jeaff. Vol. 2, p. 157.
46. Ibid. p. 159.
47. Apparently Robert Stephenson had started a long-term affair with Miss Henrietta Grace Smyth (1824-1914), who, in 1846, became the professor's last wife, and it is very probable that the child was his. There is no documentary evidence for this statement, but it has been handed down from the society of that time, and appeared to be widely accepted in London and Newcastle. DNA would provide proof positive. Robert was the child's godfather.
48. Jeaff. Vol. 2, p. 186.
49. Ibid. p. 161.
50. Ibid. p. 240.

51. Ibid. p. 251.
52. Ibid. p. 254-7.
53. Ibid. pp. 258-61.
54. Ibid. pp. 263-6.
55. *I.L.N.* 29 Oct. 1859 p. 424. The pall-bearers were: the Marquis of Chandos, chairman of the LNWR; Sir R. Murchison, president Royal Geographic Society; Geo. Carr Glyn M.P., first chairman of the LNWR; Joseph Locke M.P., president I. C. E.; Samuel Beale M.P., chairman of the Midland Rly, and George Rennie C. E.
56. The copy of Robert's will in the Probate Office, London states that it was proved at just under £400,000. Some of this he had, of course, inherited from his father. The main beneficiary was his cousin, George Robert, who acquired the interest in Robert Stephenson & Co., Snibston collieries, the leasehold and contents of the house in Gloucester Square, half the furniture and effects of 24 Great George Street plus a legacy of £50,000. (The *Titania* was sold and the proceeds went to Robert's estate.) G. P. Bidder got the other half of the office contents and £10,000; the same sum was bequeathed to his solicitor, Charles Parker. Two male cousins got £5,000 and ten female cousins £1,000 each. A total of £25,000 was distributed between friends and former assistants with George Vaughan of Snibston getting £5,000 and Messrs. G. H. Phipps, E. Clark, T. E. Harrison, each of the Berk(e)ley brothers and W. Weallens, his latest partner at Forth Street, among those receiving £2,000 each. The Institution of Civil Engineers and North of England Mining Institution as well as two religious charities received £2,000 each. Newcastle Infirmary received £10,000. The Newcastle Literary and Philosophical Institution, from which he had acquired knowledge in his youth, was rewarded with £7,000. He had already given £3,100 to the latter to pay off half of its debts on condition that the subscriptions were halved, to one guinea (£1.05), to allow poorer workmen to further their self-education. (64) As on other occasions this action belied his words as he had maintained that the superficial education obtained by workmen at reading and lecture rooms injured them as artisans! 'A really good mechanic ought to be bent on achieving *manual* perfection, throwing all his strength of body and soul into the special task assigned to him.'
57. *Proc. I. C. E.* Vol. 19, pp. 2-3.

Figure 8.4: the Britannia Bridge caused Robert more problems than any other structure that he built. Unfortunately, it no longer survives. This photo shows the removal of the damaged tubes following the fire described in Appendix 6. Photographer unknown.

APPENDIX 1

LEVELLING AND SOME DEFINITIONS.

Most accounts of early railways mention the errors in the levels which were found in the deposited plans that the engineers submitted. The blunders found in the Liverpool and Manchester plans led to considerable embarrassment for George Stephenson. How could they occur and were they excusable? may be asked. The Romans had managed to construct canals to accurate levels with fairly basic equipment, and in the fen drainage schemes, of the eighteenth century, differences of less than one foot in a mile had been worked to with optical levels. How did early railway surveyors get several feet out?

When Robert heard of the L&M errors he wrote to Michael Longridge (1 December 1825); 'Simple as the process of levelling may appear, it is one of those things that requires care and dexterity in its performance.' Later when giving evidence for a Newcastle and Carlisle Bill, Robert had told the inquiry that anyone could learn to use a level in a day. Most engineers and surveyors would agree with him. Errors are caused by faulty instruments, mistakes in reading the measuring staff, and incorrect arithmetic in converting the readings to the accepted datum. The instrument comprises a telescope with cross hairs, a sensitive spirit level and some adjusting screws necessary to centre the bubble prior to each reading. The axis of the bubble must be exactly at right angles to the line of sight, or the plane described by the horizontal cross hairs. Simple checks and adjustments will ensure this, and any residual error can be eliminated if the distance to the furthest reading beyond the instrument, 'foresight' is made the same as the distance behind it, 'backsight' (see diagram). If the ground is fairly level the extreme readings of the staff should not be more than 100 yards in each direction. On steep slopes the height of the instrument and the length of the staff obviously will limit the maximum distances. The foresight and backsight readings on the 'change points' are the most important as any errors made in them affect all subsequent levels. Minor errors in the 'intermediate sights', particularly over rough ground are not important. Levelling in the reverse direction would be normal to check the readings at least for the change points. The improved Sopwith levelling staff was introduced in 1833 to make reading simpler.

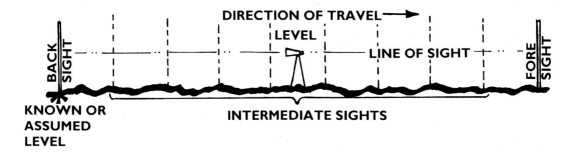

Figure A 1: a diagram showing the method of levelling over a distance of about 200 yards. J. F. A.

When levelling along a fairly straight line, like the centre line of a proposed railway, a series of pegs at one-chain (22yd or 20m) intervals would be set out to mark the route. The surveyor would set up his instrument 3½ to 4½ chains from the point that the first reading had to be taken. The level of the position, where the staff is placed for the first reading, can have been found by previous levelling or it can be a 'temporary bench mark (TBM)', with an assumed value, e.g. 100 feet. If a single surveyor is working through a railway he can relate all his levels to his starting point. On the Leicester and Swannington Railway the doorstep of the offices, with an assumed value of 180 feet above the mean water level at Liverpool, was used as the datum for all the levels. On longer railways, where a number of survey teams are employed, primary levelling can establish the value for the starting point of each team's work. Alternatively they can all start at TBMs with assumed values that have to be linked and adjusted to a single datum on completion of their levelling. If, for example, the level at the end of the first teams work, related to the correct datum, gives the value of the second teams starting TBM of 123.23 feet then all the second section levels must be adjusted to this figure. If the second team had started with an assumed a TBM value of 100 feet then 23.23 feet must be added to all their levels. In the same manner the adjustments must be found, in turn, for each subsequent section of the survey.

It was probably the arithmetic rather than the actual levelling that gave rise to the greatest errors. During the consideration of a rival scheme for the North Staffordshire Railway G. P. Bidder was able to examine the level books of the opposing surveyors and discover significant accidental errors in the reduction of their levels, which allowed him to get their scheme rejected.

During the nineteenth and early twentieth centuries the terms stress and strain were often used to describe the same thing. Strain became defined as the change in length divided by the original length, and stress as force divided by area. Stress divided by strain gives Young's Modulus, which for wrought iron is a figure around 30 million in imperial units.

John Smeaton defined the term 'resident engineer' in the eighteenth century, in the manner in which it is used today, i.e. as the engineer responsible to the client for the on-site supervision of the work by a contractor. His duties include making sure that the work is to specification, checking and agreeing quantities, and allowing minor variations. During the nineteenth century the term became used more loosely to describe assistant engineers, e.g. T. E. Harrison on the Newcastle and Berwick. It was also used to describe the engineers controlling the day-to-day maintenance of the completed lines; these were the equivalent of the divisional, district or area engineers of later years.

APPENDIX 2

LONDON AND BIRMINGHAM VIADUCTS.

The viaducts were all brick with stone facings. Their details are taken from contemporary accounts, drawings and illustrations.
River Brent. One 60 feet semi-circular arch, three 15ft. 8in. arches on each side, 28ft. between parapets. Now over North Circular Road (A406). TQ 198 838
Watford (Bushey Arches). Five 43 feet semi-elliptical arches, centre span across the road is oblique, three 10ft. blind arches, 28ft. between parapets, total length 123yds, cost £9,700. TQ 118 955
River Colne. Five 30 feet semi-circular arches, three-10ft. blind arches at each end (one buried), total length 104yds, cost £10,000. TQ 117 966
River Ouse, Wolverton. Six 60 feet semi-elliptical main arches, three small arches at one side and four on the other, 54ft. to rail level, length 220yds, cost £29,000. Near the centre of an embankment 1½ miles long. SP 815 422
Weedon Bec (over road). Five 50ft. main arches, height 35ft. SP 633 593
River Avon, Wolston (or Brandon). Nine 24ft. semi-elliptical arches, three 10ft. semi-circular arches at each end, single inverted arch spanning under the three centre arches, cost £8,600. SP 410 761
River Sowe. One 60ft. semi-circular main arch, three 17ft. semi-circular arches at each end, total length 88yds. SP 365 773
River Sherbourne. Similar to Sowe. SP 346 779
River Blythe. Two 50ft. span main arches, two 15ft. span arch at each end, 36ft. 6in. to rail level, length 70yds. SP 214 802
Lawley Street, Birmingham and River Rea. Ten 50ft. segmental main arches, skew spans over Lawley St. and River Rea, total length 237yds, cost £16,000. The longest viaduct on the line. SP 080 869

APPENDIX 3

THE DEE BRIDGE DISASTER (1)

The principle of combining wrought-iron trusses with rigid beams had been in use for building purposes for 30 to 40 years. Cast iron caused problems for bridge builders by being five times as strong in compression as it is in tension. In addition, it was difficult in the 1840s to get a sound casting for a beam more than about 40 feet long. This had led to the practice, for longer spans, of bolting two or three cast-iron beams together and post-tensioning them by means of wrought-iron trusses. After 1840 this idea was coming very much into favour, for railway bridges, usually where the clearance over a highway or navigable watercourse was critical. In these circumstances they were a fraction of the cost of a tied arch, with a suspended deck, as used on the London and Birmingham and Manchester and Leeds railways. By the time of the Dee Bridge failure there were around one hundred trussed cast-iron bridges either in use or being built, and they had almost become the equivalent, in status, to a 'Standard Bridge Type', an idea favoured later by many railways. One on the S&D over the River Tees at Thornaby, with 89 feet spans, designed by Robert Stephenson to replace Captain Brown's inadequate suspension bridge of 1829, had carried 5,000,000 tons of coal traffic since it had opened in May 1844; this suggested that they were satisfactory in service. (2)

In the middle of 1846, the opinion that the wrought-iron trusses did not aid the cast-iron beam had been expressed to Robert Stephenson, probably by Gen. Pasley, and he ordered Tom Gooch to carry out experiments. The tests were made on model cast-iron beams, 20 feet long, with and without the trusses, and suggested that the load required to break them could be increased by over 35% with the trusses properly applied. (3)

Following a paper by W. Fairbairn, at the Institution of Civil Engineers, just five weeks before the Dee Bridge collapse, the discussion of the recent failure of a trussed beam in Messrs. Gray's mill, at Oldham, was very significant. Gen. Pasley said that the official report blamed poor mortar in the walls supporting the beams as the principal cause of the disaster, and the rest of the discussion expressed conditional confidence in the beams. Robert cited the breaking of a main girder, in the early days of the Dee Bridge, '...when the whole weight was brought upon them [the truss rods], which they bore perfectly, notwithstanding the vibration of the passing trains, until the necessary repairs could be effected.' G. P. Bidder reported a similar event on the Lea Bridge. Robert ended the discussion by saying that he thought that the form of construction used at Gray's mill was not altogether bad, '...and he should not hesitate to adopt it, *if he was under the necessity of doing so; but he would provide for contingencies by adequate strength'*. He went on to endorse the use of Eaton Hodgkinson's formula for beams, which had been in use since 1831, and he had found a safe guide at all times. He stated, 'In the construction of the girders of railway bridges, the proportion of four times the breaking weight was generally adopted. The beams of pumping engines, which had the proportion of eight times the breaking weight, had been known to fail'; this failure was as a result of shock or impact loading. The tensioning of the rods was rather hit-and-miss, and he explained, that generally he had the centre rods made a quarter of an inch too short, and expanded them by heating to bring them, on cooling, 'into a perfect state of tension, and at all times to bear their proportion of the load '. **(4)** Extensometers were not used, to find the strain in the iron, until after the accident, and, surprisingly, the obvious use of turnbuckles, to adjust the tension in the centre rods, was not tried. (A drawing by John Smeaton, dated 1782, shows turnbuckles being used on trusses for the main spars of windmill sails, and, for example, the Planets used them to adjust the valves.)

In spite of the confidence that he had displayed in the discussion, one cannot help wondering if some seeds of doubt had been sown in Robert's mind and this may explain why he took an early opportunity, 'to minutely inspect the bridge ' on what turned out to be the morning prior to the accident. One hopes that his innate caution would have led him to recommend some modifications, as he should have realised that the design, particularly with respect to the depth of the girders, which may have been reasonable a few years earlier, was no longer adequate for the rapidly increasing speed and weights of trains on such a large span. **(5)** At the inquest, as Engineer-in-Chief, he took responsibility, even though, 'it had been designed by [unnamed] others'. According to F. Conder, G. P. Bidder had designed it, and he found it, 'unaccountable that the practical eye of Mr. Stephenson should have been for a moment blind' to its defects when he had been shown the proposal. **(6)**

Fig. A 2: one of the last surviving set of trussed cast-iron girders in the former No. 6 Boatyard, now 'Action Stations' museum, at Portsmouth. It was designed by Lt. Beatson in 1845. Photo J. F. A.

By 1846, two features had been used on trussed girders that could have been incorporated in the Dee Bridge. According to Gen. Pasley's evidence, 'there is a difference between this bridge and Mr. Stephenson's former iron bridges; in all his former [multi-span] bridges there is a connection from girder to girder on the central piers, from one end of the bridge to the other, by bolts, so that when a weight passes over one girder, the other girders in the same line contribute to assist it; that is the case in the bridge over the Ouse at York, the last I inspected before this'. (2) Also, in his evidence on the C&HR Bill on 5 May 1845, Robert had made it clear that the Britannia Bridge would have to be continuous at least over the centre pier. (7) Why this was ignored in the design of the Dee Bridge is a mystery.

The other feature was in the design of the floor beams for the Number 6 Boathouse at Portsmouth Naval Dockyard where Lt. Beatson R.E. had taken considerable care to ensure that the tension, applied at the ends of the trusses, was equally applied to the central section. Here he had put the centre rods under the beams and allowed their ends to pivot in lugs cast on to the bottom flanges of the main girders. (Fig. A2) **(8)(9)** If the rods had their tension correctly applied *and maintained*, to enable the 35% increase in strength, suggested by T. L. Gooch's experiments, to be realised, *and* the use of continuous beams had been employed, to reduce the maximum bending moment at the point of failure by a similar amount, then regardless of its other inadequacies, the bridge would not have collapsed.

Another factor was involved; the timber deck of I. K. Brunel's problematic cast-iron bridge over Uxbridge Road had caught fire by cinders from an engine dropping on it. The heat destroyed the girders. **(10)** To prevent this happening on the Dee Bridge, the contractor, E. L. Betts, had been ordered to spread 5 inches of stone ballast on its deck. This work had been carried out about an hour before the accident; 18 tons had been used, increasing the uniformly distributed load by a significant 20%. It has been suggested that Robert personally supervised the work, but according to all the evidence, his inspection had occurred, 'a few hours previously' and it seems to be mere coincidence that the contractor had chosen to do the work 'that broke the camel's back' on that day. (2)

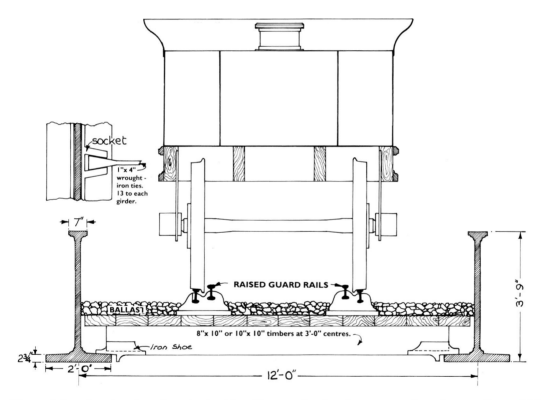

Figure A 3: a drawing, based on the Accident Report, showing the cross-section of a span from which, even compared with a modest tender of the day, the small depth of the girders is apparent. J. F. A.

The *Chester Chronicle* reports of the evidence given at the coroner's inquest, came to around 25,000 words, and in some ways differ from what Francis Conder wrote, from memory, 20 years later. Had he lived in the present day, he would not have disparaged the, 'entire unfitness of the ancient machinery of the coroner's court …to deal with questions involving such important issues'. They came up with the right verdict, after hearing complex evidence, presented in just four days, whereas it would take a modern inquiry several months, and several million pounds, to come up with the same answer! His statement that the case, 'at one time degenerated almost into a personal contest between Sir E. [Edward] Walker, the foreman of the jury, (who seemed resolved on the return of a verdict of manslaughter, or, if possible, of murder, against the Engineer, or some other unfortunate servant or representative of the company,) and Mr. Stephenson himself,' is certainly not borne out by the evidence. (6)

The opinions of the engineers differed considerably at the inquest. The coroner, John Hostage, nominated T. A. Yarrow, former bridge-master for Cheshire, as an independent engineer, to find the cause of the accident. His opinion was that the masonry abutment had failed, causing the iron girder to break. Messrs. Stephenson, Locke, Vignoles and Gooch were absolutely unable to accept that the bridge had failed merely by the passage of a normal train. They came up with the only possible, but implausible, alternative, that the tender must have somehow become derailed, causing it to strike the girder, and break it. **(11)** Knowing what was about to be said, Sir E. Walker, to try and avoid some embarrassment, told the inquest, immediately before R. Stephenson read his report, 'The opinion of the jury generally is, that the tender did not strike the girder'. However, the engineers still persisted with this view. Even the local newspaper correspondent said, 'Mr. R. Stephenson did right when he said that all he hoped was to convince the world that the fatal event resulted from an untoward circumstance, and not from any disregard for human life. That he has satisfactorily established; and *to go further is uselessly to complicate the matter'*. Evidence of James Kennedy, the locomotive and ship-builder, stated that he thought the bridge was strong enough in theory, but 'the beam has broken against all our calculations'; he did not agree with the derailment story. Henry Robertson, engineer of the S&CR, said the tension rods did not help, and he came to 'the conclusion that the girder broke in the middle from its weakness to resist the strain increased by the laying of the ballast', but he went on to say about Robert, 'there is no gentleman in the profession in whom I have greater confidence'. The inquest had been adjourned from 2 to 16 June to allow Capt. (later Field-Marshal Sir Lintorn) Simmons and James Walker, past president of the Institution of Civil Engineers, to prepare their accident report for the Commissioners of Railways. After hearing their report the jury's unanimous verdict was that the deaths had been caused by the failure of one of the cast-iron girders ' …being made of a strength insufficient to bear the pressure of quick trains passing over it'. (2)

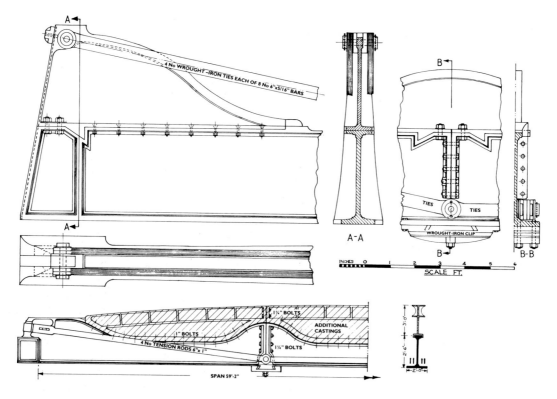

Figure A 4: Top: Construction details of the Dee Bridge girders. Bottom: Half elevation and section of a trussed girder bridge on the Trent Valley Railway showing, hatched, the castings added after the Dee Bridge failure. A 16-foot length of the centre of the girder was tested, for a fortnight, with an evenly spaced load of 100 tons. The deflection was 1.2 inches i.e. one six hundredth of the span. Similar castings were added to many of the original bridges including the two on the Florence and Leghorn Railway with 96-foot spans. Details taken from B.O.T. report and 1849 Report.

On the positive side, the accident report found that: the masonry was satisfactory; the bearing of the girders on it was ample; the cast and wrought iron were of good quality; the joints between the main castings, 'being most perfectly strong' and the deflections under load, measured on the adjacent bridge, gave no cause for concern. A train weighing 48 tons gave a deflection, at rest of 2.36 in. and, at 20 mph 1.625 in. Most engineers, at that time, would have been very complacent about these figures and would look no further for defects in the design. (Modern standards accept a deflection of 1/500th of the span, except on high-speed lines.) What was wrong with the bridge then? Firstly, as it was imperative that the wrought-iron tension rods worked correctly, an innovation had been tried. In an attempt to make the initial positive cambering of the girder easier, the ends of the trusses were attached higher than usual. **(12)** It was not realised that this meant that the rods would not retain full tension when a train passed over them. From tests on the adjacent, undamaged, bridge Capt. Simmons proved, under loading, that the top ends of the girders moved approximately 0.9in. closer together, thus reducing the initial tension very significantly. Secondly, there were no cross girders. The main girders were only connected by thirteen 4 in. by 1 in. bars, let into dovetailed sockets cast on top of their bottom flanges. Timber joists, also resting on the bottom flanges, carried the deck. This was the standard practice where clearances over a watercourse were critical, but it need not apply here; few engineers appreciated that it caused the main girders to be subjected to torsion. Again Capt. Simmons' experiments showed that when the bridge was loaded with 48 tons, the tops of the girders were brought from one to two inches nearer together. Both he and James Walker thought '...that neither Hodgkinson's, nor any other formula deduced from a fair dead pressure upon beams, was strictly applicable to this case *without great modification.*' Having taken these and most other factors into account, their conclusions were: -

'That the bridge was of sufficient strength if the cast and wrought iron be supposed to act together, each taking its equal proportion of the strain.

'That there is great difficulty in ensuring the joint action, and if this is a part of the principle of the bridge, we do not approve of it.

'That neither the wrought nor cast iron, taken separately, was sufficient for perfect stability, and that to have ensured this, the cast-iron girders alone should have been of sufficient strength to carry the whole weight, with an ample allowance for various circumstances (some of them peculiar to this bridge) which we have explained.'

They ended, '...as we entertain these opinions very decidedly, it is our duty (by no means an agreeable one) to express them'. **(13)**

As a result of the diverse evidence given by the engineers, both the inquest jury and the Commissioners of Railways recommended that there should be an inquiry into the use of iron for railway bridges. In their minute, dated 29 June 1847, the Commissioners recommended an inquiry, '...by means of a Commission appointed by the Government'; this was set up on 27 August 1847, and the report was issued on 26 July 1849 (hereinafter referred to as the 1849 Report). See Appendix 5.

In the meantime, what happened to the 100-trussed bridges, either built or being built? Those without clearance restrictions, for example, over the Dee, Ouse and Tees, were propped by substantial timber beams, extending at an angle, of about 30 degrees, from the abutment or piers to the joints in the girders. Others were strengthened by adding large iron castings above the original ones, and many of these bridges survived, as modified, for another 30 to 40 years. **(14)** Three on the Leopold Railway in Italy, over the rivers Ombrone, Bisenzio and Arno were being built with 96 ft. spans and were to be identical to the Dee Bridge. Two were modified with additional castings, and had proper cross girders bolted to the underside of the main girders, but the one over the Arno was completely redesigned. It became a hefty hogbacked cast-iron girder with horizontal chains under the bottom flange. The Arno Bridge showed very marked superiority over the Dee Bridge; a weight of 93 tons on its centre only caused a deflection of 0.95 in., whereas the Dee Bridge had given 2.4 in. with a distributed load of 48 tons. However, when describing it for the 1849 Report, Robert said that the horizontal tension bars were no better than those positioned anywhere else. He then described an experiment made the previous day, 22 March 1848, which seemed to prove the opposite. The outer ends of the tension bars had been attached, successively, to the top, middle and bottom of the girder ends, and with the same weight applied in each case, the deflection was reduced by one third, with the rods in the middle or horizontal positions. (3) Perhaps a little stubbornness was being displayed, in not accepting the evidence of his own experiment, and in proving that he could design a very sound trussed cast-iron bridge when, at this stage, a wrought-iron box girder would have been a lot cheaper. A more critical approach to the design of trussed cast-iron bridges in 1840 would have been a lot more beneficial. When giving evidence for the 1849 Report, William Fairbairn gave the reason why engineers continued to do certain things, '...in many of our operations we are the children of habit'!

Although trussed girder bridges have been almost universally condemned it is worth quoting an opposite view given by an experienced civil engineer, Conrad Gribble, in 1944: -

'One of the first jobs that I had had to do as a young engineer was to prepare drawings for the renewal of a trussed cast-iron girder bridge over the Tees at Thornaby. When the girders were removed and taken to pieces they were found to be the most perfectly manufactured girders that could possibly be imagined. The metal and workmanship were perfect, and the design was as good as it could bc. At the time of the collapse of the Dee Bridge at Chester George Stephenson visited the bridge at Thornaby. The engineer in charge was very concerned about that bridge, in view of what had happened to the Chester Bridge. Upon Stephenson's advice timber struts were put in, and those struts remained until about 1906, when the bridge was pulled down. The cast iron was found to be excellent, and some doubt was felt at the time as to whether there was any need to renew it.'**(15)**

Obviously the Tees Bridge avoided the design faults of the Dee Bridge.

NOTES AND REFERENCES

1. All italics in this section are the authors'
2. Inquest evidence as reported by the *Chester Chronicle* on; 28 May, 4, 11, 18, 25, June 1847. Microfilm copies kindly provided by Mr. R. S. Roper.
3. *Report of the Commissioners appointed to inquire into the Application of Iron to Railway Structures.* (1849 Report)
4. Discussions following a paper, by W. Fairbairn, on 'Fire-Proof Buildings'. *Proc. I. C. E.* 1847, pp 218-224. Vignoles said that he used trussed girders of 45 ft. spans over canals, as early as 1831, on what became the North Union Rly. G. P. Bidder first used trussed girders over the River Lea (60 ft. span), near Tottenham, on the Northern & Eastern Rly. (completed in 1840), and over Minories (63 ft. span) on the London & Blackwall Rly. (completed in 1841). The length and spans for the Dee Bridge are quoted incorrectly in the *Proceedings.* (p. 220)
5. E. Clark *The Britannia and Conway Tubular Bridges* Vol. 1 p. 85. '...a good proportion for the depth of large cast-iron beams had been found to be about one-fifteenth of their length,' suggesting, quite correctly, that the Dee Bridge girders should have been seven feet deep.
6. F. R. Conder. *The Men Who Built Railways*, (reprinted 1983), pp 137-142. In some cases he does not accord with verbatim evidence in the *Chester Chronicle*, or evidence in the official report. R. S's demeanour in court is reported very differently: *Chester Chronicle*: 'Mr. R. Stephenson as a railway witness, is what Mr. Scarlett was amongst advocates, or Sir Robert Peel is amongst politicians. *No man can dress a case better,* particularly when aided the by imperturbable Mr. Timothy Tyrell' (the italics are in the original); F. Conder: 'Pale and haggard, he looked more like a culprit than like a man of science, ...His manner was abrupt and dictatorial, betraying extreme irritation at the remarks of jurors ...'. There is certainly the impression of irritation and abruptness in replies to some of the more trite questions put to him.
7. E. Clark, Vol. 1 p. 49.
8. R. A. Otter. *Civil Engineering Heritage: Southern England.* pp 159-160. This building is still extant having been designed to carry the same uniformly distributed *static* load as the Dee Bridge. It now houses the 'Action Stations' exhibition at the Dockyard.
9. During his inspection, of the adjacent undamaged spans, under traffic, Capt. Simmons, '...felt a sharp jerk as the girder was relieved of its weight, the train was moving at a moderate speed'. This suggests some binding of the components of the bridge, and the jerk was it restoring itself to a state of equilibrium after the train had passed over it. The train immediately before the accident was the ballast train, weighing about 40 tons, which after standing on the bridge for some time, had moved off, reducing the load very slowly. Was it possible that this had left the bridge without its equilibrium restored, leaving the trap sprung for the passenger train?
10. E. T. MacDermot, *The History of the Great Western Railway,* Vol. 1, (1964) p. 22. See also S. C. Brees, *Railway Practice,* 3rd Series, plate 48, for the drawing of the bridge, which Brunel himself described in derogatory terms, and, although the proportions of the girders left much to be desired, it led to his, often-quoted (generally out of context) condemnation of cast-iron bridges.
11. J. Locke and C. B. Vignoles were not involved in any way with the C & H R, and had come merely to support R. S. after an event that he had always dreaded. R. S. had confided to a friend, in 1830, 'I fear that some fine morning my reputation may break under me like an egg-shell'. (Jeaff. Vol. 1 p. 155.) Joseph Locke was so outspoken in his evidence that one of his statements even led to questions being asked in Parliament, on 8 June 1847. He had claimed that I. K. B., R. S. and himself had been signatories to a letter, to Lord Dalhousie, then at the B. O. T., complaining about engineers having to design bridges to comply with, often unnecessary, clearance restrictions giving dangerously wide spans. The existence of the letter was denied.
12. Other options were being tried simultaneously. On 9 Sept. 1846, six weeks before the Dee Bridge inspection, Gen. Pasley reported on a multi-span trussed girder bridge over the River Swale, on the Richmond branch, by R. S. '... having the parts of uniform section and depth throughout their whole length, instead of making each piece of greater height at the joints and ends'.
13. There were two reports, both dated 15 June 1847; the first by Capt. Simmons only, covered his preliminary inspection and tests made on 27 May, and the other was made jointly with James Walker; together they came to just 13 pages of text. Surprisingly neither of them picked up on Gen. Pasley's remarks about continuous

beams. The success of the Britannia Bridge was wholly dependent upon the continuous beam theory, and this factor should have been well known, in engineering circles, by the late 1840s. However, even more surprisingly, on 24 Dec. 1849, Capt. Simmons, apparently without this knowledge, condemned (Sir) John Fowler's continuous, two-span wrought-iron box girder bridge at Torksey over the Trent. This caused a furore in the engineering profession. In the discussion, following W. Fairbairn's paper on 'Tubular Girder Bridges' given to the I.C.E. on 12 March 1850, (*Proceedings* p. 282) it appears neither Simmons nor Fairbairn, appreciated the extra strength that the bridge obtained, by being continuous over the centre pier. After much argument, the bridge was passed, as safe for passenger traffic from 25 April 1850, amazingly over a month after Simmons had passed the first tube of the Britannia Bridge! Happily, Simmons and Fowler later became very good friends. Copies of the report kindly supplied by J. C. Dean.

14. PRO. MT6 5/35. Capt. Simmons' report for the inspection for re-opening the modified Dee Bridge dated 23 March 1848. *The Builder*, 8 Jan. 1848, p 23, quotes a letter to Sir E. Walker and Sir J Jervis (M. P. for Chester) confirming that the trussed girder bridges on the Trent Valley line had already been strengthened to the satisfaction of the inspecting officers. In a letter to R. S., dated 6 June 1847, two weeks after the accident, Fairbairn commended the use of tubular girders as replacements. But according to remarks made by Capt. Simmons, at the inquest, even the Railway Inspectorate was concerned about the expense of total replacement. R. S. had, of course, started using small tubular girders at Camden the previous September. Tubular girders were as susceptible to design faults as any other type. One, of 63ft. span, near Birmingham, collapsed *after* an engine and two ballast wagons had passed over it; the designer later also became president of the Institution of Civil Engineers! See MacDermot's *Great Western Railway,* pp. 173-4.

15. *Journal of the I. C. E.,* Oct. 1944, pp. 294-5. 'Discussion on the strength of cast-iron girder bridges.' Conrad Gribble was chief engineer on the Bridge Stress Committee in the 1920s, and had carried out investigations for the Ministry of Transport, in 1939, along with Professors Southwell and Pippard, into masonry and cast-iron bridges.

APPENDIX 4

THE 1849 REPORT

The Commission was chaired by John, Lord Wrottesley (1798-1867), an Oxford graduate who had qualified, but not practised, as a barrister; he served on a number of Royal Commissions and was a founder and leading light of the Royal Astronomical Society. Rev. Professor Robert Willis, F.R.S., Capt. (Sir) Henry James, R.E., F.R.S., George Rennie, (Sir) William Cubbit, and Professor Eaton Hodgkinson assisted him; the secretary was Lt. (Sir) Douglas Galton R.E. The report came to around 450 pages, and covered accounts of the special experiments made, and the written and verbal evidence given by engineers and iron founders. The budget of £3,000 and the time available limited the scope of the experiments, but enough information was found on the strength of materials, metal fatigue and impact loading to enable some sound recommendations to be made. (1) This parsimonious sum was less than half that spent on the experiments for the Britannia and Conwy bridges.

Eaton Hodgkinson, William Fairbairn, and others had already carried out various experiments into the use and strength of metals. However, it was soon evident to the Commission, '...that the effects of heavy bodies moving with great velocity upon structures had never been made the subject of direct scientific investigation, and as it also appeared in the opinion of practical and scientific engineers such an inquiry was highly desirable, our attention was directed to the devising of experiments for the purpose of elucidating this matter.' When the series of experiments was made on the effect of weights, passing at various speeds, over iron bars, it was found that, although a load of 4,150 lbs. was required to break the bars, if applied at rest, only 1,778 lbs. was needed if it passed over them at 30 miles per hour. It was appreciated that the use of the small bars dramatised the effects, and that the power of the beam to resist impact increases with its weight. Full-scale trials were also carried out on bridges over roads, where scaffolding could be set up, to allow precise deflections to be measured. They found that an engine weighing 39 tons was able to produce the deflection equivalent to a static load of 45 tons when it travelled at 50 miles per hour. This was contrary to the results that Capt. Simmons and others had got with moving trains, leading some of them to a false sense of security about impact loads. (2) The analogy was used of an ice skater being able to move safely over ice that was unable to bear his weight when he was standing still.

There had been a dawning of awareness of the possibility of metal fatigue from the late 1830s, although the actual term 'fatigue' was not used until 1849. (3) Experiments by the Commission not only proved its existence, but also established the extremely important fact that fatigue would not occur if the repeated stress remained below a third of the breaking stress. The Commission recommended, in order to keep the deflection of the iron below a third that the greatest weight on railway bridges should not exceed one-sixth of the ultimate breaking load that was applied on the centre of the span. Tests with impact, bending and rolling loads applied up to 100,000 times, on iron bars, were used in these experiments. Significantly, this seems to be the first scientific use of the repetitive stress tests, which are now considered indispensable in the development of many components. **(4)**

It was appreciated that uneven track and the irregular motion, or jerks, of the engines could cause larger deflections. Early locomotives did not run very steadily, and in attempts to improve them, their centre of gravity was kept as low as possible, longer wheelbases were tried, and their cylinders were placed between the frames, rather than outside them. One gentleman had even increased the gauge by 50%! A few locomotive manufacturers had started to realise that the lack of balancing, of the revolving machinery of the engines, was a major cause of the unsteadiness, and some were taking reasonably successful measures to improve matters. (5) Locomotive balancing was one of the things not looked into by the Commission, and, in fact, the significant effects of 'hammer-blow' on bridges, caused by steam engines, was not investigated for another 75 years. **(6)** Most railway companies had ignored it, and based their bridge designs on axle weights with a factor added to cover 'lurching'.

The Commission started questioning witnesses on 27 November 1847, and veteran engineer John Rastrick was the first to be called. In all, nineteen engineers, builders and iron founders gave verbal and/or written evidence. **(7)** Robert Stephenson was the only witness to be called more than once, appearing on 16 and 23 March 1848. As was to be expected, there were considerable variations in the opinions of those who gave evidence. It was a time when a number of important breakthroughs were being made, and within a few years most of the witnesses would have given totally different answers to many of the questions. For example, neither Stephenson nor Brunel viewed lattice trusses with great enthusiasm. Lattice trusses would only need a few more years' development to become a very successful form of bridge construction. **(8)** Also the idea of combining materials with different properties in the trussed beams was frowned upon by many, but thousands of modern bridges use concrete beams, pre or post-tensioned by high tensile steel wires, with complete success.

One topic that produced a large number of questions, and an awful lot of experimental data, was the mixing of iron to eliminate inconsistencies of quality. Iron selected from sources all over the country was mixed, in order to get, in an engineer's opinion, the best product for his bridge. This was all simplified as a result of a suggestion by Charles Fox, and the Commission advised, '...engineers in contracting for castings to stipulate for iron to bear a certain weight instead of endeavouring to procure a specified mixture'. This left the iron founders with the problem of producing a material of suitable strength.

Although trussed cast-iron bridges were covered in the questioning, it was obvious that their day was over, but as a man who had once condoned them was now building tubular bridges of unprecedented size, the soundness of this new type had to be substantiated. Eaton Hodgkinson and Edwin Clark gave full details of the experiments that had been carried out for the Britannia and Conwy bridges. (9) Clark was called on 10 June 1848 and, as the first tube of the Conwy Bridge had been open to passengers since 1 May 1848, he was able to give very positive evidence of its success. It had been tested with a load of 300 tons and had given a deflection of 3 in. (1/1600th of the span). When questioned about the vibration caused by the passage of the trains, he said there was none, and that the only way of producing a tremor was by firing a cannon mounted on top of the tube! (10)

Considering that Robert Stephenson was in a somewhat defensive position, he really attacked the Commission while being questioned regarding any rules being made as a result of the inquiry. The dialogue was as follows: -

'Have you any suggestion to make, as to the conduct of the inquiry referred to the Commissioners, or to the course to be pursued by them? - My opinion is rather strong, that a collection of facts of all kinds, is highly desirable, in reference to the shape of girders. We are not yet quite clear as to the best proportions for girders, but I am convinced that the Commissioners will have infinite difficulty in laying down anything like rules. I cannot conceive myself being tied down in executing such a line, for instance, as the Holyhead, or the London and Birmingham. I cannot conceive myself going on successfully, and being tied down by pre-conceived rules.

'What do you understand by rules? - Some limitation as to the extent to which cast iron should be used, and the forms it should be used in.

'You mean by that a Legislative enactment? - Yes, of course I do. I apprehend that any decision you come to here would become a Legislative enactment.

'Our object will be rather to make rules similar in nature to those Mr. Hodgkinson has already laid down? - I cannot use his formulae always, and I should be sorry to be tied down to them.

'We rather wish by the powers given to us to obtain opinions and information, so as to form a collection of facts and observations to lay before the profession for their benefit? - I think it would be most valuable; but if you collect facts; and if you attempt to draw conclusions from those facts, and confine engineers even in a limited way to those conclusions, I am quite sure that it will tend to hamper the profession very much.'(11)

I. K. Brunel held the same views and they won, thanks to the good sense of the Commissioners, and much to the relief of the profession. In their summary the Commissioners said: -

'The investigation in which we have been concerned has made it evident that the novelty of the railway system has introduced a variety of new mechanical causes, the effects of which have not yet had time fully to develop themselves, on account of the extent and number of new railways, and the rapidity with which they were constructed, in many cases scarcely giving breathing time to the engineers, by which to observe and profit by the experience of each successive new construction. Thus it has happened that some portions of the mechanism and structure have been made too weak, or placed in unfavourable combinations; and hence some unavoidable, but most lamentable and sometimes fatal accidents, have been occasioned. It also appears that there exists a great want of uniformity in practice in many most important matters relating to railway engineering, which shows how imperfect and deficient it yet is in leading principles. . .

'And in conclusion, considering that the attention of engineers has been sufficiently awakened to the necessity of providing a superabundant strength in railway structures, and also considering the great importance of leaving the genius of scientific men unfettered for the development of a subject as yet so novel and so rapidly progressive as the construction of railways, we are of the opinion that any legislative enactments with respect to the forms and proportions of the iron structures employed therein would be highly inexpedient.' (12)

The publication of the report ended one of the unhappiest incidents in Robert Stephenson's life.

NOTES AND REFERENCES

1. *The Builder,* 5 Oct. 1850 p. 476.
2. Chettoe, Davey and Mitchell, 'The Strength of Cast-Iron Bridges' *Journal of I. C. E.* Oct. 1944, p. 288, Table V gives examples of the erratic nature of 'dynamic effect'. On one bridge the deflection caused by a 10.3-ton static load was compared with those when the same load passed over it at speeds between 15 and 25 mph. The static deflection was reduced by *either* 7 *or* 19% at 15 mph. increased by 7% at 20 mph. and reduced by 10% at 25 mph!
3. Joshua Field, president of I. C. E. 1848-1849, suggested the term 'fatigue'. *Proc. I. C. E.* 1854 p.467.
4. Repeated hammering of iron bars to induce failure is known to have been carried out earlier at Coalbrookdale and Crewe.
5. *Gauge Evidence,* p. 18. See chapter 3.
6. The Bridge Stress Committee was appointed in 1923 and they published their report in 1928. The damage that could be caused by unbalanced forces was dramatically demonstrated when a seriously out-of-balance G W R mixed traffic locomotive was driven, at high speed, to Swindon Works for repairs. The effect was that, several miles of crippled rails, had to be removed from the track immediately. See P. S. A. Berridge, *The Girder Bridge.* Plate 45.
7. The witnesses were: Civil Engineers; P. W. and W. H. Barlow, I. K. Brunel, E. Clark, J. Cubitt, W. Fairbairn, C. Fox, J. Glynn, T. L. Gooch*, J. Hawkshaw, J. Locke, R. B. Osborne*, J. U. Rastrick, R. Stephenson, C. H. Wild, Builder; T. Cubitt, Iron Manufacturers, etc.; H. Grissell, C. May, J. D. Morries Stirling. * Written evidence only. Notable among those missing were C. B. Vignoles, who was building Kiev Bridge at the time, and G. P. Bidder.
8. W. T. Doyne, 'Description of a Wrought-Iron Lattice Bridge, constructed over the line of the Rugby and Leamington Railway.' *Proc. I. C. E.*1850 p. 355. Doyne, who had completed the 150 ft. lattice road bridge in 1849, stated that the 1849 Report regarded lattice bridges as being of doubtful merit, ' ...this unfavourable opinion has been drawn from bridges badly constructed, and which should not therefore condemn the principle;'
9. 1849 Report. Details of E. Hodgkinson's experiments appeared in Appendices A and A.A.
10. Ibid. p. 339 Questions 925 to 929.
11. Ibid. p. 366 Questions1265 to 1272.
12. Ibid. pp xvii, xviii.

APPENDIX 5

THE FAIRBAIRN – STEPHENSON CONTROVERSY.

In his presidential address to the Institution of Civil Engineers on 8 January 1850, William Cubitt said of the tubular bridges: -

'The world already duly appreciates this great undertaking, and we should not be behindhand in testifying our estimate of the bold conception of Mr. Robert Stephenson in the original idea, his professional skill in the design and execution, and his care and caution in availing himself of the talents and experience of Mr. W. Fairbairn and Mr. Eaton Hodgkinson, whose scientific investigations respecting the strength of cast-iron are so well known to the world and so highly appreciated by our profession, and his entrusting the general construction and elevation to Mr. Frank Forster and Mr. Edwin Clark. Upon the merits of all these gentlemen we may look with pardonable pride and partiality; - their labours speak for themselves.'(1)

This should have put an end to the controversy; however, certain recent publications have raised the subject, and unfairly given too much credit to one of the contenders either by inadequate research or by deliberately suppressing the facts.

It appears that neither Fairbairn nor Stephenson started the dispute, and it seems to result from a rider to a previous report in the *Manchester Guardian* about the launching of the first Conwy tube. This appeared in the edition of the 15 March 1848 and said: -

'We ought to have stated on Wednesday [8 Mar.], that the whole of the operations connected with the floating and raising of the tube have been carried out under the superintendence of Mr. Fairbairn, of this town, who has been appointed by the company their engineer for the construction and erection of the tubular bridges.'

This was wide of the truth. Fairbairn had been appointed on 13 May 1846, '...to superintend, in conjunction with Mr. Stephenson, the construction and erection of the tubes.' (2) He tendered his resignation after 'misunderstandings' with the directors, in May 1847, mainly regarding his reassignment of the contract they had awarded to him for the fabrication of 2,000 tons of the tubes for the Britannia Bridge. He had profited by transferring this contract, worth over £60,000, to Ditchburn and Mare, without even asking the directors. Stephenson placated the directors and got him to withdraw his resignation. According to Clark '...though not in any active capacity, he continued to assist Mr. Stephenson, in conjunction with the Author in watching the progress of the manufacturing of the Conway Bridge; and he took no share in the floating or the raising, he occasionally visited the works, and was present at these operations in March 1848.'(3)

The piece in the *Manchester Guardian* provoked G. P. Bidder to write the letter that appeared in the paper on 22 March. It included, 'The Company look to Mr. Robert Stephenson alone, as their engineer, for the proper construction and erection of all their bridges and works.' The editor agreed and said that the argument was basically a play on words! Fairbairn said he had no involvement in the original statement, 'with all its inaccuracies', and Stephenson claimed he had no prior knowledge that Bidder was going to write his letter. (4) There is no reason to doubt either gentleman's word, and J. F. Bateman, who was Fairbairn's son-in-law, probably provoked the dispute on his own initiative. (5)

After the report of the dinner celebrating the opening of the first Conwy tube appeared in the *Manchester Guardian,* on 20 May 1848, Bateman wrote a long letter to the paper objecting to inaccuracies in Robert Stephenson's speech. It was a relaxed after-dinner speech, and not an address to a learned society, and for the sake of his audience, he had attempted to compress the story with the inevitable loss of accuracy. In the circumstances he could have been more careful. The relevant part of his speech that was to cause the dispute is quoted exactly as it appeared in the *Manchester Guardian*: -

'It is now upwards of six, or about seven years, since I entertained the idea of constructing bridges with wrought-iron plates, riveted together. I was called upon, - in a smaller case I admit, but not a very simple one - to construct a bridge authorised by act of parliament, but with such limitations that it became a matter of extreme difficulty. All the ordinary kinds of bridges were discussed, and I eventually hit on the notion, and the designs were completed, for a thin tubular bridge, although not precisely the same as the present, yet in principle exactly the same. That was effectually completed, and answers its purpose, and may now be seen on the Northern and Eastern Railway. From that time, however, to the period commencing the Chester and Holyhead Railway, the idea fell, or dropped rather, for the time, in the consequence of the expense of wrought iron rather exceeding that of cast. On undertaking the C & H R, you will all remember that the original designs for crossing the Conway River and the Menai strait, were by cast-iron arches of very large dimensions - from 400 to 450 feet span. The execution of the latter work over the strait, would have been one, under the circumstances, of extreme difficulty, and would have required the utmost facilities to be afforded by those interested in the navigation of the strait. It is familiar to you all that the project or proposal met with a strenuous opposition - whether reasonable or unreasonable it would be very improper of me to stop here to discuss. But it is sufficient to say that parliamentary powers were granted for the construction of a bridge over the strait at the Britannia rock, with such conditions attached to it as rendering it all but, if not absolutely, impracticable. It was then, to use a common expression, that I felt myself "fairly driven into a corner". No existing species of bridge was at all applicable under the operation of the act of parliament as granted; and it was after an anxious investigation of every possible description of bridge, that it occurred to me, that by reviving the old notion of seven years ago, that by extending it might enable me to get over the difficulty. Approximate calculations were immediately made, and the results of those calculations were such as to satisfy me of the perfect feasibility of the work. And I well remember, when going into the committee room of the house of commons afterwards, when a change of direction of the line was applied for, and when the description of the bridge was announced, on expressing it to the committee, and giving it in evidence, I well remember, I say, the surprise, and the incredulous glances that I received from all parts of the room. - (Hear, laughter and applause) However, I had satisfied myself that the idea was practicable, and I stood by it. - (Hear, and applause) As soon as the bill was obtained, and it became time to commence, I obtained the consent of the directors to institute a very laborious, and elaborate, and expensive series of experiments, in order, most thoroughly, to test experimentally the theory I had formed, and also to add suggestions for its full development. It was then that I called in the aid of two gentlemen, eminent, both of them, in their professions, - Mr Fairbairn and Mr Hodgkinson. They had both distinguished themselves for elaborate series of experiments on cast-iron bridges, and although this was a different material, still from their accomplishments and skill, they were well qualified to aid me in my research. They heartily went into it, and the result is what you now see under the walls of your venerable old castle. - (Great applause.) But, having mentioned those two names, there is another gentleman that I wish to call to your notice, - a gentleman to whose talents, to whose zeal and ability, from the commencement of this undertaking, I am much indebted; and indeed the full development of the principles of tubular bridges is by no means in a small degree indebted to him; - I allude to my assistant, Mr Edmund Clarke. (Applause.) He has been my closet companion **(6)** from the commencement of the preliminary investigation; no variation or inconsistency in the experiment eluded his keen perception; he was always on the lookout for contingencies that might effect the success - though not the principle, still the success of the operation - of the undertaking; and he and the other gentlemen, who I have just named, are the three to whom I feel deeply indebted for having brought the theory I first broached to such perfection, and I thus publicly tender them my acknowledgments.- (Hear, and applause)'

Bateman complained that 'Mr. Stephenson's remarks implied that he was not indebted for any assistance to Mr. Fairbairn until "after the act was obtained, and it became necessary to construct the works"'. (The remarks about the bridge on the Northern and Eastern Railway also were to come into the dispute at a later stage.) During the three weeks between their first meeting and the Select Committee hearing Fairbairn had assisted Stephenson with calculations to prove the feasibility of a tubular bridge, and nine weeks later, following the Act being passed, Fairbairn had been sufficiently involved to enable the first simple tube to be tested.

Bateman went on to say the following, which he had gleaned from access to Fairbairn's letters: -

'The almost immediate appreciation of the peculiar advantages and disadvantages of the properties of the material to be dealt with, - the suggestion of means of overcoming the difficulties and anomalies as they were developed by the experiments, - the relative proportions of the various parts, - the mode of riveting, in which the most important improvement was introduced, - the manner of floating, and the mode of raising, - are all there spontaneously suggested and matured by Mr. Fairbairn.' (7)

With these, and other claims made, Robert Stephenson could not let the matter rest, and on 31 May 1848, he wrote to the paper and quoted a letter that Fairbairn had written, during their exchange of correspondence, regarding the patenting of the small box, or tubular girders, in October 1846. In this Fairbairn gave every credit to Stephenson for the *original* idea of the bridge, and concluded, '…you may rest assured of my best efforts in supporting the claim to which you are entitled.' Stephenson went on with no personal claim except that he had to take the ultimate responsibility: -

'This extract shows sufficiently Mr. Fairbairn's feelings at the time when his letter was written, which was subsequent to the passing of the act; and I will only add to it, that I have never attempted to detract in any way from the merits of any party connected with the work, but have always freely acknowledged the valuable assistance which has been afforded to me during its progress by Mr. Fairbairn, Mr. Hodgkinson and Mr. Clark; but that Mr. Fairbairn devised, or had charge of the whole construction, is simply a mis-statement of the facts. He, in common with the other two gentlemen named, aided me by his advice, and I acted upon it, or otherwise, as I thought proper. The company looked to me as alone responsible; and in my discretion every other party who has been concerned in the progress of these bridges was engaged.' (8)

William Fairbairn's *An account of the Construction of the Britannia and Conway Tubular Bridges* appeared in July 1849. It was very favourably received in *The Builder,* and much less so in *The Civil Engineer and Architect's Journal,* and by Sir Francis Bond Head in *The Quarterly Review.* **(9)** *The Civil Engineer and Architect's Journal* concluded: -

'But enough is before us to warrant us in affirming that Mr. Fairbairn deals unfairly both with his own fame and with that of his colleagues, in assuming a controversial tone – unfairly towards them, by endeavouring to depreciate their merits, - unfairly towards himself; because the attempt will re-act against himself, in the minds of those who will estimate his labours by personal, and not by purely scientific considerations.' (10)

Sir Francis Head, who had written his own account of the bridges, was highly critical of some of William Fairbairn's remarks and actions. On 15 December 1849 Thomas Fairbairn responded in his father's defence, against Sir Francis, in his pamphlet *Truths and Tubes.* In view of T. Fairbairn's objections, Sir Francis Head moderated some of his statements, in the 1850 edition of his book *Highways and Dry-ways,* but still stuck to his main arguments. **(11)** He even added a two-page supplement featuring correspondence he had had with the C&HR board. This included the statement: 'That the Directors made the appointment of Mr. Fairbairn at Mr. Stephenson's request, to assist him, but that they looked to Mr. Stephenson as responsible to them.' (12) This may be absolutely correct, but it is not exactly what is implied either by their board minute or, as stated publicly, in their half-yearly report, regarding Fairbairn's appointment.

Regardless of the semantics, what did William Fairbairn achieve? His employment in the bridges was for one year carrying out experiments, followed by two years 'to superintend, in conjunction with Mr. Stephenson, the construction and erection of the tubes.' The experiments were brought to a satisfactory conclusion but took a lot longer than they need to have done, and this may have resulted from a rift between Fairbairn and Hodgkinson. **(13)** Although Fairbairn had recommended Hodgkinson for the project in August 1845, by the following March the latter had requested that his 'work should be performed separately under his own control; and as Mr. Stephenson acceded to this, Mr. Hodgkinson had no further connection with Mr. Fairbairn's proceedings.' (14) After his full appointment in May 1846, Fairbairn was involved with Edwin Clark in the initial contract drawings and specifications, which were produced, by the end of September, as far as the inconclusive experiments had allowed. He spent some time, at the close of the year, visiting manufacturers to find those with a large enough capacity to do some of the fabrication of the tubes. (15) Later, quotations from contractors, for the tubes, had to be asked for on a tonnage basis as the exact size and cross-section had still to be determined. The fabrication of the first Conwy tube started on 8 April 1847, and within two months Fairbairn handed in his resignation for the first time. The statement by Clark that he did very little after this time has not been refuted. Fairbairn's yard at Millwall had lost £100,000 since 1840, and he had to dispose of it in 1848, so this, and his other substantial business interests, may have taken up a great deal of his time. (16) Within the five year period from the Act being passed, and the completion of the Britannia Bridge, he was only fully involved for two years, making his claims somewhat exaggerated.

The reference to the bridge on the Northern and Eastern Railway caused offence to Fairbairn, though few in Stephenson's immediate audience, and even fewer among the newspaper readers, would understand it to be the least slight to him. The bridge was not on the railway but was required by its enabling Act to carry a road over the River Lea in Hertfordshire. The first idea, because of very limited clearances, had been for a cellular deck resembling the tops and bottoms of the tubular bridges. Fabrication of this would have been difficult, so instead it was constructed with riveted wrought-iron main girders, and 'arranged as in an ordinary cast-iron bridge.' Fairbairn considered that it could not have given any inspiration to Stephenson for the tubular bridges as 'it is exceedingly defective in design' and 'an imperfect structure.'! When giving evidence for the 1849 Report, Charles Fox said of it; 'The only wrought-iron bridge that I know that is made of wrought-iron flat girders is not a railway bridge, it is a bridge near Hertford for carrying a public road over the River Lea; they have constantly very heavy vibratory loads going over them, and they are in perfect order; it is the best specimen of that kind of [simple girder] structure I know.' (17) It was Fairbairn's unjustified criticisms that *The Civil Engineer and Architect's Journal,* and others, most objected to.

This journal also raised doubts about the originator of the idea for the drawing resembling the final tubes that appeared with Fairbairn's letter dated 20 September 1845. When describing the drawing he said that the problems with the first experiments '…have suggested a new arrangement'. The journal asks 'To w*hom* [it. sic] did the suggestion occur? – Is the writer to be understood as expressing his own ideas only, or the collective deliberations of several persons present at the experiments described?' (18) Whether it was Stephenson's, Fairbairn's, Hodgkinson's, or a combination of all three's ideas, the question must be: – Why were another ten months wasted before the concept was properly tested, and then with square cells at the top only? Fairbairn claims ' …the entire conduct of the investigation was entrusted to me; and as an experimenter, I was left free to exercise my own discretion, of whatever form or conditions of the structure might appear to me best calculated to secure a safe passage across the Straits.' (19) If it was his idea why did he not get on with it? A general comment by Clark may offer the explanation: - 'It is difficult to retrace the steps by which any design is perfected; and it is remarkable that the first conceptions are frequently returned to, and discovered to have been correct.' (20)

Another distorted argument was about the permanent use of suspension chains to assist the bridge. Fairbairn's version of Stephenson's views, which he claims were held until December 1846, is: -

> 'He was strongly impressed with the primary importance of the use of chains, placing his reliance in them as the principal support of the bridge; and **he never for a moment entertained the idea of making the tube self supporting**. The wrought-iron tube, according to his idea, indeed was entirely subservient to the chains, and intended to operate from its rigidity and weight as a stiffener, and to prevent, or at least to some extent counteract the undulations due to the catenary principle of construction.' (21)

The evidence that Stephenson gave to the Select Committee for the second C&HR bill on 5 and 6 May 1845 is printed in full in Edwin Clark's work. It seems pretty obvious, even at this early stage, that he is not very enthusiastic about retaining the chains. In his evidence on the 5th he stated: -

> '…We should have to erect a chain platform for the purpose of the building. Then the question would arise, whether the chains should be allowed to remain, or whether they should be taken down. My own opinion is, that a tube of wrought iron would possess sufficient strength and rigidity to support a railway train….Then, in going into the calculation of the strength of the tube, I found that I did not require the chains themselves, and therefore I have since proceeded upon the idea of the plating merely and the simple tubes.'

He had 25 years of, sometimes bitter, experiences with parliamentary committees, and as he was putting an almost unbelievable proposal to them he had to tread very carefully. He had the conditional support of the Inspector-General of railways, who wanted chains, so the tactful avoidance of an argument at this juncture was essential. When recalled for further questioning on 6th he was asked: -

> 'You have not made up your mind as to the safety of dispensing of the chains? – No, I have not.
> 'It would be impossible to do so until it is constructed, would it not? – I would rather leave that, because I would make the design so that the chains might either be taken away or left; and during construction we should have ample opportunity of ascertaining whether we could safely take away the chains or not.'

Later, at the end of a series of questions, Gen. Pasley was asked if the chains could be removed without the sanction of the government, he said, 'I do not know. I do not see any objection to their being there; **I should recommend their not being removed.'** (22)

The contention is raised again when Stephenson, Fairbairn, and Hodgkinson presented separate reports to the C&HR directors in February 1846. Fairbairn was totally against the chains, Hodgkinson recommended their retention as an auxiliary to reduce the amount of metal required in the tubes, and Stephenson reported: -

> 'The application of chains as an auxiliary has occupied much of my attention, and I am satisfied that the ordinary mode of applying them to suspension-bridges is wholly inadmissible in the instance; if, therefore, it be hereafter found necessary or desirable to employ them in conjunction with the tube, another mode of applying them must be devised, as it is absolutely essential to attach them in such a manner as to preclude the possibility of the slightest oscillation…I have, therefore, turned my attention to other modes of employing them in conjunction with the wrought-iron tube (as suggested by Mr. Hodgkinson), **if such be found necessary upon further investigation.'** (23)

Taking Stephenson's evidence, as a whole, the balance is certainly against the retention of the chains, and Fairbairn's statement is again wide of the mark. Five months after these reports Robert decided to abandon the chains altogether, and to rely upon the floating and lifting of the complete tubes.

In a letter to Samuel Smiles, on 1 December 1864, Fairbairn wrote, when complaining about the recently published *The Life of Robert Stephenson,* 'It seems to have been got up for the praise of

Stephenson and his school, - claiming the merit of a great discovery, to which they have not the shadow of a title, beyond a very crude idea of a wrought-iron suspended cylinder, which I afterwards proved useless.' (24) Professor Pole was responsible for the technical content of *The Life of Robert Stephenson,* so it is surprising, after this outburst, that Fairbairn's family insisted that the professor should edit William Fairbairn's biography. In his conclusion to his introduction to the 1970 reprint of *The Life of Sir William Fairbairn, Bart.,* Professor A. E Musson says, 'It appears that, in his later life, Fairbairn was perhaps too much concerned with being a public figure and establishing his status as a scientist and writer...'. Earlier he seems to be trying, unnecessarily, to increase his status as an engineer. He was extremely good in his chosen fields, and contributed a great deal to early Victorian mechanical and civil engineering. In his obituary the *Engineer* said '...it is difficult to discover a branch of the art of mechanical engineering to which Fairbairn has not contributed something. His footprints may be found on every path which the engineer can tread, and the sands of time will never efface them.' (25) It is a great pity that he was ever goaded into this controversy, as he does not come out of it too well. One thing is certain; the Britannia Bridge could have been completed without William Fairbairn, but it could not without Robert Stephenson.

Robert's feelings are indicated in a letter that he wrote to Professor J. D. Forbes (1809-1868), then at Edinburgh University, from the yacht *Titania*, at Southampton, on 5 November 1855.

'My Dear Sir,

'I am exceedingly obliged for your kindness in permitting me to peruse that portion of your article on mathematical and physical science, which refers to the part I took in originating "tubular bridges". You have done me more justice than I have hitherto had from scientific authors.

'I have from the beginning of this matter, shrunk from entering into the painful controversy, which arose upon the subject. My silence has no doubt contributed to the opinion which has for so long a time been prevalent regarding the respective merits of those who joined me in the experimental investigation, namely, that I occupied but a secondary position. Few people ventured on the study of Mr. Edwin Clark's work on the subject of tubular bridges. You have yourself evidently read it with care, and a sincere desire to do justice to all parties, which I believe you have effectually done.' (26)

NOTES AND REFERENCES

1. *Proc. I. C. E.* 1850, Vol. 9 p. 136. If anyone had a gripe it would be Frank Forster whose input is generally ignored.
2. C&HR Minutes.
3. Clark op. cit. p. 812.
4. W. Fairbairn, *An Account of the Construction of the Britannia and Conway Tubular Bridges,* 1849, p. 169.
5. John Frederic La Trobe Bateman F.R.S. (1810-1889). A prominent water supply engineer; was president of I. C. E. 1877-1879. See *Trans. Newcomen Society,* Vol. 52 pp. 119-138,
6. Some modern writers have interpreted the phrase 'closet companion' to imply a homosexual relationship. Consultation of a decent dictionary would have indicated to them that this phrase, like the word 'gay', had no sexual connotations until the latter half of the twentieth century.
7. *Manchester Guardian*, 27 May 1848. Microfilm copies kindly obtained by Mr. R. S. Roper.
8. Ibid. 3 June 1848.
9. Sir F. B. Head P.C. (1793-1875) had served in the Royal Engineers until 1825, before going to South America to manage a mine. This is during the period that R. S. was there, and they may have got to know (of) each other. He served as a diplomat in Canada until 1837. He wrote a number of books and articles, and was privileged to have full access to the site during the floating of the first Britannia tube.
10. *Civil Engineer and Architect's Journal,* Aug. 1849 pp. 251-3.
11. F. B. Head, *High-ways and Dry-ways*, p. 73. The damaging statement regarding the transfer of the contract still remains in the 1850 edition: '...which contract, to the great displeasure of the Directors, he [Fairbairn] immediately sold at a profit of several thousand pounds to Mr. Mare of Blackwall:' A recent booklet, on the Britannia Bridge, dismisses it as 'nasty rumours', but T. Fairbairn, (*Truths and Tubes,* p. 46.) could not refute it, and neither does Fairbairn's own ambiguous version which appears in his *Life* p. 208, 'This transfer was afterwards satisfactorily arranged by my son, and approved by the Company.'
12. Ibid. pp. 84-5.
13. W. Fairbairn p. 22. Hodgkinson comes in for criticism in a footnote. ' The drawings and the designs of the Britannia and Conway bridges were made out and parts proportioned without the aid of Mr. Hodgkinson's formula and above all, as with all other hollow girder bridges have since been constructed without that gentleman's assistance.' Clark added in his own copy 'This is directly false.' When Fowler and Fairbairn were involved in the B. O. T. refusal to pass the box girder Torksey Bridge, Hodgkinson was one of those called in to help with his calculations!
14. W. Pole *The Life of Sir William Fairbairn Bart.* (1970 edition), p. 205.

15. Ibid. p.207.
16. Ibid. p.342.
17. 1849 Report, p. 301. This bridge must be one of the very earliest examples of a riveted wrought-iron plate girder bridge, and as such is of considerable historical importance.
18. *C. E. & A. J.*, Aug. 1849, p. 252.
19. Clark, p. 84.
20. W. Fairbairn, op. cit.
21. Ibid. p. 2.
22. Clark, pp. 47-71.
23. Ibid. pp. 135-154.
24. S. Smiles, *Industrial Biography*, (1878), p. 330.
25. W. Pole, p.436.
26. Letter at St. Andrew's University.

APPENDIX 6

THE DESTRUCTION OF THE BRITANNIA BRIDGE.

On the evening of 23 May 1970 two schoolboys who had trespassed on to the Britannia Bridge to look for birds and bats, started a fire in the Bangor abutment. A tarred hessian curtain covered the recess in the masonry where the tube's end moved to allow for expansion or contraction. The boys used a lighted paper to see into this recess and while doing so set fire to the hessian. The fire travelled to the top of the tube, and, as they failed to raise the alarm, the fire was soon out of control. The fire brigade was only called when flames were observed above the blazing timber roof of the room at the top of the abutment. The arched timber covering that had been built to protect the tops of the tubes from corrosion, provided a perfect passage to funnel the flames along the full length and width of the bridge. Over the years, the covering had acquired a coating of tar, up to 50mm thick; in addition a workshop above the tubes in the Britannia tower contained a significant quantity of inflammable material. Although the fire brigades at both sides of the bridge made heroic efforts to put the fire out, the odds were stacked against them. The heat caused by the blazing timber, tar and other consumables was so intense that, in the early hours of the next day, the junction plates in the Britannia tower cracked. The crack widened to 400mm, and resulted in the main spans sagging up to 1100mm. This and other heat damage to the wrought iron sounded the death knell of the fine old bridge. Four years to build and just four hours to destroy! Coincidentally, it failed on the anniversary of the Dee Bridge disaster. (1)

An assessment of the damage found that the main spans were in imminent danger of collapse, and that the sagging tubes were irreparable. 'The structural continuity [which Stephenson had taken such pains to achieve] of both the Up and Down line tubes was broken at the three main tower supports, the main spans were sagging severely and the sides of the tubes were showing a pattern of serious vertical corrugations,' There was cracking in the roofs and sides of the tubes, also the expansion bearings in the side towers were severely damaged. However, the masonry towers were structurally sound and could be incorporated in a reconstruction. The first task was to render the tubes safe, and the Royal Engineers were called in to provide temporary support to the ends of the tubes. In order to achieve this they built up Bailey bridge sections within the recesses in the towers that Robert Stephenson had used to raise the tubes.

The possibility of providing either temporary or permanent supports for the tubes by means of suspension cables or post-stressing systems was rejected because it was difficult to find suitable anchorages. The removal of the damaged tubes presented a real problem. To lower them, as full spans, would require two of the world's largest floating cranes, but, as 120 years earlier, the tidal currents would still cause considerable risk and expense. The tubes were too damaged to attempt reversing the original method of erection, and lowering them by the means of jacks. Ultimately it was decided that the design of the replacement spans must allow for them to support the original tubes until these could be cut up into small sections, and removed over the new structure. Regrettably, in these circumstances, it was not possible to rebuild the bridge to resemble the old design. (2)

It was decided to replace the main spans with spandrel-braced steel arches, and to use steel box girders for the side spans. The railway was re-opened as a single line on 30 January 1972. **(3)** The opportunity was taken to include provision in the design for an upper road deck to carry a diversion of the A5 trunk road to relieve Telford's heavily overloaded Menai Suspension Bridge. This was the only benefit arising from the disaster. The Prince of Wales formally opened the completed double-deck bridge on 1 July 1980. The cost of the replacement, together with the new road, came to ten million pounds, but the total cost, allowing for all the disruption, was estimated at over £50 million. A very expensive bit of nature study! (1)

NOTES AND REFERENCES

1. F. W. Hitchinson, O.B.E. 'The Britannia Tubular Bridge Fire: 23 May 1970.' *Permanent Way Institution, Journal and Report of Proceedings,* 1985 Part 2. pp. 146-161. Information kindly supplied by Alan Blower, then Editor of the *PWIJ.*
2. H. C. Husband, 'Reconstruction of the Britannia Bridge.' *Proc. I. C. E.* Vol.58, Feb. 1975, pp. 25-66.
3. A British Transport Film of the reconstruction of the bridge shows small sections of the arches being again floated in on pontoons. The film has been made available on video by the British Film Institute as Volume Seven: *Civil Engineering 1.*

Figure A 5: the rebuilt Britannia Bridge with the road on the upper deck, and a single-track railway on the lower. Photo J. F. Addyman.

APPENDIX 7

RAILWAYS THAT ROBERT STEPHENSON WAS INVOLVED WITH IN 1847 (from *The Post Office Railway Directory*).

London and North Western Railway – consulting engineer with Joseph Locke.
*Aylesbury Railway.
*Bedford and London and Birmingham Railway.
*Buckinghamshire Railway.
*Dunstable Railway.
*East and West India Docks and Birmingham Junction Railway (North London Railway) - with H. D. Martin as acting engineer.
*West London Railway.
Trent Valley Railway - with G. P. Bidder, acting engineer T. L. Gooch.
North Staffordshire Railway – with G. P. Bidder and T. L. Gooch.
Shrewsbury and Hereford Railway – consulting engineer with H. Robertson as engineer.
Chester and Holyhead.
Fleetwood, Preston and West Riding Junction Railway – consulting engineer with Samuel. P. Bidder and Philip Park as engineers.
South Eastern Railway – consulting engineer with P. W. Barlow as assistant engineer.
Reading, Guildford and Reigate Railway – consulting engineer with Francis Giles as engineer.
Eastern Counties Railway – from 1844 with J. Braithwaite.
Northern and Eastern Railway – from 1839 with G. P. Bidder.
Norfolk Railway - with G. P. Bidder.
Newmarket and Chesterford Railway - with M. A. Borthwick.
Midland Railway – consulting engineer with W. H. Barlow as engineer and J. H. Merchant as assistant.
Birmingham and Gloucester Railway - from 1843.

York and North Midland Railway – consulting engineer with T. Cabry and J. C. Birkinshaw as engineers.

Leeds and Bradford Railway (via Shipley) - with T. L. Gooch.

York, Newcastle and Berwick Railway - with T. E. Harrison.

Londonderry and Enniskillen Railway - with A. M. Ross; replaced J. B. Macneill from 1845, at the request of the directors, and provided a £209,000 cheaper route.#

Londonderry and Coleraine Railway.

Cork and Brandon Railway – consulting engineer.

Sambre and Meuse Railway.

West Flanders Railway.

Enfield and Edmonton Railway (absorbed by Eastern Counties in 1847) - with M. A. Borthwick.

Liverpool, Manchester and Newcastle-upon-Tyne Junction Railway - with John Hawkshaw (scheme totally abandoned).

Birmingham, Wolverhampton and Stour Valley Railway - with William Baker.

Pontop and South Shields Railway – Chairman.

* Branches off the L&B (LNWR) # H. G. Lewin *The Railway Mania and its Aftermath* (1936) p. 234. Missing from this list is the **Florence and Leghorn Railway.**

APPENDIX 8

ROBERT STEPHENSON'S MEMBERSHIPS AND HONOURS   **By R. S. Roper**

DAY	YEAR	MEMBERSHIP OR HONOUR
	1815	Reading member of Newcastle Literary and Philosophical Society
	1823	Member of Newcastle Literary and Philosophical Society
21 Sept	1827	Installed as a Free Mason in New York
20 Apr	1830	Member of the Institution of Civil Engineers
	1837-9	On Council of Institution of Civil Engineers
	1840	Member of the Athenaeum Club by invitation
19 July	1841	Awarded the Chevalier de l'Ordre de Leopold by the Belgians
	1842	Member of the Royal Society of Arts
	1845-7	On the Council of the Institution of Civil Engineers
2 Apr	1845	Elected Fellow of the Geological Society
	1847	President of the Smeatonian Society of Civil Engineers
	1847	Member of the Institution of Mechanical Engineers
30 July	1847	Elected M. P. for Whitby
	1848	Awarded Grand Cross of St. Olaf by the Norwegians
	1848-55	Vice president of the Institution of Civil Engineers
1 Feb	1848	Elected to the Carlton Club
	1849-53	President of the Institution of Mechanical Engineers
7 June	1849	Elected Fellow of the Royal Society
19 June	1850	Awarded Master of Arts at Durham University
9 Aug	1850	Elected Fellow of Royal Yacht Squadron
	1850	Became member of Royal Thames Yacht Club
	c. 1851	Became member of Yorkshire, London, Mersey and Welsh Yacht Clubs
	1855-59	President of Newcastle Literary and Philosophical Society
19 Feb	1855	Hon. Fellow of Royal Society of Edinburgh
26 Apr	1855	Member of Royal Society Club
25 June	1855	Elected Fellow of Royal Geographical Society
	1855	Chevalier de la Légion d'Honneur
	1856-7	President of the Institution of Civil Engineers
	1856	President of the Smeatonian Society of Civil Engineers
	1857-9	President of the British Meteorological Society
24 June	1857	Awarded Hon. Doctor of Civil Law at Oxford University
	1858-9	Member of the Council of the Royal Geographical Society

INDEX

Pages with illustrations are shown **bold**

GEORGE STEPHENSON 1781-1848 (in rough chronological order)

ROBERT STEPHENSON 1803-1859

Above: Top: the inside of Robert Stephenson & Co's works in the 1840s. Below: a view of the outside of the factory about the time of Robert's death.

Rear cover: (top) the London and Birmingham Railway's crossing of the Grand Junction Canal at Long Buckby with reasonable clearances for the boats and askew of 30 degrees presented problems. These were solved by using a bowstring cast-iron bridge with the deck suspended from the arch (see page 71). Photo of the original 1930s drawing by Laura Haworth with the kind permission of Ove Arup. Below: one of the two 'great ventilating shafts' at Kilsby in 1838 (J.C. Bourne), and a view of it above ground today. Photo, J. F. Addyman.